PLANE TRIGONOMETRY

C. V. NEWSOM
Consulting Editor

BRITTON AND SNIVELY: *Algebra for College Students*
Intermediate Algebra

MORRILL: *Plane Trigonometry*, Revised

NORTHCOTT: *Mathematics of Finance*

PLANE TRIGONOMETRY

Revised Edition

WILLIAM KELSO MORRILL
Associate Professor of Mathematics
The Johns Hopkins University

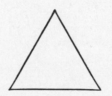

RINEHART & COMPANY, INC.
Publishers   *New York*

PREFACE

When this text was first published in 1938, its purpose was to enable the student to obtain quickly the fundamentals of trigonometry that would permit him to proceed with analytic geometry and the calculus. Although it may still be used for that purpose, it is now a much more complete text.

An entire chapter has been devoted to the right triangle. In practical, everyday experiences, trigonometry is probably used more in the solution of problems involving the right triangle than in any other way. The problems in elementary physics, engineering, and navigation which appear in this chapter illustrate to the student the application of trigonometry to these sciences.

Sections have been included on the use of significant figures and the slide rule. Most of the exercises have been set up to show the use of significant figures. Detailed instruction on the use of the slide rule has been omitted, since booklets of instructions are included with each rule.

The chapter on graphs has been enlarged, and graphs of the inverse functions, the exponential function, and the logarithmic function have been included.

Many more word problems have been added to the chapters on triangles.

In order to encourage the student to think for himself, a question "why?" has been inserted occasionally after statements based on a fact previously mentioned in the text or some fundamental algebraic or geometric fact that the student has had before.

The author wishes to express his sincere appreciation to

v

Professor Abraham Cohen, who made many valuable suggestions in the rewriting of the book; to Dr. John Williamson, who assisted greatly in the original writing; to Mr. Samuel G. Bourne, who read the revised copy and made some valuable suggestions and criticisms; to Mr. Mathew Bilyk, who contributed a number of the exercises pertaining to engineering; to Mrs. William S. Quinn, who checked many of the exercises; and to Mrs. F. Macaulay for her help in the typing.

W. K. Morrill

The Johns Hopkins University
Baltimore, Maryland
July, 1946

CONTENTS

Chapter I
THE ANGLE AND RECTANGULAR CO-ORDINATES

Chapter II
THE TRIGONOMETRIC FUNCTIONS

Chapter III
SIGNIFICANT FIGURES AND THE NUMERICAL VALUES OF THE TRIGONOMETRIC FUNCTIONS

*May be omitted for a brief course.

CONTENTS

Chapter IV
LOGARITHMS

Chapter V
THE RIGHT TRIANGLE

Chapter VI
IDENTITIES

*May be omitted for a brief course.

Chapter VII
THE GENERAL TRIANGLE

*Chapter VIII
TRIGONOMETRIC EQUATIONS AND THE INVERSE TRIGONOMETRIC FUNCTIONS

*Chapter IX
GRAPHS

*May be omitted for a brief course.

Appendix

PLANE TRIGONOMETRY

GREEK ALPHABET

A, α	. . . . .	Alpha	N, ν	Nu
B, β	. . . . .	Beta	Ξ, ξ	Xi
Γ, γ	. . . . .	Gamma	O, o	Omicron
Δ, δ	. . . . .	Delta	Π, π	Pi
E, ε	. . . . .	Epsilon	P, ρ	Rho
Z, ζ	. . . . .	Zeta	Σ, σ	Sigma
H, η	. . . . .	Eta	T, τ	Tau
Θ, θ	. . . . .	Theta	Υ, υ	Upsilon
I, ι	. . . . .	Iota	Φ, φ	Phi
K, κ	. . . . .	Kappa	X, χ	Chi
Λ, λ	. . . . .	Lambda	Ψ, ψ	Psi
M, μ	. . . . .	Mu	Ω, ω	Omega

Chapter I

THE ANGLE AND RECTANGULAR CO-ORDINATES

1. The angle

Centuries ago, while working on problems in surveying and astronomy, mathematicians discovered that certain relations existed between the sides and the angles of a triangle. Out of these relations came a new branch of mathematics called trigonometry. Although there are modern applications of trigonometry which are not directly concerned with angles, it seems appropriate in this book to place major emphasis upon traditional ideas.

We begin our study of trigonometry, therefore, with a discussion of the angle. As in geometry, we shall think of an angle as being formed by two half-lines OX and OP meeting at a point O. (See Fig. 1.) By a half-line we mean that portion of a straight line extending in one direction from O.

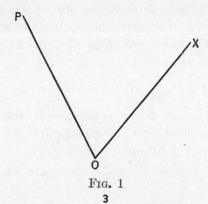

Fig. 1

Now let us consider OX as fixed, and permit the half-line OP to rotate in the plane about O, starting from the initial position OX. (See Fig. 2.) An arrowhead is used to indicate the path of rotation. When OP comes to rest we shall say an angle has been generated. The point O is called the *vertex* of the angle, the half-line OX is called the *initial side* of the angle, and the half-line OP is called the *terminal side*, or *generating side*, of the angle.

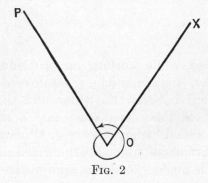

FIG. 2

If the terminal side rotates in a counterclockwise direction, the angle generated is said to be *positive;* if it rotates in a clockwise direction, the angle is said to be *negative*.

When OP makes a complete circuit and again coincides with OX, it has completed *one revolution*. Since there is no restriction on the number of revolutions through which OP may turn, there is no limit to the size of the angle that may be generated. If the vertex of an angle is at the center of a circle and the sides are radii of the circle, the angle is called a *central angle*.

2. Measure of the angle*

a. Sexagesimal or degree system. — If the circumference of a circle is divided into 360 equal parts, the central angle which is subtended by one of these parts is said to have a

---

* A third unit of measure for an angle, known as the mil, is discussed in the appendix.

measure of one degree and is often selected as a unit of angular measure. Hence, when the generating side completes one revolution, the measure of the angle generated is 360°; when the generating side completes two revolutions, an angle of 720° is generated, and so on. In order to make more accurate measurements, a degree is divided into 60 equal parts and the measure of each part is called a *minute*. In turn, a minute is divided into 60 equal parts and the measure of each part is called a *second*. The following relations exist:

$1° = 60'$ (read "one degree equals 60 minutes.")

$1' = 60''$ (read "one minute equals 60 seconds.")

b. Radian measure. — Another unit of measure for the angle is the radian. A radian is the measure of a central angle subtended by an arc equal in length to the radius. Thus, if arc $AB = r$, it follows that $\angle AOB = 1$ radian.

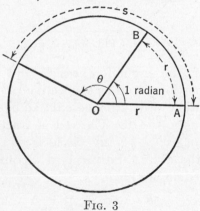

FIG. 3

Let $\angle AOC$ be any central angle other than $\angle AOB$. Denote the length of its intercepted arc by s, and let θ equal the radian measure of $\angle AOC$. We know from geometry that the measures of central angles are proportional to their intercepted arcs. Hence it follows that

(1)
$$\frac{\angle AOC}{\angle AOB} = \frac{\theta}{1} = \frac{s}{r}.$$

This means that *the radian measure of a central angle is equal to the length of the intercepted arc divided by the radius of the circle.*

From (**1**) it follows that the respective arcs of the sectors of two circles with equal central angles are proportional to the corresponding radii, since $\dfrac{\theta}{1} = \dfrac{s_1}{r_1} = \dfrac{s_2}{r_2}.$ (See Fig. 4.)

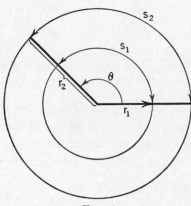

FIG. 4

In particular, the circumferences C_1 and C_2 of any two circles are proportional to their respective radii.   We denote the constant ratio C/r by 2π, where it can be calculated that π is approximately 3.1416.   Cleared of fractions, it follows that the circumference of any circle is equal to 2π times the radius of the circle.   So in (**1**) if s equals the circumference of the circle, we have

$$\frac{\theta}{1} = \frac{2\pi r}{r} = 2\pi, \text{ or}$$

there are 2π radians in the central angle subtended by the circumference.

c. The relation between degrees and radians. — Since the measure of the central angle subtended by the circumference is equal to 360° or 2π radians, it follows that

(**2**) $360° = 2\pi$ radians.

By dividing both sides by 360, we obtain

$1° = \pi/180$ radians $= 0.0175$ radians, approximately.

If we divide both sides of (2) by 2π, we obtain

1 radian $= 180°/\pi = 57° \ 17' \ 45''$, approximately.

With these relations, it is a simple matter to change $\theta°$ into radians or θ radians into degrees.

Example 1:

Change 90° to radians.

Since $1° = \pi/180$, we have $90° = 90\pi/180$ radians $= \pi/2$ radians.

Example 2:

Change $\pi/4$ radians to degrees.

Since 1 radian $= 180°/\pi$, we have $\pi/4$ radians $= \dfrac{180°}{\pi} \times \dfrac{\pi}{4} = 45°$.

3. Length of arc

By formula (1), § 2, the measure in radians of a central angle θ is equal to the length of arc s divided by the radius r. Clearing of fractions, we obtain

$$s = r\theta.$$

This means that *the length of the arc of a circle is equal to the radius of the circle multiplied by the subtended angle in radians.*

Example:

Given a circle of radius 10 feet, find the length of arc subtending an angle of 120°.

Since $120° = \dfrac{2\pi}{3}$ radians, we have

$$s = 10\left(\frac{2\pi}{3}\right) \text{ ft.} = \frac{20\pi}{3} \text{ ft.}$$

EXERCISES

1. Change the following angles into radians: 30°, 135°, −15°, −150°.

2. Change the following angles into radians: −60°, 150°, 1025°, −480°.

3. Change the following angles into degrees: 4 radians, 0.23 radians, 0.5 radians, $-\pi/6$ radians.

4. Change the following angles into degrees: -1.4 radians, 9.6 radians, $-3\pi/2$ radians, 2 radians.

5. What angle in degrees is subtended by an arc of 20 feet if the radius of the circle is 45 inches?

6. What is the radius of the circle if an arc of 8 yards subtends an angle of 120°?

7. A horse, tethered to a stake by a 30-foot rope, grazes while moving in such a way that the rope remains taut. When the rope has generated an angle of 240°, over what arc has the horse grazed?

8. What is the angular speed in radians per second of a wheel of an army truck if the wheel is 30 inches in diameter and the truck is going 45 miles per hour? Hint: θ/t is defined to be angular speed in uniform rotation, where θ is in radians and t denotes time.

9. A trackman running on a circular track 50 feet in diameter runs a lap in 20 seconds. What is his average speed? Hint: s/t is defined as average speed.

10. If the earth is considered to be a perfect sphere 7900 miles in diameter, what is the length of an arc at the equator that subtends an angle of 2° at the center of the earth?

4. The rectangular co-ordinate system

Let $X'X$ and $Y'Y$ be two mutually perpendicular lines. (See Fig. 5.) These lines, called *reference lines* or *axes*, divide the plane into four parts or *quadrants*. The quadrants are called I, II, III, and IV, starting with the upper right-hand quadrant and reading counterclockwise. The point of intersection of the axes is called the *origin*. The line $X'X$ is called the *axis of abscissas*, or *x-axis*, and is generally taken to be horizontal. The line $Y'Y$ is called the *axis of ordinates*, or *y-axis*, and is generally taken to be vertical. Starting from the origin O, all distances measured along the axis of abscissas to the *right* are considered positive; all distances measured along the axis of abscissas to the *left* are considered negative; all distances measured along the axis of ordinates *upward* are considered positive; and all distances measured along the axis of ordinates *downward* are considered negative.

Positive distances are represented by positive numbers, and negative distances are represented by negative numbers. Such distances are frequently known as directed distances, inasmuch as the signs associated with the numbers indicate direction.

Any point in the plane is uniquely located by its directed distances from the axis of ordinates and the axis of abscissas, respectively. The two numbers that represent these distances are called the *co-ordinates* of the point. When written they are enclosed in parentheses and separated by a comma. The first number is called the *abscissa* of the point and the second number is called the *ordinate* of the point. For example, consider the point whose co-ordinates are (3,2). The abscissa 3 represents the horizontal distance of the point from the y-axis, and, since it is positive, the distance is measured to the right. The ordinate 2 represents the vertical distance of the point from the x-axis, and, since it is also positive, the distance is measured upward. In locating, or plotting, a point it is convenient to start at the origin O and measure first the abscissa; then from the terminal point of the abscissa measure vertically the ordinate. To locate the point (3,2), for example, we start at O and measure 3 units to the right along the x-axis. Then, from the point (3,0), we measure 2 units upward to the point (3,2). (See Fig. 5.)

A point in quadrant I, such as (3,2), has both of its co-ordinates positive. A point in quadrant II, such as $(-5,1)$, has a negative abscissa and a positive ordinate. A point in quadrant III, such as $(-2,-2)$, has a negative abscissa and a negative ordinate. A point in quadrant IV, such as $(4,-2)$, has a positive abscissa and a negative ordinate. If a point lies on one of the axes, the co-ordinate representing the distance from that axis to the point is zero. Thus (6,0) is a point on the axis of abscissas, (0,0) is the origin, and $(0,-4)$ is a point on the axis of ordinates. An arbitrary point in the plane may be represented by (x,y). It is very important to note that the letters x and y are variables which may represent positive, negative, or zero distances, depending upon the position of the point in the plane. The abscissa, or x, is always measured from the $Y'Y$ axis along a line parallel to the $X'X$ axis, usually from the origin to the foot of the perpendicular drawn from the point to the x-axis. The ordi-

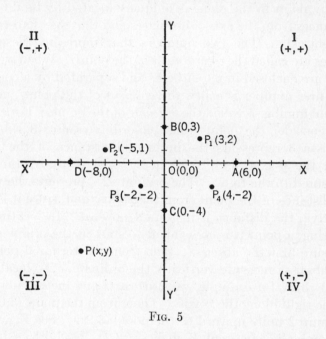

FIG. 5

nate, or y, is always measured from the $X'X$ axis along a line parallel to the $Y'Y$ axis. Throughout this text, whenever x and y are considered as co-ordinates of a point, x will represent a horizontal distance and y a vertical distance.

Example:

In Figure 6, $x = BP = OA$ and is negative since it is measured to the left; $y = AP = OB$ and is positive since it is measured upward. The direction of measurement is made specific by writing BP, not PB; likewise the measurement upward from A to P is denoted by AP, not PA.

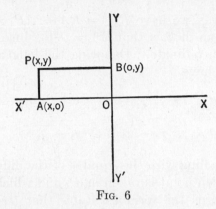

Fɪɢ. 6

5. The distance between two points

In order to find the length of the segment from P_1 to P_2 we construct a right triangle having the segment P_1P_2 for its hypotenuse and the segments P_1R and RP_2 for its sides, where P_1R is parallel to the x-axis and RP_2 is parallel to the y-axis. (See Fig. 7.)

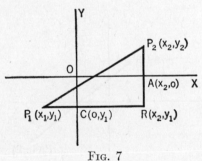

Fɪɢ. 7

It is a simple matter to express the length of the segment in terms of the co-ordinates of the end points of the segment. From the Pythagorean theorem, we have

$$(P_1P_2)^2 = (P_1R)^2 + (RP_2)^2.$$

It is apparent that $P_1C = -x_1$, since $CP_1 = x_1$ by definition of an abscissa. Consequently,

$$P_1R = P_1C + CR = -x_1 + x_2.$$

In the same way we have $RP_2 = RA + AP_2 = -y_1 + y_2$. This follows from the fact that $RA = -y_1$, since $AR = y_1$ by definition of an ordinate. Denoting the length of the segment by d, we have

$$d^2 = (x_2 - x_1)^2 + (y_2 - y_1)^2, \text{ or}$$

$$d = \sqrt{(x_2 - x_1)^2 + (y_2 - y_1)^2}.$$

Since we are dealing with the squares of the differences, it is immaterial which point is taken as P_1 and which as P_2.

In other words the formula states that *the length of a segment is equal to the square root of the sum of the squares of the difference of the abscissas of the end points and the difference of the ordinates of the end points.*

Example:

Find the distance between the points $P_1(-1,2)$ and $P_2(4,-2)$.

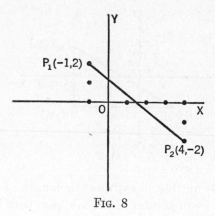

FIG. 8

We have

$$d = \sqrt{(x_2 - x_1)^2 + (y_2 - y_1)^2} = \sqrt{(4 - (-1))^2 + (-2 - 2)^2}$$
$$= \sqrt{25 + 16} = \sqrt{41}.$$

Hence the length of the segment P_1P_2 is $\sqrt{41}$ units.

EXERCISES

1. Define carefully the meaning of an abscissa of a point; an ordinate of a point. State how we locate a point in the plane.

2. In using the distance formula, why does it make no difference which point is called P_1 and which is called P_2?

3. In Figure 6 is PB an abscissa of P? Is PA an ordinate of P? Explain.

4. Plot the following points: $(0,-1)$, $(3,-7)$, $(2,3)$, $(-4,6)$, $(-2,-1)$, $(0,5)$, $(0,0)$, $(6,0)$, $(-8,2)$.

5. Find the distances between the following pairs of points:

(a) $P_1(-1,3)$, $P_2(5,-2)$.   (d) $P_1(-2,0)$, $P_2(0,6)$.
(b) $A(7,-3)$, $B(4,2)$.   (e) $Q(3,-2)$, $R(3,-8)$.
(c) $L(3,2)$, $M(-5,7)$.   (f) $A(-2,7)$, $B(3,-1)$.

6. Prove that the triangle whose vertexes are $P_1(3,0)$, $P_2(-3,0)$, and $P_3(0,-3\sqrt{3})$ is an equilateral triangle.

7. Three vertexes of a rectangle are, in order, $P_1(0,0)$, $P_2(0,-3)$, and $P_3(7,-3)$; what is the fourth vertex?

8. Prove that the triangle whose vertexes are $P_1(0,0)$, $P_2(0,8)$, and $P_3(-6,4)$ is an isosceles triangle.

9. Prove that $(0,0)$, $(-1,2)$, $(1,3)$, and $(2,1)$ are vertexes of a rectangle.

10. Prove that $(-1,1)$, $(1,3)$, and $(-\sqrt{3},2+\sqrt{3})$ are vertexes of an equilateral triangle.

11. Prove that $(2,3)$, $(-2,5)$, and $(-1,-3)$ are vertexes of a right triangle.

12. What is the path of a point which moves in such a way that its ordinate is always -3?

13. What is the path of a point which moves in such a way that its abscissa is always 2?

14. What is the path of a point which moves in such a way that its distance from the origin is always 5?

6. Angles referred to the co-ordinate system

An angle is said to be in *standard position* when the vertex coincides with the origin O of the rectangular co-ordinate system and the initial side coincides with the positive half of the x-axis. As the terminal side rotates about O in a *counterclockwise* direction, a positive angle is generated in standard position. As the terminal side rotates about O in a *clockwise* direction, a negative angle is generated in standard position.   An angle in standard position is said to be *in* the quadrant that contains its terminal side.   So an angle of 145° in standard position lies in quadrant II.   (See Fig. 9.)

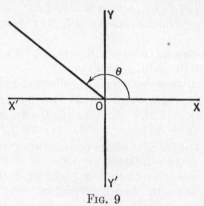

Fɪɢ. 9

EXERCISES: CHAPTER I

1. Change into radians: 35°, 265°, 120°, −315°, −225°, 765°, 17.5°, −435°.

2. Change into radians: 135°, 240°, 330°, −45°, −810°, 1055°, −30°, 750°.

3. Change into degrees: $\pi/3$ radians, $-2\pi/3$ radians, −1.5 radians, 2 radians, π radians, −4 radians, $\frac{1}{2}$ radian, $3\pi/4$ radians.

4. Change into degrees: $\pi/4$ radians, 3 radians, $-\pi$ radians, 8 radians, $-7\pi/3$ radians, −2 radians, $\pi/6$ radians, $-5\pi/3$ radians.

5. Divide 113° 18′ 43″ by 7.

6. Divide 203° 17′ 13″ by 3.

7. Change 14.836° to degrees, minutes, and seconds.

8. Change 14.836° to minutes; to seconds.

9. Draw a rough sketch of each of the following angles in standard position: 120°, −60°, $3\pi/4$ radians, 1260°, $-7\pi/8$ radians, −180°, 1535°, $5\pi/4$ radians, −120°, −330°, 693°.

10. In what quadrants do the terminal sides of the following angles lie: −120°, −612°, $5\pi/6$ radians, 825°, 4 radians, −1100°, −2 radians, 273°, −315°, 1325°, −20°?

11. Locate the points: (3,−4), (−2,−3), (0,6), (−2,0), (0,0), (4,8), (3,0), (−1,6), (−3,−3), (5,−1), (6,2), (−3,−2), (−5,4), (−8,−6), (0,−2).

12. Locate the points: $(-3,2)$, $(0,4)$, $(-3,0)$, $(-6,7)$, $(8,-10)$, $(3,4)$, $(0,-6)$, $(7,0)$, $(-5,2)$, $(-3,2)$, $(4,0)$, $(-7,1)$, $(4,-5)$, $(2,3)$.

13. A central angle of $\frac{3}{5}$ radians intercepts an arc of 4 feet. Find the radius of the circle.

14. An angle of 3.505 radians at the center of a circle is subtended by an arc 25 inches long. Find the radius.

15. If an arc of 20 feet subtends an angle of 4 radians, what is the radius of the circle?

16. In a circle whose radius is 12 feet, find in radians, and in degrees, the angle subtended by a length of arc equal to 40 feet.

17. In a circle whose radius is 12 feet find the length of arc which subtends an angle of 120°.

18. Through what clockwise angle does the hour hand of a clock turn in one hour? in one minute? in one second?

19. If the minute hand of a clock has moved $7\pi/6$ radians in a clockwise direction from 12 noon, what time is it?

20. Calculate the time after the minute hand of a clock has moved through an angle of $25\pi/6$ radians from 12 noon.

21. If we assume the earth to be a perfect sphere of radius 3959 miles, find the length of an arc at the equator that subtends an angle of 12° at the center of the earth.

22. What is the distance between two points located on the same meridian of the earth if one point is 10° south of the equator and the other point is 28° south of the equator?

23. What is the distance between two points on the same meridian if one point is 22° north of the equator and the other point is 8° south of the equator?

24. The circumference of a circle is 2000 feet. Find in degrees, minutes, and seconds the central angle subtended by an arc of length (**a**) 200 feet; (**b**) 20 feet; (**c**) 1500 feet; (**d**) 750 feet.

25. Through what angle will a spoke of a wheel 6 feet in diameter turn in going 120 yards? How many revolutions has the wheel made?

26. A mail truck whose wheels are 36 inches in diameter travels at the rate of 30 miles per hour. How many revolutions per minute does a wheel make? What angle does a wheel turn through in going 50 feet?

27. A wheel 4 feet in diameter rolls along the ground at the rate of 40 feet per second. Through how many degrees does it turn in one second? In ten seconds?

28. In 15 minutes the minute hand of a clock turns through how many degrees? How many radians?

29. The end of a 24-inch pendulum describes an arc of 3 inches. Find the angle through which the pendulum swings.

30. The minute hand of a clock is 6 inches long. How far does its end travel in 25 minutes? If the hour hand is 4 inches long, how far does its end travel in the same time?

31. The minute hand of a clock is 8 inches long. How far does its end travel in 55 minutes? In 2 hours and 10 minutes?

32. Through what angle does the hour hand of a clock turn in an hour? In 5 hours? In 30 minutes? In 17 minutes?

33. In 3 hours what angles have been generated by the hour hand, the minute hand, and the second hand, respectively, of a clock?

34. Assume the earth to be a sphere of radius 3959 miles. Find the length of an arc which subtends an angle of 1 minute at the center of the earth. Give the result in feet. This length is known as a *nautical mile*.

35. What angle at the earth's center is subtended by 5 nautical miles? (See problem 34.)

36. A pendulum, 3 feet in length, swings through an angle of 25° 18′ 30″. What is the length of arc described by its end point?

37. If a wheel makes 300 revolutions per minute, through how many degrees does it turn per second?

38. If a wheel makes 500 revolutions per hour, through how many radians does it turn per minute?

39. Find the distance traveled by the end of the minute hand of a clock during a period of 40 minutes if the minute hand is 10 inches long. Through what angle does the hour hand turn in this time?

40. The propeller of an airplane is spinning at the rate of 1000 revolutions per minute. Through what angle does it turn each minute?

41. Draw the co-ordinate axes and arbitrarily locate a point $P(x,y)$ in quadrant III. What are the co-ordinates of the three other points symmetric to P with respect to the x-axis, the y-axis, and the origin respectively?

42. Plot the points $(-1,3)$ and $(4,2)$. By constructing a right triangle having these points as ends of the hypotenuse and sides parallel to the axes find the distance between the two points.

43. What is the length of the segment joining the points $(6,2)$ and $(12,-6)$?

44. Plot the points $(5,0)$ and $(0,-6)$. Find the area of the triangle formed by the co-ordinate axes and the line joining the two given points.

45. One side of a square has its end points at $P_1(2,-1)$ and $P_2(2,3)$.   Find the co-ordinates of the other vertexes.   How many solutions are there to the problem?

46. The ends of a diagonal of a square are $P_1(3,1)$ and $P_2(0,4)$. Find the other vertexes.

47. What is the path of a point which moves in such a way that its abscissa is always -3?

48. What is the path of a point which moves in such a way that its ordinate is always 5?

49. What is the path of a point which moves in such a way that its abscissa is always equal to its ordinate?

Chapter II

THE TRIGONOMETRIC FUNCTIONS

7. Variable, function

We shall define a variable as a symbol representing any one of a collection of numbers. For example, the collection of numbers could be all the positive and negative numbers, or all the numbers between and including 1 and 2, or all the numbers representing the angular measures from 0° to 360°. As a special case the collection of numbers may consist of just one number.

If two collections of numbers are so related that to each value of one collection there exists a unique value of the second collection, we say that the variable designating the second collection is a *single-valued function* of the variable associated with the first collection.

For example, suppose the first collection of numbers consists of all the positive integers (1, 2, 3, 4, . . .) and suppose we agree that to each number K in this collection there corresponds the number $2K$ in a second collection. Then the second collection is uniquely determined and is a function of the first collection. The positive even integers compose the second collection of numbers.

The variable designating the collection of numbers that determines the function is called the *independent variable*. Hereafter in this text, *variable* is to be understood to mean *independent variable*.

Frequently the relation between a variable and the function it determines is expressed by means of an algebraic equation.   For example, we might say the area of a circle is a function of the radius of the circle.   This would mean that the area of a circle is determined when its radius is known.   Algebraically the actual relationship between A and r is given by $A = \pi r^2$, where π is a constant.   Since r is the radius, it may be any positive number.   The collection of numbers associated with A consists also of all positive numbers.   Why?

One might ask, couldn't the radius of the circle be a function of the area?   The answer is yes, and algebraically we have $r = \sqrt{A/\pi}$, where the positive radical is used, since r is a positive number.

Other examples follow:

1. A man is walking at the rate of 3 miles per hour.   His speed remains fixed, while the distance that he walks changes with the time.   If we assume that distance is to be determined, it follows that time is the variable and the desired distance is a function of the time.   Algebraically, we would state this as: $d = 3t$, where t is time and d is distance.

2. If $y = 3x^3 - 2x$, we say y is a function of x, since for each value assigned to x, a value of y is determined.

3. The formula for finding the volume of a right circular cylinder is $V = \pi r^2 h$, where V is the volume, r is the radius of the base, and h is the altitude of the cylinder.   Here there are two independent variables, and V is said to be a function of both r and h.   This means that both r and h must be assigned values before V can be determined.

EXERCISES

1. Express the area of a square as a function of the length of a side.

2. If b is the base of a rectangle and h is the altitude, express the area as a function of b and h.

3. Express the area of a triangle as a function of its base and its altitude.

4. If a man, walking at the rate of x miles per hour, walks for t hours, express the distance the man walks as a function of x and t.

5. Express the diagonal d of a square as a function of a side s.

6. Express each base angle of an isosceles triangle as a function of the third angle.

7. A well-known formula in physics states that under certain conditions pressure times volume is a constant. This is written $pv = k$. Rewrite this formula in two ways, first making the pressure a function of the volume and then making the volume a function of the pressure.

8. Express the area of an equilateral triangle as a function of a side.

9. Express the radius of a circle as a function of the area.

10. Express the volume of a right circular cone as a function of its radius and its altitude.

8. The trigonometric functions

We are now going to describe six different collections of numbers which define, respectively, the six *trigonometric functions.* We shall find that, *in general*, values assigned to an angle θ determine unique values of each of the six trigonometric functions. We say "in general," since some of the trigonometric functions do not exist for certain values of the angle θ.

To define the trigonometric functions we proceed as follows: Generate an angle θ in standard position and select an arbitrary point $P(x,y)$, except the origin, upon the terminal side. For illustrative purpose we have placed θ in two positions.

In both Figures 10 and 11 we have $x = OM$ and $y = MP$. The segment $OP = r$, called the *distance*, is measured along the terminal side of θ and is *always considered a positive distance.* As before, x and y represent directed distances and are positive, negative, or zero depending upon the position of the point P in the plane.

The six ratios associated with the distances x, y, and r are determined by the angle θ and are defined as the trigonometric functions of θ. If we consider any other point, $P' = (x',y')$, on the terminal side of θ, then $x' = OM'$, $y' = M'P'$, and $r' = OP'$. (See Figs. 10 and 11.) The triangle $OM'P'$

is similar to the triangle OMP. Hence the numerical values of the ratios associated with the distances x', y', and r' are equal to the corresponding values of the ratios associated

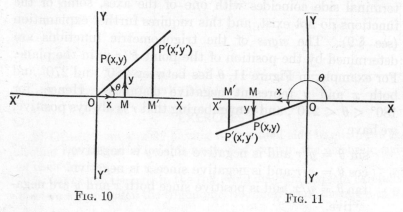

FIG. 10   FIG. 11

with the distances x, y, and $r;$ also the signs are the same. Therefore the trigonometric functions are independent of the choice of the position of the point P on the terminal line.

We *define:*

$$\text{sine } \theta = \frac{\text{ordinate}}{\text{distance}} = \frac{y}{r}. \qquad \text{cosecant } \theta = \frac{\text{distance}}{\text{ordinate}} = \frac{r}{y}.$$

$$\text{cosine } \theta = \frac{\text{abscissa}}{\text{distance}} = \frac{x}{r}. \qquad \text{secant } \theta = \frac{\text{distance}}{\text{abscissa}} = \frac{r}{x}.$$

$$\text{tangent } \theta = \frac{\text{ordinate}}{\text{abscissa}} = \frac{y}{x}. \qquad \text{cotangent } \theta = \frac{\text{abscissa}}{\text{ordinate}} = \frac{x}{y}.$$

The names of the six trigonometric functions are abbreviated as follows: sin θ for sine θ, cos θ for cosine θ, tan θ for tangent θ, cot θ or ctn θ for cotangent θ, sec θ for secant θ, and csc θ for cosecant θ.

From the definitions it is clear that when sin θ, cos θ, and tan θ are known and are not equal to 0, csc θ, sec θ, and cot θ are uniquely determined, since sin $\theta = 1/\text{csc } \theta$, cos $\theta = 1/\text{sec } \theta$, and tan $\theta = 1/\text{cot } \theta$. These are known as

sent them graphically by means of single directed segments, and then, using these, to study how the functions change in value as the angle increases from 0° to 360°.

Draw a circle of radius 1 with center at the origin and generate an angle θ in standard position in quadrant I. At the point A where the circle cuts the x-axis draw a vertical tangent to the circle, and at the point B where the circle cuts the y-axis draw a horizontal tangent. Denote by P, T,

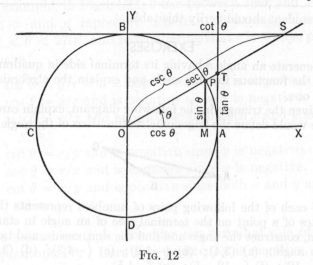

FIG. 12

and S the points where the terminal side of θ cuts the circle, the vertical tangent, and the horizontal tangent, respectively. As a consequence of this construction certain of the segments have their *directed lengths* equal to the various trigonometric functions. Since $OP = 1$, we have $\sin \theta = MP/OP = MP$, and $\cos \theta = OM/OP = OM$. Now $\tan \theta = MP/OM$, but since $OM \neq 1$ this does not give us a line segment representation. From similar triangles it follows that $MP/OM = AT/OA$, and so $\tan \theta = AT$ since $OA = 1$. In the same way $\cot \theta = OM/MP = BS/OB = BS$ since $OB = 1$. Likewise, $\sec \theta = OP/OM = OT/OA = OT$; and $\csc \theta = OP/MP = OS/OB = OS$. In order that $\sec \theta$ and csc θ may also be considered as directed segments, we define distances measured from the origin *along the terminal side* of the angle to be positive and those measured from the origin *along the terminal side extended in the opposite direction* to be negative.   In Figure 12 the names of the functions have been written beside the segments that represent them.

Now let us consider θ in quadrant II.   (See Fig. 13.)   As

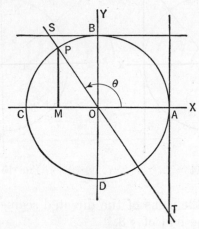

FIG. 13

before, the circle is a unit circle and $OA = OB = OP = 1$. Hence $\sin \theta = MP/OP = MP$, $\cos \theta = OM/OP = OM$, $\tan \theta = MP/OM = AT/OA = AT$, $\cot \theta = OM/MP = BS/OB = BS$, $\sec \theta = OP/OM = OT/OA = OT$,   and $\csc \theta = OP/MP = OS/OB = OS$.   In interpreting the signs of the functions, we notice that:

MP is positive, since it is measured upward;

OM is negative, since it is measured to the left;

AT is negative, since it is measured downward;

BS is negative since it is measured to the left;

OT is negative, since it is measured along the terminal side extended in the opposite direction;

OS is positive, since it is measured along the terminal side.

In Figures 14 and 15 the circle is a unit circle and θ has been generated in quadrants III and IV, respectively. In each case $\sin \theta = MP$, $\cos \theta = OM$, $\tan \theta = AT$, $\cot \theta = BS$, $\sec \theta = OT$, and $\csc \theta = OS$.

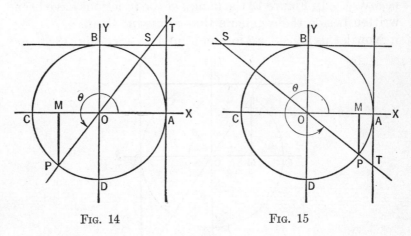

FIG. 14   FIG. 15

Verify that the signs of the directed segments agree with the table at the end of § 8.

The line segment representation is very useful. We can use it to determine easily and quickly how the trigonometric functions vary in both magnitude and sign as θ varies.* It is especially helpful in considering the limiting cases when the terminal side coincides with one of the co-ordinate axes.

For our first example, we shall consider $\sin \theta$. In Figures 12 to 15, $\sin \theta = MP$. As θ approaches 0°, M approaches A and the directed segment MP approaches 0. So *we define* $\sin 0° = 0$. (See Fig. 12.) As θ increases from 0° to 90°, M approaches the origin and MP increases from 0 to 1 and *we define* $\sin 90° = 1$. As θ continues to increase from 90° to 180°, M approaches C and the directed segment MP again approaches 0, and *we define* $\sin 180° = 0$. (See Fig. 13.) As θ increases from 180° to 270°, M again approaches the origin

* See Chapter IX for another graphic way of determining how the functions vary as θ varies.

and the directed segment MP decreases from 0 to -1. *We define* sin $270° = -1$. (See Fig. 14.) Finally, as θ increases from 270° to 360°, M approaches A, MP approaches 0, and *we define* sin $360° = 0$. (See Fig. 15.) As θ continues to increase to values greater than 360° it is clear from our line segment representation that the trigonometric functions repeat themselves.

As a second illustration, we shall consider the variation of tan θ. Again using the unit circle, tan $\theta = AT$. As θ approaches 0, T approaches A and the directed segment AT approaches 0. *We define* tan $0° = 0$. (See Fig. 12.) As θ increases from 0° to 90°, AT increases indefinitely. When $\theta = 90°$, the terminal side of the angle and the tangent line to the circle at A are parallel and AT does not exist. Hence tan 90° does not exist. When θ is slightly greater than 90°, AT does exist, but now it is negative. (See Fig. 13.) So the line segment representation tells us that tan 90° does not exist but that if θ approaches 90° in a counterclockwise direction, tan θ increases positively, while if θ approaches 90° in a clockwise direction, tan θ is negative and decreases indefinitely. As θ leaves 90° and approaches 180°, AT approaches 0 and *we define* tan $180° = 0$. (See Fig. 13.) As θ increases from 180° to 270°, AT behaves exactly as it did for θ changing from 0° to 90°. Hence tan 270° does not exist. (See Fig. 14.) Finally after θ leaves 270° and approaches 360°, AT approaches 0, and *we define* tan $360° = 0$. (See Fig. 15.)

It should be clear from these two illustrations that when the terminal side of θ coincides with the axes, we define the trigonometric functions of θ to be the limiting values of the line segments that represent them. When there is no limiting value, the trigonometric function does not exist.

EXERCISES

1. Trace the changes in cos θ as θ increases from 0° to 360°.
2. Trace the changes in cot θ as θ increases from 0° to 360°.
3. Trace the changes in csc θ as θ increases from 0° to 360°.

4. Trace the changes in sec θ as θ increases from 0° to 360°.

5. Which of the six trigonometric functions are restricted in value?   What are the restrictions?

6. Give the numerical values of the following: cos 0°, sin 90°, tan 180°, sec 180°, csc $(-90°)$, sin 2π, cos $(-\pi)$, cot 810°, sin $\dfrac{3\pi}{2}$.

7. Give the numerical values of the following: sin 0°, cos 90°, tan 0°, sec $(-\pi)$, csc 90°, cos 2π, sin $(-\pi)$, tan 720°, cos $\dfrac{3\pi}{2}$.

8. Given each of the following points on the terminal side of an angle in standard position, sketch the line segment representation of each function of each of the angles, and find the directed lengths of the segments that represent them: $(1,-3)$; $(3,4)$; $(5,12)$; $(-12,5)$; $(-1,-1)$.

10. Construction of the angle

It is apparent from a study of the table in § 8 that it is usually impossible to determine uniquely a positive angle less than 360° when only one of the trigonometric functions of the angle is given.   Suppose we have given sin $\theta = \frac{3}{4}$. The terminal side of the angle may be in either quadrant I or quadrant II.   We construct the two angles as follows: With the origin as the center and the radius equal to 4, draw a circle.   Measure 3 units in a positive direction on the y-axis

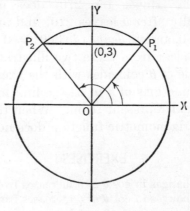

F<small>IG</small>. 16

and draw the line through the point (0,3) parallel to the
x-axis.   It cuts the circle at two points, P_1 and P_2, in quadrants I and II, respectively.   The angles XOP_1 and XOP_2
are the required angles.   Why?

However, if we know that $\sin \theta = \frac{3}{4}$ and that $\cos \theta$ is negative, θ must lie in quadrant II.   In order to find the numerical values of the functions of $\angle XOP_2$ we find the abscissa x
of P_2 in Figure 16 by using the Pythagorean theorem.   We
have $x^2 = 16 - 9 = 7$, or $x = -\sqrt{7}$, since P_2 lies in quadrant II.   Then, from the definitions of the functions, we have
$\cos \angle XOP_2 = -\sqrt{7}/4$, $\tan \angle XOP_2 = -3/\sqrt{7}$, $\cot \angle XOP_2$
$= -\sqrt{7}/3$, $\sec \angle XOP_2 = -4/\sqrt{7}$, and $\csc \angle XOP_2 = 4/3$.

Find the functions of $\angle XOP_1$, employing the data given
above.

In general when *one* function of an angle is given, two
positive angles less than 360° are determined.   On the other
hand, if two of the trigonometric functions of an angle which
are not reciprocals are known, a positive angle less than 360°
is uniquely determined.   In fact, the angle is determined if
one of the functions and the *sign* of a second one, not the
reciprocal of the first, are known.

As a second example let us construct a positive angle θ

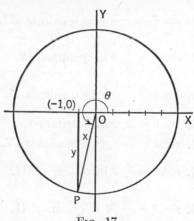

FIG. 17

$< 360°$, given that $\cos\theta = -\frac{1}{5}$ and $\tan\theta$ is positive. By definition, $\cos\theta = x/r$, and since r is always positive, we let $x = -1$ and $r = 5$. Since the cosine is negative, θ lies in either quadrant II or quadrant III. Since $\tan\theta$ is positive, θ must lie in either quadrant I or quadrant III. Because of these two requirements, it follows that θ lies in quadrant III. Why? With the origin as a center, draw a circle of radius 5. Locate the point $(-1,0)$ and from it draw the ordinate to the circle at P in the third quadrant. Then $\theta = \angle XOP$ is the desired angle. (See Fig. 17.)

To find the remaining functions of θ we find the ordinate of P by using the Pythagorean theorem. We have

$$y^2 + 1 = 25, \text{ or } y = -\sqrt{24} = -2\sqrt{6}. \text{ So } \sin\theta = -\frac{2\sqrt{6}}{5},$$

$$\tan\theta = 2\sqrt{6}, \cot\theta = \frac{1}{12}\sqrt{6}, \sec\theta = -5, \text{ and } \csc\theta = -\frac{5}{12}\sqrt{6}.$$

EXERCISES

Given the following conditions, construct the positive angle less than 360° which satisfies them, and find the remaining trigonometric functions:

1. $\cot\theta = 2$, θ in quadrant I.

2. $\sin\theta = -\dfrac{3}{5}$, θ in quadrant III.

3. $\cos\theta = \dfrac{2}{3}$, θ in quadrant IV.

4. $\tan\theta = \dfrac{-1}{5}$, θ in quadrant II.

5. $\sec\theta = 2$, θ in quadrant I.

6. $\csc\theta = -3$, θ in quadrant IV.

7. $\cot\theta = \dfrac{3}{7}$, θ in quadrant III.

8. $\sin\theta = \dfrac{5}{13}$, θ in quadrant II.

9. $\cos \theta = -\dfrac{12}{13}$, θ in quadrant III.

10. $\tan \theta = \dfrac{4}{9}$, θ in quadrant I.

11. $\csc \theta = \dfrac{5}{3}$, θ in quadrant II.

12. $\cot \theta = -2$, θ in quadrant IV.

13. $\sec \theta = \dfrac{-13}{5}$, θ in quadrant II.

14. $\sin \theta = \dfrac{-2}{3}$, θ in quadrant IV.

15. $\cos \theta = \dfrac{1}{5}$, θ in quadrant I.

11. Functions of an acute angle

Many of the applications of trigonometry deal with the trigonometric functions of an acute angle of a right triangle. Suppose we are given a right triangle ABC in any position in the plane. Let C be the right angle and A and B the acute angles. Represent the lengths of the sides opposite the angles A, B, and C by a, b, and c, respectively.

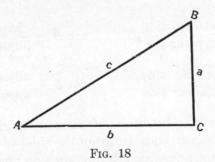

FIG. 18

Construct an axis system so that the angle B appears in standard position, and mark off the point (a,b). Then the vertex of the angle C is at the point (a,o). By definition,

$\sin B = b/c,\;\cos B = a/c,\;\tan B = b/a,\;\cot B = a/b,$
$\sec B = c/a,\;\csc B = c/b.$ In terms of the right triangle
ABC, b is the opposite side to $\angle B$, a is the adjacent side, and

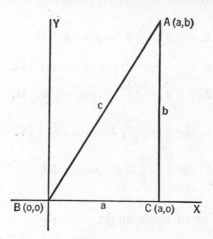

Fig. 19

c is the hypotenuse. Hence, for *any acute angle of a right triangle*, we have

$$\sin B = \frac{\text{opposite side}}{\text{hypotenuse}}, \qquad \csc B = \frac{\text{hypotenuse}}{\text{opposite side}},$$

$$\cos B = \frac{\text{adjacent side}}{\text{hypotenuse}}, \qquad \sec B = \frac{\text{hypotenuse}}{\text{adjacent side}},$$

$$\tan B = \frac{\text{opposite side}}{\text{adjacent side}}, \qquad \cot B = \frac{\text{adjacent side}}{\text{opposite side}}.$$

So we see that the functions of an acute angle of a right triangle can be expressed in terms of the sides of the triangle and, hence, it is *not* necessary to put such an angle in standard position before finding its functions.

Example:

Find the trigonometric functions of angle A in Figure 20.

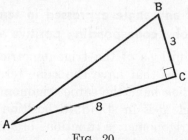

FIG. 20

Since A is an acute angle of a right triangle, it does not need to be put into standard position. We find the length of the hypotenuse by using the Pythagorean theorem. Thus: $(AB)^2 = 64 + 9 = 73$, or $AB = \sqrt{73}$.* Hence, we have $\sin A = 3/\sqrt{73}$, $\cos A = 8/\sqrt{73}$, $\tan A = 3/8$, $\cot A = 8/3$, $\sec A = \sqrt{73}/8$, and $\csc A = \sqrt{73}/3$.

EXERCISES

Find the trigonometric functions of the angle θ in each of the following right triangles:

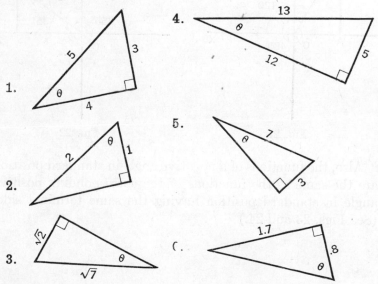

* When no sign precedes a radical the positive sign is understood; so $\sqrt{73} = +\sqrt{73}$.

12. Function of any angle expressed in terms of the same function of a corresponding positive acute angle

From the definitions of the trigonometric functions it is clear that all angles that have the same terminal side *when in standard position* have the same trigonometric functions. Hence if an angle θ is in standard position and is greater than 360°, the trigonometric functions of θ are the same as the functions of the angle that remains after all the integral multiples of 360° are removed from θ. (See Figs. 21 and 22.)

Example 1:

$$\sin 480° = y/r = \sin 120°$$

Example 2:

$$\cos 755° = x/r = \cos 35°$$

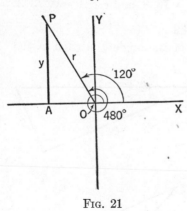

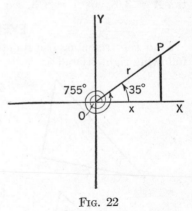

FIG. 21   FIG. 22

Also, the functions of a negative angle in standard position are the same as the functions of the corresponding positive angle in standard position having the same terminal side. (See Figs. 23 and 24.)

Example 3:

$$\cos(-120°) = x/r = \cos 240°$$

Example 4:

$$\tan(-315°) = y/x = \tan 45°$$

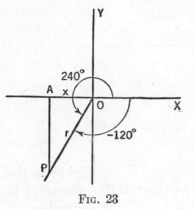

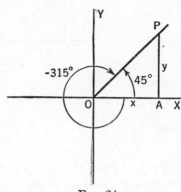

Fɪɢ. 23   Fɪɢ. 24

So we see that the problem of determining the trigonometric functions of an angle greater than 360°, or of a negative angle, reduces to the problem of finding the trigonometric functions of a positive angle less than 360°. Now, any positive angle less than 360° and greater than 90° can be written in one of the following ways:

$180° - \theta$, terminal side in quadrant II;
$180° + \theta$, terminal side in quadrant III;
$360° - \theta$, terminal side in quadrant IV;

where θ is a positive acute angle. Examples are:

$$120° = 180° - 60°;$$
$$210° = 180° + 30°;$$
$$315° = 360° - 45°.$$

Finally, we shall see that any function of these angles can be expressed in terms of the *same* function of the positive acute angle θ.

Generate an angle $180° - \theta$ in standard position, and select an arbitrary point P on the terminal side of the angle.

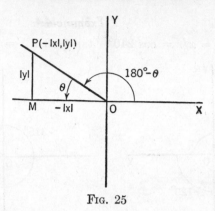

Fig. 25

Project P on the x-axis at M and let $|x|$,*$|y|$, and r be the lengths of the sides of the right triangle OMP. According to this notation the abscissa of P is $-|x|$, the ordinate of P is $|y|$, r is always positive, and the trigonometric functions of $180° - \theta$ are

$$\sin (180° - \theta) = \frac{|y|}{r}, \qquad \csc (180° - \theta) = \frac{r}{|y|},$$

$$\cos (180° - \theta) = \frac{-|x|}{r}, \qquad \sec (180° - \theta) = \frac{r}{-|x|},$$

$$\tan (180° - \theta) = \frac{|y|}{-|x|}, \qquad \cot (180° - \theta) = \frac{-|x|}{|y|}.$$

Since OMP is a right triangle, θ does not need to be in standard position for the determination of its functions and we can read at once that

$$\sin \theta = \frac{|y|}{r}, \qquad \csc \theta = \frac{r}{|y|},$$

$$\cos \theta = \frac{|x|}{r}, \qquad \sec \theta = \frac{r}{|x|},$$

$$\tan \theta = \frac{|y|}{|x|}, \qquad \cot \theta = \frac{|x|}{|y|}.$$

* The symbols $|\quad|$ are absolute-value symbols and imply the positive or unsigned value. So $|-7| = 7$; $|x| = x$ if x is positive and it is $-x$ if x is negative.

If we compare the two sets of results, we have

$$\sin\,(180° - \theta) = \sin\theta, \qquad \csc\,(180° - \theta) = \csc\theta,$$
$$\cos\,(180° - \theta) = -\cos\theta, \qquad \sec\,(180° - \theta) = -\sec\theta,$$
$$\tan\,(180° - \theta) = -\tan\theta, \qquad \cot\,(180° - \theta) = -\cot\theta.$$

Now generate an angle $180° + \theta$, and let P be a point on the terminal side of this angle.

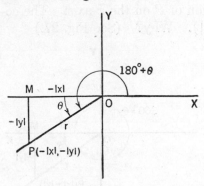

Fig. 26

Let M be the projection of P on the x-axis, and let $-|x|$ be the abscissa and $-|y|$ be the ordinate of P. As before, we have

$$\sin\,(180° + \theta) = \frac{-|y|}{r}, \qquad \csc\,(180° + \theta) = \frac{r}{-|y|},$$

$$\cos\,(180° + \theta) = \frac{-|x|}{r}, \qquad \sec\,(180° + \theta) = \frac{r}{-|x|},$$

$$\tan\,(180° + \theta) = \frac{-|y|}{-|x|}, \qquad \cot\,(180° + \theta) = \frac{-|x|}{-|y|}.$$

Since θ is an acute angle of a right triangle, we have

$$\sin\theta = \frac{|y|}{r}, \qquad \csc\theta = \frac{r}{|y|},$$

$$\cos\theta = \frac{|x|}{r}, \qquad \sec\theta = \frac{r}{|x|},$$

$$\tan\theta = \frac{|y|}{|x|}, \qquad \cot\theta = \frac{|x|}{|y|}.$$

Again, comparing the two sets of values, observe that

$$\sin (180° + \theta) = - \sin \theta, \qquad \csc (180° + \theta) = - \csc \theta,$$
$$\cos (180° + \theta) = - \cos \theta, \qquad \sec (180° + \theta) = - \sec \theta,$$
$$\tan (180° + \theta) = \tan \theta, \qquad \cot (180° + \theta) = \cot \theta.$$

Finally, let us generate an angle $360° - \theta$ in standard position. Choose a point P on the terminal side, and let M be the projection of P on the x-axis. The co-ordinates of P are $(|x|, -|y|)$. Why? (See Fig. 27.)

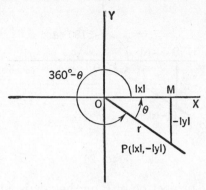

FIG. 27

The functions of $360° - \theta$ are

$$\sin (360° - \theta) = \frac{-|y|}{r}, \qquad \csc (360° - \theta) = \frac{r}{-|y|},$$

$$\cos (360° - \theta) = \frac{|x|}{r}, \qquad \sec (360° - \theta) = \frac{r}{|x|},$$

$$\tan (360° - \theta) = \frac{-|y|}{|x|}, \qquad \cot (360° - \theta) = \frac{|x|}{-|y|}.$$

Referring to the right triangle OMP, we see that

$$\sin \theta = \frac{|y|}{r}, \qquad \csc \theta = \frac{r}{|y|},$$

$$\cos \theta = \frac{|x|}{r}, \qquad \sec \theta = \frac{r}{|x|},$$

$$\tan \theta = \frac{|y|}{|x|}, \qquad \cot \theta = \frac{|x|}{|y|}.$$

So it follows that

$$\sin (360° - \theta) = -\sin \theta, \qquad \csc (360° - \theta) = -\csc \theta,$$
$$\cos (360° - \theta) = \cos \theta, \qquad \sec (360° - \theta) = \sec \theta,$$
$$\tan (360° - \theta) = -\tan \theta, \qquad \cot (360° - \theta) = -\cot \theta.$$

We see, therefore, that if θ is a positive acute angle the trigonometric functions of the angles $180° - \theta$, $180° + \theta$, or $360° - \theta$ are exactly the same as the trigonometric functions of θ except for the *sign* that belongs to the function of the original angle. (See the table at the end of § 8.) The student can probably best remember this result in the following way. Draw the angle whose function is required in the standard position. The function of this angle is *always* the same as the function of the *acute* angle that exists between the terminal side of the angle and the x-axis, prefixed by the *sign* that originally belonged to the function of the given angle.

Examples:

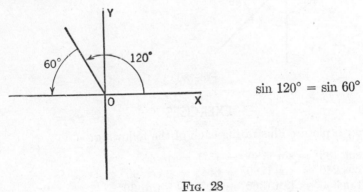

$$\sin 120° = \sin 60°$$

Fig. 28

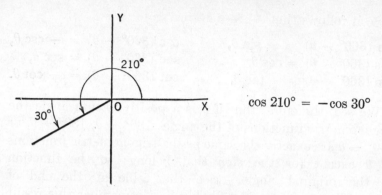

$$\cos 210° = -\cos 30°$$

Fig. 29

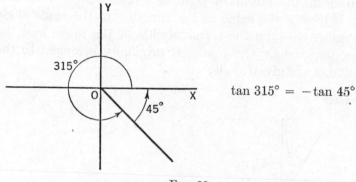

$$\tan 315° = -\tan 45°$$

Fig. 30

EXERCISES

Draw a picture illustrating each of the following:

1. $\sin 135° = \sin (180° - 45°) = \sin 45°.$
2. $\cos 240° = \cos (180° + 60°) = -\cos 60°.$
3. $\tan 330° = \tan (360° - 30°) = -\tan 30°.$
4. $\sin (-45°) = -\sin 45°.$
5. $\cos 1235° = \cos (1235° - 1080°) = \cos 155° = -\cos 25°.$
6. $\sin (-125°) = -\sin 125° = -\sin (180° - 55°) = -\sin 55°.$

If $f(k\pi \pm \theta)$ represents any one of the six trigonometric functions of $k\pi \pm \theta$, where k is an integer and θ a positive acute angle, and if $f(\theta)$ represents the same trigonometric function of θ, then the conclusion of this section can be summed up in a single formula:

$$f(k\pi \pm \theta) = \epsilon f(\theta),$$

where ϵ is $+1$ or -1 according as $f(k\pi \pm \theta)$ is positive or negative.

EXERCISES

1. Express each of the following as a function of a positive acute angle.

(a) $\sin 140°$.

(b) $\cos 225°$.

(c) $\tan 310°$.

(d) $\cot (-25°)$.

(e) $\sin 1095°$.

(f) $\cos 112° 33'$.

(g) $\sec 237° 44'$.

(h) $\cos (-135°)$.

(i) $\tan (-42° 34' 20'')$.

(j) $\sin 116° 33' 30''$.

(k) $\cos (-60° 20')$.

(l) $\sin 2135° 8' 12''$.

(m) $\tan 145° 30' 30''$.

(n) $\cot 130° 15' 10''$.

(o) $\csc (-20° 10' 30'')$.

2. Given that θ is a positive acute angle, use the line segment representation to find the relations between the functions of $180° - \theta$, $180° + \theta$, and $360° - \theta$ and the functions of θ.

13. The functions of $-\theta$ in terms of the functions of θ

By the methods explained in § 9 it is a simple matter to express the functions of $-\theta$ in terms of the same functions of θ, if θ is any angle.

Consider an angle θ whose terminal side falls in quadrant III. Then the terminal side of $-\theta$ will fall in quadrant II. (See Fig. 31.)

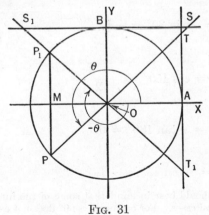

Fig. 31

Let P and P_1 be the points where the terminal sides of θ and $-\theta$, respectively, intersect the *unit* circle. From § 9 we know that $\sin \theta = MP$, $\cos \theta = OM$, $\tan \theta = AT$, $\cot \theta = BS$, $\sec \theta = OT$, and $\csc \theta = OS$; and also that $\sin (-\theta) = MP_1$, $\cos (-\theta) = OM$, $\tan (-\theta) = AT_1$, $\cot (-\theta) = BS_1$, $\sec (-\theta) = OT_1$, and $\csc (-\theta) = OS_1$. Since the segments P_1P and T_1T are bisected by the x-axis, and the segment S_1S is bisected by the y-axis, it follows that $MP_1 = -MP$, $AT_1 = -AT$, $BS_1 = -BS$, $OT_1 = OT$, and $OS_1 = -OS$. From these relations, it follows that

$$\sin (-\theta) = MP_1 = - MP = - \sin \theta,$$
$$\cos (-\theta) = OM = \cos \theta,$$
$$\tan (-\theta) = AT_1 = - AT = - \tan \theta,$$
$$\csc (-\theta) = OS_1 = - OS = - \csc \theta,$$
$$\sec (-\theta) = OT_1 = OT = \sec \theta,$$
$$\cot (-\theta) = BS_1 = - BS = - \cot \theta.$$

Except for the special cases when the terminal sides of θ coincide with the axes, the above relations hold for every value of θ since P and P_1 and T and T_1 are always on opposite sides of the x-axis, and S and S_1 are always on opposite sides of the y-axis. Since we do not distinguish between $+0$ and -0, the relations also hold for the special cases.*

Example 1:
$$\sin (-30°) = -\sin 30° = -\tfrac{1}{2}.$$

Example 2:
$$\cos (-150°) = \cos 150° = -\frac{\sqrt{3}}{2}.$$

Example 3:
$$\tan (-180°) = -\tan 180° = 0.$$

Example 4:
$$\tan (-45°) = -\tan 45° = -1.$$

* The student should bear in mind that some of the functions are not defined for the special cases. For example, $\csc 0°$ does not exist.

EXERCISES

1. Let the terminal side of θ fall in quadrant IV, and derive the relations between the functions of $-\theta$ and the functions of θ.

2. Repeat problem 1 with the terminal side of θ in quadrant II.

3. Repeat problem 1 with the terminal side of θ in quadrant I,

4. Evaulate: $\sin(-60°)$, $\cos(-240°)$, $\cot(-90°)$, $\sin(-180°)$. $\tan(-120°)$, and $\sec(-30°)$.

14. Relations between complementary angles

If A and B are positive acute angles and $A + B = 90°$, they can be the acute angles in a right triangle, and it follows readily that the trigonometric functions of each angle are equal, respectively, to the conamed trigonometric functions of the other.

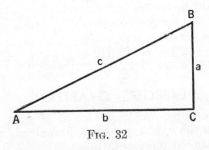

FIG. 32

We have

$$\sin A = a/c = \cos B, \qquad \cot A = b/a = \tan B,$$
$$\cos A = b/c = \sin B, \qquad \sec A = c/b = \csc B,$$
$$\tan A = a/b = \cot B, \qquad \csc A = c/a = \sec B.$$

Conversely, if A and B are positive acute angles and if $\sin A = \cos B$, $\tan A = \cot B$, or $\sec A = \csc B$, then $A + B = 90°$.

Proof: Suppose $\sin A = \cos B$. Since A is acute there exists a right triangle having A as one angle. (See Fig. 32.) But this fixes for us the value of a/c and there is only one positive acute angle that has this for its cosine. Since B, the other acute angle of the triangle, has a/c for its cosine, it follows that when $\sin A = \cos B$, $A + B = 90°$.

The same argument holds when $\tan A = \cot B$, or $\sec A = \csc B$.

Example:

Find θ if $\tan 2\theta = \cot (\theta + 30°)$, where 2θ and $\theta + 30°$ are positive acute angles. Since we must have $2\theta + (\theta + 30°) = 90°$, it follows that $3\theta = 60°$ or $\theta = 20°$.

EXERCISES

Find θ in each of the following exercises if the angles appearing are positive acute angles:

1. $\sin 2\theta = \cos \theta$.
2. $\tan (\theta + 40°) = \cot (2\theta - 30°)$.
3. $\sec (2\theta - 10°) = \csc\theta$.
4. $\cot (\theta - 10°) = \tan 3\theta$.
5. $\csc (\theta + 5°) = \sec 2\theta$.
6. $\cos (\theta/2) = \sin 3\theta$.
7. $\tan [(3\theta/2) - 2°] = \cot (\theta/2)$.
8. $\sin (\theta - 15°) = \cos (\theta/2)$.

EXERCISES: CHAPTER II

1. Define the trigonometric functions of an angle whose terminal side lies in the fourth quadrant, and obtain their algebraic signs and line segment representations.

2. Generate an angle θ whose terminal side lies in quadrant III. Define the trigonometric functions of θ, explain their algebraic signs, and give the line segment representation.

3. Construct an angle whose cosine is $-\frac{3}{5}$. Is there only one solution?

4. Given that $\cos \theta = -\frac{3}{5}$ and $\sin \theta$ is negative, find the remaining functions.

5. Construct the angles if $\cot \theta = -3$. Find the remaining functions if $\sin \theta$ is negative.

6. Construct the angles θ, given that:

(a) $\tan \theta = 1.3$.
(b) $\sin \theta = \frac{2}{3}$.
(c) $\sec \theta = 2$.
(d) $\cos \theta = -\frac{2}{5}$.
(e) $\tan \theta = -\frac{2}{3}$.
(f) $\cot \theta = -4$.
(g) $\sin \theta = -1$.
(h) $\csc \theta = \frac{3}{2}$.
(i) $\tan \theta = 2$.
(j) $\cos \theta = \frac{1}{2}$.
(k) $\sec \theta = -4$.
(l) $\sin \theta = \frac{1}{3}$.
(m) $\cos \theta = 0$.
(n) $\sin \theta = -\frac{2}{5}$.
(o) $\csc \theta = -3$.

7. Construct the angle whose cosecant is 7 and whose tangent is negative. Find the remaining trigonometric functions.

8. Given $\sin \theta = \frac{2}{3}$ and $\csc \theta = \frac{3}{2}$ construct $\theta < 360°$. Are there one or two solutions?

9. Using the line segment representation, explain the changes in $\cos \theta$, $\tan \theta$, and $\csc \theta$ as θ varies from $0°$ to $360°$.

10. For a given sine, is there only one angle θ less than $360°$ associated with it? How many are greater than $360°$?

11. Is it possible to construct θ if $\sin \theta = 2$? Why? Which of the trigonometric functions are restricted in value? Which are not?

12. If θ is any positive acute angle, the angles whose terminal sides lie in the other three quadrants may be represented by $\pi - \theta$, $\pi + \theta$, and $2\pi - \theta$, respectively. Write out carefully the relations between the functions of $\pi - \theta$, $\pi + \theta$, and $2\pi - \theta$ and the functions of θ.

13. How are the results of problem 12 applied to angles greater than $360°$?

14. Find the relations between the trigonometric functions of the positive acute angle θ and the functions of the following angles:

(a) $90° + \theta$. *Hint*: Draw a circle. Generate a positive acute angle θ. Construct $90° + \theta$. Compare similar triangles, being careful to note directions of the lengths involved.

(b) $90° - \theta$.   (c) $270° + \theta$.   (d) $270° - \theta$.

15. Compare the results obtained in the above four exercises with the results of problem 12. What is the outstanding difference?

16. Express the trigonometric functions of the following angles in terms of the functions of a positive acute angle:

(a) $120°$.   (f) $480°$.   (k) $360°$.
(b) $315°$.   (g) $-240°$.   (l) $540°$.
(c) $-60°$.   (h) $1395°$.   (m) $-276°$.
(d) $-210°$.   (i) $-765°$.   (n) $1095°$.
(e) $150°$.   (j) $-45°$.   (o) $123° 18' 29''$.

17. Express the trigonometric functions of the following angles in terms of the functions of a positive acute angle:

(a) $223° 48' 10''$.   (f) $-23° 15' 47''$.   (k) $3\pi/4$ radians.
(b) $344° 43' 32''$.   (g) $650° 30' 30''$.   (l) $-5\pi/6$ radians.
(c) $-212° 24' 35''$. (h) $209° 8' 25''$.   (m) 3 radians.
(d) $95° 6' 4''$.   (i) $312° 38' 19''$.   (n) $4\pi/3$ radians.
(e) $428° 25' 12''$.   (j) $-214° 21' 51''$. (o) $18\pi/5$ radians.

18. Using the results of problem 14, express the functions of the following angles in terms of the conamed functions of a corresponding acute angle.

(a) 60°. (g) 315°. (m) 780°.
(b) 28°. (h) 265°. (n) 140°.
(c) 112°, (i) 340°. (o) 240°.
(d) 150°. (j) −130°. (p) −345°.
(c) 210°. (k) −30°. (q) $3\pi/4$ radians.
(f) 230°. (l) −225°. (r) $-5\pi/6$ radians.

19. By using § 12 and § 14, reduce the following trigonometric functions to equivalent expressions in terms of a positive angle no greater than 45°.

(a) cos 60°. (f) sin 281°. (k) tan 100° 29′.
(b) sin 125°. (g) cos (−163°). (l) sin 213° 34′.
(c) tan (−52°). (h) cos 1019°. (m) cos 133° 20′.
(d) cot 235°. (i) sin 464°. (n) sin (−210° 25′).
(e) sec 120°. (j) cot (−2000°). (o) sec 312° 15′.

20. Solve the following equations for θ, where in each case the angles appearing are positive acute angles:

(a) tan $(2\theta - 4°) = $ cot $(\theta - 2°)$.
(b) sin $(\theta - 3°) = $ cos $(3\theta + 2°)$.
(c) sec $\theta = $ csc $(4\theta - 5°)$.
(d) cos $3\theta = $ sin 2θ.
(e) cot $\theta = $ tan 3θ.
(f) cos $(2\theta - 10°) = $ sin $(\theta + 20°)$.
(g) sec $(\theta - 60°) = $ csc $(\theta + 20°)$
(h) sin $(\theta + 30°) = $ cos 2θ.
(i) sin $(\theta + 30°) = $ cos $(2\theta - 15°)$.
(j) tan $(2\theta + 10°) = $ cot $(\theta + 50°)$.
(k) sec $(\theta - 20°) = $ csc $(\theta + 20°)$.
(l) cos $(3\theta + 40°) = $ sin 2θ.
(m) tan $(\theta + 10°) = $ cot $(\theta + 70°)$.
(n) sin $(2\theta - 45°) = $ cos $(\theta + 15°)$.

Chapter III

SIGNIFICANT FIGURES AND THE NUMERICAL VALUES OF THE TRIGONOMETRIC FUNCTIONS

In the previous chapter the trigonometric functions of any angle were defined, the angle was constructed when the functions of it were given, the changes in the functions were studied for the angle varying from 0° to 360°, and it was shown that a trigonometric function of any angle could be expressed in terms of the same function of a corresponding positive acute angle. In this chapter we shall learn how to use tables and from them find the *approximate* numerical values for the functions of any angle. Much of the work from now on is concerned with numerical calculations, and so we start this chapter with a brief discussion of the meaning of significant figures.

15. Significant figures*

In any work in which physical measurements are to be made it is impossible to be 100 per cent accurate. Since we must approximate, we want our approximations to be as accurate as possible and we want persons reading the problem to understand what the numbers mean. This requires some consideration of *significant figures*. The following examples will illustrate the nature of our problem.

If a carpenter needs to cut a piece of board 3 feet long from a larger piece, experiment has shown that he must be careful not to vary by more than $\frac{1}{32}$ of an inch. Since $\frac{1}{32} = 0.03125$

* May be omitted for a brief course.

47

exactly, the length of his piece of board must not be more than 36.03125 inches or less than 35.96875 inches. The carpenter would therefore probably interpret 3 feet to mean not more than about 36.03 inches and not less than about 35.97 inches.

If one were to measure an object one foot long with an ordinary meter stick, one would probably read the length to be 30.5 centimeters. This means that the true length is equal to or more than 30.45 centimeters and less than 30.55 centimeters. It would give a false impression if an answer of 30.50 were given, since 30.50 suggests an error of not more than .005, a greater degree of precision than it is possible to obtain with the meter stick. No more digits should appear in a measurement than the accuracy of the data warrants.

The "significant figures" of any approximate number begin with the first figure on the left that is not 0 and end with the last figure on the right. So 1200, 2.364, 0.01300, and 0.002000 all have four significant figures. If any of the figures that appear are not significant, this should be so stated in the problem. For example, in a problem dealing with the content of a bin we might read the volume to be "130,000 cubic inches correct to three significant figures." This would mean the volume was less than 130,500 and more than or equal to 129,500 but we would not know how much less or how much more. We always read the significant figures from left to right. So, for our example, the significant figures are 1, 3, and 0.

The number of significant figures should not be confused with the position of the decimal point. As an illustration, 238, 2.38, 0.0238 all have three significant figures, namely 2, 3, and 8.

The best way to write a number so that the significant figures are apparent is to write it as a number between 1 and 10, in which all the significant figures appear, multiplied by an integral power of 10. For example, 132,000 would be written 1.32000×10^5. If 132,000 is correct to only three significant figures, we would indicate this by writing 1.32×10^5. The number 0.00460 would be written 4.60×10^{-3}. The exponent that is attached to the 10 is $+K$ or $-K$, where K is the number of places through which the decimal point has been moved. When the decimal is moved to the left, the number is made smaller; so to bring it back to its original value we must multiply it by 10^K, where K is a positive integer.

Example:

$134.6 = 1.346 \times 10^2$.

If the decimal is moved to the right, the number is increased; so we must multiply it by 10^{-K}, where K is a positive integer.

Example:

$0.00423 = 4.23 \times 10^{-3}$.

This method of writing numbers is particularly useful and beneficial in the sciences, where very large numbers or very small numbers are constantly in use. For example, there are approximately 602,000,000,000,000,000,000,000 molecules in a gram molecule of any substance. Here 6, 0, and 2 are significant, and a much more convenient way of writing this number is 6.02×10^{23}.

16. Operations with approximate numbers*

It may happen, in carrying out the computation of a problem, that more figures appear in the result than are considered significant. When this does occur we *round off* our number to the desired number of significant figures. By this we mean that if the digit to the right of the last figure that is regarded as significant is greater than or equal to 5, we add 1 to the last significant figure, but if it is less than 5

* May be omitted for a brief course.

we drop it.*   For example, if a surveyor is measuring the distance between two trees and his calculations come out to be 136.47 feet he would probably round off his result to either 136.5 feet or even 136 feet if he did not trust the determination of the fraction.

If an artilleryman calculates the range of an enemy battery to be 3243.6 yards away, the .6 would have little significance. In fact the significant figures would probably be 3, 2, and 4 and the measurement could well be indicated by 3.24×10^3 yards.   This result would mean that the enemy is less than 3245 yards away and more than or equal to 3235 yards away.

When adding or subtracting data that have been obtained from approximate measurements whose significant figures do not have the same terminal places, we first write our numbers in appropriate columns for adding or subtracting.   Then the terminal place of the significant figure of the result should, in general, agree with that number whose terminal place is furthest to the left.

Example 1:

The following measurements were taken and their sum is required: 314.2, 21.368, 1.45, and 0.0026.

$$
\begin{array}{r}
314.2 \\
21.368 \\
1.45 \\
0.0026 \\
\hline
337.0206
\end{array}
$$

Since 314.2 has its terminal place furthest to the left, we would write our result as 337.0 or 3.370×10^2.

Example 2:

The difference between the approximate numbers 13.46 and 2.173 is required.   Obviously, $13.46 - 2.173 = 11.287$, but 13.46 has its terminal place furthest to the left, so the result should be given as 11.29, or 1.129×10.

---

* When the digit to be discarded is 5, some calculators prefer to add 1 to the last significant figure if it makes that figure even and otherwise to drop it. Using this convention 0.001025 is 0.00102 to three significant figures while 0.001035 is 0.00104 to three significant figures.

In the multiplication and division of approximate numbers, the number of significant figures in the result should, in general, be the same as that of the number appearing in the problem having the least number of significant figures.

Example 3:

A rectangular field is measured and its dimensions found to be 31.5 rods by 17.6 rods.   What is its approximate area?

The direct product is 554.40 square rods.   Since each length is given to three significant figures, the approximate area is usually given as 554 square rods, or 5.54×10^2 square rods.

Example 4:

Evaluate 13.4/27, where numerator and denominator are approximate numbers.   Here the result should be given to two significant figures.   We carry the calculations to three figures and round off the result.   We have 13.4/27 = 0.496, which may be written as 5.0×10^{-1} when properly rounded off.

If a problem involves repeated multiplication, or multiplication and division, and the factors appearing do not all contain the same number of significant figures, it is advisable, before carrying out the calculation, to round off each factor to one more significant figure than is required in the result.

Example 5:

Evaluate $(3.1416 \times 0.0020)/0.6735$.   Since the result should have two significant figures, we rewrite our problem
$$(3.14 \times 0.0020)/0.674 = 0.00933,$$
or 9.3×10^{-3} after rounding off the result.

Most of the exercises appearing hereafter in this text have been worked according to the ideas expounded in this section, and the answers have been rounded off to the number of significant figures consistent with the data in the exercises.

It is hoped that after reading § 15 and § 16 the student will be familiar with the general idea of significant figures. He must be sure he understands that the *number of figures to be considered significant* is determined by the particular problem under discussion.

EXERCISES

1. Round off each of the following numbers to three significant figures and write the result as a number between 1 and 10 times an integral power of 10.

5128;   0.03127;   13,050;   0.6046.

2. Approximate each of the following computations involving approximate numbers to the proper number of significant figures:

(a) 1.367×0.42.   (d) $0.29735/0.0400$.

(b) 0.265×34.0.   (e) $(0.4826 \times 134.68)/2.90$.

(c) $72.36/0.49$.   (f) $(1.8 \times 243.6)/0.425$.

17. Numerical computations for the trigonometric functions of 0°, 30°, 45°, 60°, and 90°

For the general problem of evaluating the trigonometric functions, tables have been computed. In order to understand how these tables are compiled it is necessary to be familiar with more advanced mathematics. With the aid of plane geometry, however, it is possible to evaluate exactly the trigonometric functions of certain angles.

a. The functions of 45°. — Construct an isosceles right triangle OPR. The acute angles are each equal to 45°. Let the length of each of the sides adjacent to the right angle be equal to 1. Then the length of the hypotenuse is equal to $\sqrt{2}$. By the definition of the functions of an acute angle of a right triangle, we have

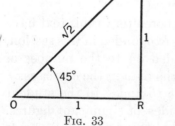

$$\sin 45° = 1/\sqrt{2} = \cos 45°,$$

$$\tan 45° = 1 = \cot 45°,$$

$$\sec 45° = \sqrt{2} = \csc 45°.$$

Fig. 33

b. The functions of 30° *and* 60°. — Construct an equilateral triangle ABC and let the lengths of the sides be equal to 2.

Bisect angle B and let D be the point where this bisector meets AC.   Then ADB is a right triangle in which $AD = 1$ and $BD = \sqrt{3}$, so we have

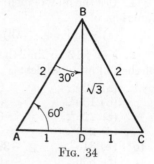

$\sin 60° = \sqrt{3}/2 = \cos 30°$,
$\cos 60° = \frac{1}{2} = \sin 30°$,
$\tan 60° = \sqrt{3} = \cot 30°$,
$\cot 60° = 1/\sqrt{3} = \tan 30°$,
$\sec 60° = 2 = \csc 30°$,
$\csc 60° = 2/\sqrt{3} = \sec 30°$.

FIG. 34

c. The functions of 0° *and* 90°. — These have already been discussed in § 9, and we shall merely list the results here.

$\sin 0° = 0.$ $\sin 90° = 1.$
$\cos 0° = 1.$ $\cos 90° = 0.$
$\tan 0° = 0.$ $\tan 90°$ does not exist.
$\cot 0°$ does not exist. $\cot 90° = 0.$
$\sec 0° = 1.$ $\sec 90°$ does not exist.
$\csc 0°$ does not exist. $\csc 90° = 1.$

The following table gives the results for the sine, cosine, and tangent of 0°, 30°, 45°, 60°, 90°, 180°, 270°, and 360°.

Function	0°	30°	45°	60°	90°	180°	270°	360°
sine	0	$\frac{1}{2}$	$\frac{\sqrt{2}}{2}$	$\frac{\sqrt{3}}{2}$	1	0	−1	0
cosine	1	$\frac{\sqrt{3}}{2}$	$\frac{\sqrt{2}}{2}$	$\frac{1}{2}$	0	−1	0	1
tangent	0	$\frac{1}{\sqrt{3}}$	1	$\sqrt{3}$	Does not exist	0	Does not exist	0

Exercise:

Complete the table for the cotangent, the secant, and the cosecant.

EXERCISES

1. Use the line segment representation to find the trigonometric functions of:

(a) π radians.   (b) $3\pi/2$ radians.   (c) $360°$.   (d) $450°$.

2. Use § 12 to find the values of the trigonometric functions of the following angles:

(a) $120°$.	(k) $1395°$.	(u) $\pi/4$ radians.
(b) $150°$.	(l) $-765°$.	(v) $-\pi$ radians.
(c) $225°$.	(m) $-45°$.	(w) $\pi/6$ radians.
(d) $210°$.	(n) $390°$.	(x) $-4\pi/3$ radians.
(e) $315°$.	(o) $540°$.	(y) $-3\pi/2$ radians.
(f) $330°$.	(p) $-270°$.	(z) $-\pi/3$ radians.
(g) $240°$.	(q) $1110°$.	(aa) $-5\pi/2$ radians.
(h) $300°$.	(r) $-720°$.	(ab) $7\pi/6$ radians.
(i) $-210°$.	(s) $-240°$.	(ac) $-5\pi/6$ radians.
(j) $-60°$.	(t) $-480°$.	(ad) $-7\pi/6$ radians.

3. Verify numerically that:

(a) $\sin 60° = 2 \sin 30° \cos 30°$.

(b) $\cos 60° = 1 - 2 \sin^2 30°$.

(c) $\cos 60° = 2 \cos^2 30° - 1$.

(d) $\sin 90° = 2 \sin 45° \cos 45°$.

(e) $\cos 90° = \cos^2 45° - \sin^2 45°$.

(f) $\cos (90° - 30°) = \cos 90° \cos 30° + \sin 90° \sin 30°$.

4. Verify that the following relations are true:

(a) $\cos 90° = \cos 60° \cos 30° - \sin 60° \sin 30°$.

(b) $\sin 120° = \sin 180° \cos 60° - \cos 180° \sin 60°$.

(c) $\sin 30° = \sin 60° \cos 30° - \cos 60° \sin 30°$.

5. Find the values of each of the following:

(a) $(\sin 30°)(\tan 60°)(\cos 60°)(\cot 45°)$.

(b) $(\cos 120°)(\sin 150°)(\sec 180°)(\cos 60°)$.

(c) $(\cos \pi)\left(\sin \dfrac{3\pi}{2}\right)\left(\tan \dfrac{\pi}{4}\right)$.

(d) $\left[\cot\left(-\dfrac{\pi}{4}\right)\right]\left[\tan \dfrac{3\pi}{4}\right]\left[\cos 2\pi\right]\left[\sin \dfrac{\pi}{6}\right]$.

6. What is the perimeter of a right triangle if one acute angle is $45°$ and the hypotenuse is 37 feet? What is the area of the triangle?

7. A ladder leaning against a house is 23 feet long. If it makes an angle of 60° with the horizontal, how far is the foot of the ladder from the house?

8. Find the area of an equilateral triangle if the length of a side is 38 inches.

9. Two consecutive milestones are located at A and B on a straight road, and a pole is erected at C some distance from the road.   If angles CAB and CBA are each found to be 60°, how far is the pole from the road?

10. Find the unknown sides and angles of the following right triangles.   *Hint.* Use the definitions of the trigonometric functions.

(a)   (b)

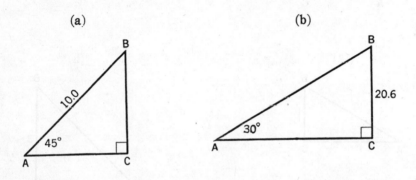

(c)   (d)

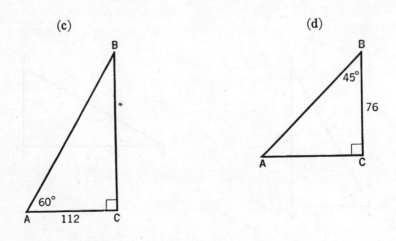

(e)

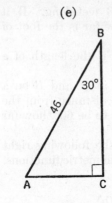

(f)

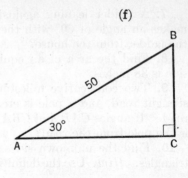

(g)

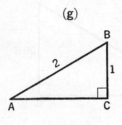

(h)

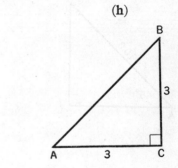

(i)

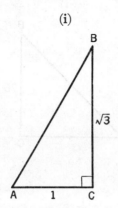

(j)

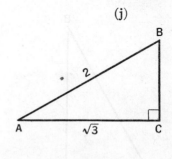

18. Numerical values of the functions of any angle

Tables of the values of the trigonometric functions have been calculated, correct to a certain number of decimals. These tables usually give the values of the sine, cosine, tangent, and cotangent of angles from 0° to 90°. To find the functions of *angles greater than 90°* the results given in § 12 < must be used. Turning to a table of the natural trigonometric functions, we find, for angles less than 45°, that the degrees are indicated at the *top* of the page and that the minutes are in the *left-hand* column. The trigonometric functions of the angles appear in the columns to the right of the minute column. For angles greater than 45°, the degrees are indicated at the *bottom* of the page, the minutes are in the *right-hand* column, and the trigonometric functions of the angles are read from the columns to the *left* of the minute column. As an example, let us find cos 26° 39′ in a table listing the values of the trigonometric functions to five significant figures. First turn to the page *headed* by 26°, next look down the column of minutes *at the left* for 39′, and finally read the number opposite 39′ in *the cosine column* to be .89376.

Hence   cos 26° 39′ = 0.89376.

To find sin 63° 21′ we look at the bottom of the page for 63°. Now look up the right-hand minute column for 21′, and finally read the number opposite 21′ in the *sine column* to be 0.89376. Notice that this is the same result as for cos 26° 39′. Why?

By using § 12 we can easily obtain the functions of any angle.

Example 1:

Evaluate cos 257° 18′.

From § 12 it follows that cos 257° 18′ = cos (180° + 77° 18′) = −cos 77° 18′. From the tables we find cos 77° 18′ = 0.21985. Hence cos 257° 18′ = −0.21985.

Example 2:

Evaluate tan $(-528°\ 36')$.

Step by step, it follows that tan $(-528°\ 36')$ = tan $(-168°\ 36')$ = tan $191°\ 24'$ = tan $11°\ 24'$ = 0.20164.

EXERCISES

Evaluate the following by use of a table:

1. sin 22° 33'.	**11.** sin 63° 40'.	**21.** cos 111° 10'.
2. cos 19° 45'.	**12.** cos 75° 16'.	**22.** sin 203° 40'.
3. tan 43° 7'.	**13.** tan 59° 24'.	**23.** tan $(-20°\ 30')$.
4. cot 34° 25'.	**14.** cot 80° 14'.	**24.** cot 315° 10'.
5. cos 61° 34'.	**15.** sin 112° 20'.	**25.** tan 106° 20'.
6. sin 45° 50'.	**16.** cos 203° 35'.	**26.** sin 330° 28'.
7. tan 12° 9'.	**17.** tan 315° 30'.	**27.** cos $(-44°\ 6')$.
8. cot 61° 44'	**18.** sin $(-30°\ 50')$.	**28.** cot 206° 18'.
9. cos 73° 36'.	**19.** cot 104° 32'.	**29.** sin $(-113°\ 52')$.
10. tan 80° 51'.	**20.** tan 412° 20'.	**30.** cos $(-212°\ 3')$.

19. Interpolation

When an angle is measured to seconds we find the functions of the angle by a process known as interpolation. The method of interpolation assumes that the differences between angles are proportional to the differences between their trigonometric functions. For angles differing only by seconds, no error is introduced when four-place or five-place tables are used. By this we mean that the error due to the assumption would appear somewhere after the sixth decimal place.

Example 1:

Evaluate sin 33° 16′ 27″.

Since sin θ *increases* with θ in quadrant I, it follows that
$$\text{sin } 33°\ 16' < \text{sin } 33°\ 16'\ 27'' < \text{sin } 33°\ 17'.$$

From the tables

$$\begin{aligned}
\text{sin } 33°\ 17' &= 0.54878, \\
\text{sin } 33°\ 16' &= \underline{0.54854,} \\
\text{sin } 33°\ 17' - \text{sin } 33°\ 16' &= 0.00024.
\end{aligned}$$

Now $\sin 33° 16' 27'' = \sin 33° 16' + x = 0.54854 + x$. We assume that

$$\frac{x}{0.00024} = \frac{27}{60} = \frac{9}{20}, \text{ or } x = 0.00011, \text{ approximately.}$$

Therefore

$$\sin 33° 16' 27'' = 0.54865.$$

A convenient way of arranging the above calculations is the following:

$$60\left\{ \begin{array}{l} \sin 33° 17' \quad\quad = 0.54878 \\ 27\left\{ \begin{array}{l} \sin 33° 16' 27'' = 0.54854 + x \\ \sin 33° 16' \quad\quad = 0.54854 \end{array} \right\} x \end{array} \right\} 0.00024$$

Hence $\quad\quad\quad\quad \dfrac{x}{0.00024} = \dfrac{27}{60}, \text{ or } x = 0.00011.$

Therefore

$$\sin 33° 16' 27'' = 0.54865.$$

NOTE: Since we are interested in carrying our results to five places only, we shall drop the sixth place, adding either 0 or 1 to the fifth place, depending upon whether or not the number in the sixth place is less than, greater than, or equal to 5. (See § 16.)

Example 2:

Find $\cos 53° 33' 18''$.

Since $\cos \theta$ *diminishes* as θ increases in quadrant I, it follows that

$$\cos 53° 33' > \cos 53° 33' 18'' > \cos 53° 34'.$$

The calculations follow:

$$60\left\{ \begin{array}{l} \cos 53° 34' \quad\quad = 0.59389 \\ 18\left\{ \begin{array}{l} \cos 53° 33' 18'' = 0.59412 - x \\ \cos 53° 33' \quad\quad = 0.59412 \end{array} \right\} x \end{array} \right\} 0.00023$$

Interpolating,

$$\frac{x}{0.00023} = \frac{18}{60}, \text{ or } x = 0.00007, \text{ approximately.}$$

Therefore

$$\cos 53° 33' 18'' = 0.59405.$$

Example 3:

Find θ, given that $\tan \theta = 1.6939$.

We look in the *tangent columns* of the tables for the numbers between which 1.6939 lies, and then proceed as follows:

$$60\left\{\begin{array}{l} \tan 59°\ 27' \quad = 1.6943 \\ y\left\{\begin{array}{l} \tan 59°\ 26'\ y'' = 1.6939 \\ \tan 59°\ 26' \quad = 1.6932 \end{array}\right\}0.0007 \end{array}\right\}0.0011$$

Interpolating,

$$\frac{y}{60} = \frac{0.0007}{0.0011}, \text{ or } y = 38, \text{ approximately.}$$

Therefore
$$\theta = 59°\ 26'\ 38''.$$

This is not the only possible value. From the table in § 8 and the first paragraph of § 10 we know that a given trigonometric function generally determines two positive angles less than 360°. The tangent is positive if the terminal side of θ lies in quadrant I or quadrant III and hence, by § 12, we have

$$\theta = 59°\ 26'\ 38'', \text{ or } \theta = 239°\ 26'\ 38''.$$

Example 4:

Find θ, given that $\cot \theta = 0.99314$.

This time looking in the cotangent columns, we find:

$$60\left\{\begin{array}{l} \cot 45°\ 12' \quad = 0.99304 \\ y\left\{\begin{array}{l} \cot 45°\ 11'\ y'' = 0.99314 \\ \cot 45°\ 11' \quad = 0.99362 \end{array}\right\}0.00048 \end{array}\right\}0.00058$$

Interpolating,

$$\frac{y}{60} = \frac{0.00048}{0.00058}, \text{ or } y = 50, \text{ approximately.}$$

Since for $\cot \theta$ positive, the terminal side of θ lies in quadrant I or quadrant III, we have

$$\theta = 45°\ 11'\ 50'', \text{ or } \theta = 225°\ 11'\ 50''.$$

Example 5:

Find cos 150° 20′ 32″.

By § 12 we know that cos 150° 20′ 32″ = cos (180° − 29° 39′ 28″)
= − cos 29° 39′ 28″.

From the tables:

$$60\left\{\begin{array}{l}\quad\cos 29°\ 40′\qquad = 0.86892 \\ 28\left\{\begin{array}{l}\cos 29°\ 39′\ 28″ = 0.86906 - x \\ \cos 29°\ 39′\qquad = 0.86906\end{array}\right\}x\end{array}\right\}0.00014$$

Interpolating,

$$\frac{x}{0.00014} = \frac{28}{60}, \text{ or } x = 0.00007.$$

Hence

$$\cos 29°\ 39′\ 28″ = 0.86899.$$

Therefore

$$\cos 150°\ 20′\ 32″ = -0.86899.$$

Example 6:

Find θ, given that sin θ = −0.39461.

Since sin θ is negative, θ may be in quadrant III or quadrant IV.

Let α be the positive acute angle such that sin α = 0.39461; then θ = 180° + α, or θ = 360° − α. We find α as follows:

$$60\left\{\begin{array}{l}\quad\sin 23°\ 15′\qquad = 0.39474 \\ y\left\{\begin{array}{l}\sin 23°\ 14′\ y″ = 0.39461 \\ \sin 23°\ 14′\qquad = 0.39448\end{array}\right\}13\end{array}\right\}26$$

and

$$\frac{y}{60} = \frac{13}{26}, \text{ or } y = 30.$$

Hence

$$\alpha = 23°\ 14′\ 30″.$$

Therefore

$$\theta = 203°\ 14′\ 30″, \text{ or } \theta = 336°\ 45′\ 30″.$$

Example 7:

Sometimes the table of the natural functions contains only the angles in intervals of 5 minutes. In this case we must interpolate to find the functions of the intervening angles. So to find $\sin 35° 13'$, we would have

$$5\left\{ 3\left\{\begin{matrix} \sin 35° 15' = 0.57715 \\ \sin 35° 13' = 0.57596 + x \\ \sin 35° 10' = 0.57596 \end{matrix}\right\} x \right\}119$$

Interpolating,

$$3/5 = x/119, \text{ or } x = 71, \text{ approximately.}$$

So $\sin 35° 13' = 0.57667.$

EXERCISES

1. Find the value of each of the following:
   (a) $\sin 31° 22'$.
   (b) $\cos 82° 14'$.
   (c) $\tan 10° 35'$.
   (d) $\cot 15° 21'$.
   (e) $\cot 41° 32' 27''$.
   (f) $\sin 101° 29' 12''$.
   (g) $\tan 79° 25' 22''$.
   (h) $\cot 53° 3' 30''$.
   (i) $\cos 129° 43' 14''$.
   (j) $\sin (-5° 46' 30'')$.
   (k) $\cos 238° 19' 43''$.
   (l) $\cos (-812° 78')$.
   (m) $\tan 315° 14' 10''$.
   (n) $\sin 28° 51' 11''$.
   (o) $\tan 68° 6' 25''$.
   (p) $\cos 79° 23' 14''$.
   (q) $\tan 321° 31' 17''$.
   (r) $\sin 231° 4' 26''$.

2. Find the positive angles less than 360° satisfying each of the following:
   (a) $\sin x = 0.67123$.
   (b) $\cos x = 0.41286$.
   (c) $\tan x = 0.31984$.
   (d) $\sin A = -0.71147$.
   (e) $\cot A = 0.29316$.
   (f) $\cos y = 0.65344$.
   (g) $\cot \theta = 3.1246$.
   (h) $\cos y = 0.91248$.
   (i) $\tan x = -2.3617$.
   (j) $\sin B = 0.71245$.
   (k) $\cos B = -0.21036$.
   (l) $\tan \theta = 1.6422$.
   (m) $\sin \theta = 0.29468$.
   (n) $\tan y = 3.1664$.
   (o) $\cos y = -0.34216$.
   (p) $\cot x = -0.98175$.
   (q) $\sin x = -0.46238$.
   (r) $\cos \theta = 0.87855$.

EXERCISES: CHAPTER III

1. Without using the tables, find the trigonometric functions of the following angles:

(a) 120°.   (h) 1395°.   (o) −720°.
(b) 315°.   (i) −765°.   (p) 1950°.
(c) −60°.   (j) −405°.   (q) $4\pi/3$ radians.
(d) −210°.   (k) 390°.   (r) $13\pi/4$ radians.
(e) 150°.   (l) 600°.   (s) $-5\pi/6$ radians.
(f) −480°.   (m) −270°.   (t) $-5\pi/2$ radians.
(g) −240°.   (n) 1110°.   (u) $-3\pi/4$ radians.

2. Evaluate the following trigonometric functions:

(a) sin 130° 29′ 33″.   (i) tan (−210° 45′ 50″).
(b) cos 200° 18′ 27″.   (j) cos 115° 40′ 20″.
(c) tan (−34° 35′ 10″).   (k) tan 740° 38′ 20″.
(d) cot 26° 40′ 13″.   (l) cot 419° 22′ 30″.
(e) sin 210° 30′ 40″.   (m) sin (−235° 10′ 50″).
(f) cos (−135° 15′ 35″).   (n) cos 310° 15′ 25″.
(g) sin 330° 20′ 43″.   (o) tan (−34° 28′ 45″).
(h) cot 210° 35′ 20″.   (p) cot (−420° 18′ 10″).

3. Find the smallest positive angle less than 360° satisfying each of the following relations:

(a) sin x = 0.53162.   (i) tan A = 0.31497.
(b) cos θ = 0.72139. (j) cos x = 0.34612.
(c) tan x = 1.4127.   (k) sin B = 0.64425.
(d) sin θ = 0.23974. (l) tan x = −1.3214.
(e) tan θ = −2.3461. (m) cos y = 0.29218.
(f) cot A = 0.42793.   (n) cot A = −2.6176.
(g) cos θ = −0.86144. (o) sin θ = 0.42983.
(h) sin θ = −0.73515.

4. Find all the positive angles less than 360° satisfying each of the following:

(a) sin $\alpha = \frac{2}{3}$.   (g) cos $\alpha = \frac{1}{4}$.   (m) tan $y = -\frac{2}{5}$.
(b) cos $\alpha = -\frac{3}{4}$.   (h) sin $\alpha = \frac{2}{9}$.   (n) cos $\alpha = -\frac{1}{6}$.
(c) tan $x = \frac{3}{5}$.   (i) tan $\beta = \frac{4}{3}$.   (o) sin $\alpha = -\frac{2}{3}$.
(d) cot $x = \frac{2}{7}$.   (j) sin $\beta = \frac{7}{8}$.   (p) sec $x = -2$.
(e) sec $\theta = 3$.   (k) sec $x = \frac{5}{3}$.   (q) csc $x = -\frac{7}{6}$.
(f) csc $\theta = \frac{8}{5}$.   (l) cot $y = \frac{5}{9}$.   (r) cot $\theta = -\frac{6}{7}$.

5. A field has the shape of a right triangle. If one acute angle is 30°, and the length of the hypotenuse is 123 rods, what is the perimeter of the field to the nearest tenth of a rod?

Chapter IV

LOGARITHMS

20. Introduction

An important use of logarithms is to simplify numerical computations. With the aid of logarithms a problem of multiplication is replaced by one of addition, a problem of division is replaced by one of subtraction, and the more difficult problem of raising to a power or extracting a root is replaced by one of multiplication or division, usually by a simple number.

An understanding of logarithms requires familiarity with the definitions and laws of exponents. For purpose of review, we shall state some of these definitions and laws here.

Definitions:

1. $a^o = 1$; thus $3^o = 1$.

2. $a^{-n} = 1/a^n$; thus $2^{-3} = \dfrac{1}{2^3}$.

3. $a^{\frac{1}{n}} = \sqrt[n]{a}$; thus $7^{\frac{1}{3}} = \sqrt[3]{7}$.

4. $a^{\frac{p}{q}} = \sqrt[q]{a^p} = (\sqrt[q]{a})^p$; thus $5^{-\frac{2}{3}} = 1/5^{\frac{2}{3}} = 1/(\sqrt[3]{5})^2$.

Laws:

5. $a^m a^n = a^{m+n}$; thus $2^3 \cdot 2^2 = 2^5$; and $3^{\frac{1}{2}} \cdot 3^{\frac{2}{3}} = 3^{\frac{7}{6}}$.

6. $a^m/a^n = a^{m-n}$; thus $2^5/2^2 = 2^3$; and $5^{-3}/5^{\frac{1}{2}} = 5^{-\frac{7}{2}}$.

7. $(a^m)^n = a^{mn}$; thus $(2^3)^2 = 2^6$; and $(2^{\frac{1}{3}})^5 = 2^{\frac{5}{3}}$.

8. $a^m b^m = (ab)^m$; thus $3^2 \cdot 2^2 = (3 \cdot 2)^2$.

9. $a^m/b^m = (a/b)^m$; thus $3^2/2^2 = (3/2)^2$.

64

EXERCISES

1. Evaluate the following:
   (a) 3^4; $2^2 2^4$; $(3^2)^3$; $(2/3)^3$; $3^5/3^2$; $(-7)^0$; $3(4^0)$.
   (b) 4^{-2}; $1/2^{-3}$; $2(3^{-3})$; $1/(4 \cdot 2^{-1})$; $2^0/3^{-1}$; $2^{-2}(-3)^0$.
   (c) $\sqrt{16}$; $8^{\frac{1}{3}}$; $32^{-\frac{3}{5}}$; $1/8^{-\frac{2}{3}}$; $3(2^{-1})(4^{-\frac{3}{2}})$; $5^0/(3 \cdot 16^{-\frac{3}{4}})$.

2. Write with positive exponents:
   $a^{-1}/2b^{-2}$; $(a - b)^{-1}$; $a^{-1} - b^{-1}$; $1/(a^{-1} + b^{-1})$;
   $(1/2a^{-1}) + 2a^{-1}$.

21. Definition of a logarithm

If we are given the three numbers N, a, and b such that

(1) $$N = a^b,$$

we call N the number (or antilogarithm), a the base, and b the exponent or logarithm. We state this in words as follows:

The logarithm of a number to a given base is the exponent which must be applied to the base in order to obtain the given number.

Another way to write (1) is

(2) $$\log {}_a N = b,$$

where N is a positive number* and the base a must be *positive* and not equal to 0 or 1. Usually the base is taken to be greater than 1. Equations (1) and (2) are equivalent statements and, to distinguish between them, we shall speak of (1) as being in *exponential form* and (2) as being in *logarithmic form*.

Example:

In $2^3 = 8$, 2 is the *base*, 3 is the *logarithm*, and 8 is the *number* (*or antilogarithm*). We can also write this in the logarithmic form as $\log_2 8 = 3$.

---

* The discussion of logarithms of negative numbers is beyond the purpose and scope of this book.

Example:

In $\log_4 16 = 2$, 4 is the *base*, 2 is the *logarithm* and 16 is the *number*. We can also write this in the exponential form, $4^2 = 16$.

EXERCISES

1. Rewrite the following in logarithmic form:

(a) $3^2 = 9$.   (g) $10^{-3} = .001$.   (m) $5^{-1} = \frac{1}{5}$.

(b) $2^4 = 16$.   (h) $81^{\frac{1}{4}} = 3$.   (n) $4^{\frac{3}{2}} = 8$.

(c) $5^3 = 125$.   (i) $8^0 = 1$.   (o) $10^{-1} = .1$.

(d) $7^{-1} = \frac{1}{7}$.   (j) $\sqrt{\frac{1}{4}} = \frac{1}{2}$.   (p) $\sqrt{64} = 8$.

(e) $2^{-3} = \frac{1}{8}$.   (k) $\sqrt[3]{8^2} = 4$.   (q) $10^0 = 1$.

(f) $\sqrt{9} = 3$.   (l) $10^2 = 100$.   (r) $4^{-2} = \frac{1}{16}$.

2. Rewrite the following in exponential form:

(a) $\log_3 9 = 2$.   (h) $\log_{\frac{1}{4}} \frac{1}{2} = \frac{1}{2}$.   (n) $\log_4 8 = \frac{3}{2}$.

(b) $\log_4 16 = 2$.   (i) $\log_2 \frac{1}{8} = -3$.   (o) $\log_2 32 = 5$.

(c) $\log_2 1 = 0$.   (j) $\log_{10} .01 = -2$.   (p) $\log_7 7 = 1$.

(d) $\log_{10} 1000 = 3$ (k) $\log_6 36 = 2$.   (q) $\log_{25} \frac{1}{125} = -\frac{3}{2}$.

(e) $\log_9 3 = \frac{1}{2}$.   (l) $\log_{16} 2 = \frac{1}{4}$.   (r) $\log_{16} 4 = \frac{1}{2}$.

(f) $\log_{10} 0.1 = -1$.   (m) $\log_3 27 = 3$.   (s) $\log_{27} 3 = \frac{1}{3}$.

(g) $\log_5 5 = 1$.

3. Solve the following examples for x:

(a) $x = \log_3 9$.   (g) $\log_x 27 = 3$.   (m) $\log_{10} x = 3$.

(b) $x = \log_{10} 1000$.   (h) $\log_x \frac{1}{64} = -\frac{3}{2}$.   (n) $\log_8 x = \frac{2}{3}$.

(c) $x = \log_{10} 0.1$.   (i) $\log_x 3 = \frac{1}{2}$.   (o) $\log_4 x = -1$.

(d) $x = \log_5 25$.   (j) $\log_x 4 = \frac{2}{3}$.   (p) $\log_{16} x = -\frac{3}{4}$.

(e) $x = \log_2 \frac{1}{8}$.   (k) $\log_x \frac{1}{16} = -2$.   (q) $\log_b x = 1$.

(f) $x = \log_{64} 16$.   (l) $\log_x 10 = 1$.   (r) $\log_b x = a$.

4. Show that:

(a) $a^{\log_a x} = x$.   (c) $\log_a \frac{1}{a} = -1$.

(b) $\log_b(b^x) = x$.   (d) $\log_b a \, \log_c b \, \log_a c = 1$.

22. The fundamental theorems of logarithms

We have seen that a logarithm is an exponent and from this fact arise some important theorems. Those of especial utility in this course are:

Theorem 1: *The logarithm of 1 to any base a equals 0.*

Proof: $a^0 = 1$. Hence by the definition of a logarithm, it follows that

$$\log_a 1 = 0.$$

Theorem 2: *The logarithm of a to the base a equals 1.*

Proof: $a^1 = a$, therefore

$$\log_a a = 1.$$

Theorem 3: *The logarithm of the product of two numbers is equal to the sum of the logarithms of the numbers; that is,*

$$\log_a(MN) = \log_a M + \log_a N.$$

Proof: Let $\log_a M = x$ and $\log_a N = y$. Then $M = a^x$ and $N = a^y$, and the product is given by the formula,

$$MN = a^x a^y = a^{x+y}.$$

Hence, by definition,

$$\log_a (MN) = x + y, \text{ or } \log_a (MN) = \log_a M + \log_a N.$$

Theorem 4: *The logarithm of a quotient is equal to the logarithm of the dividend minus the logarithm of the divisor; that is*

$$\log_a \frac{M}{N} = \log_a M - \log_a N.$$

Proof: Let $\log_a M = x$ and $\log_a N = y$. Then $M = a^x$ and $N = a^y$; therefore the quotient is given by the formula

$$\frac{M}{N} = \frac{a^x}{a^y} = a^{x-y}.$$

Hence

$$\log_a \frac{M}{N} = x - y, \text{ or } \log_a \frac{M}{N} = \log_a M - \log_a N.$$

Theorem 5: *The logarithm of a power of a number is equal to the exponent times the logarithm of the number; that is,*

$$\log_a(M^k) = k \log_a M,$$

where k is any number, integral or fractional, positive or negative, rational or irrational.

Proof: Let $\log_a M = x$. Then $M = a^x$, and $M^k = (a^x)^k = a^{kx}$. Hence

$$\log_a (M^k) = kx = k \log_a M.$$

Theorem 6: $\log_a M = \log_b M \log_a b$.

Proof: Let $\log_b M = x$; then $M = b^x$. Taking the logarithms of both sides of the exponential equation to the base a, and using Theorem 5, we have

$$\log_a M = \log_a (b^x) = x \log_a b, \text{ or}$$

$$(1) \qquad\qquad \log_a M = \log_b M \log_a b.$$

If $M = a$, we have the interesting result,

$$1 = \log_b a \log_a b.$$

If $a \neq b$, and we solve (1) for $\log_b M$, we obtain

$$\log_b M = \log_a M / \log_a b.$$

By means of this result we can determine the logarithm of a number to any base if we know the logarithms of numbers to some other base. For example, if we know $\log_{10} 2 = 0.30103$ and $\log_{10} 3 = 0.47712$, then $\log_2 3 = \log_{10} 3 / \log_{10} 2 = 0.47712/0.30103$. Consequently, $\log_2 3 = 1.585$ to four significant figures.

EXERCISES

1. Prove: $\log_a(MNQ) = \log_a M + \log_a N + \log_a Q$.

2. Given $\log_{10} 2 = 0.30103$, $\log_{10} 3 = 0.47712$, and $\log_{10} 5 = 0.69897$; find the following logarithms:

(a) $\log_{10} 10$.	(j) $\log_{10} 50$.	(s) $\log_{10} \dfrac{1}{5^3}$.
(b) $\log_{10} 15$.	(k) $\log_{10} \dfrac{1}{6}$.	(t) $\log_{10} 15^4$.
(c) $\log_{10} 6$.	(l) $\log_{10} 0.001$.	(u) $\log_{10} \sqrt{45}$.
(d) $\log_{10} \dfrac{3}{2}$.	(m) $\log_3 2$.	(v) $\log_{10} 30$.
(e) $\log_{10} 3^2$.	(n) $\log_{10} \sqrt{6}$.	(w) $\log_{10} \sqrt[7]{15}$.
(f) $\log_{10} 100$.	(o) $\log_{10} 27$.	(x) $\log_{10} \dfrac{15}{2}$.
(g) $\log_{10} \sqrt{3}$.	(p) $\log_{10} 32$.	(y) $\log_2 3$.
(h) $\log_{10} \sqrt[3]{5}$.	(q) $\log_{10} \sqrt[5]{2}$.	(z) $\log_2 9$.
(i) $\log_{10} 20$.	(r) $\log_{10} \dfrac{3}{5}$.	(aa) $\log_2 5$.

23. The common system of logarithms*

The common system of logarithms is characterized by having the base 10 and is the most useful in numerical computations. Since, in this system, the logarithm of a number N is that number x such that $10^x = N$, we shall omit the subscript 10 in future logarithmic statements and simply write $\log N$ for $\log_{10} N$.

Hence we have the following equivalent statements:

$$10^3 = 1000, \qquad \log 1000 = 3,$$
$$10^2 = 100, \qquad \log 100 = 2,$$
$$10^1 = 10, \qquad \log 10 = 1,$$
$$10^0 = 1, \qquad \log 1 = 0,$$
$$10^{-1} = 0.1, \qquad \log 0.1 = -1,$$
$$10^{-2} = 0.01, \qquad \log 0.01 = -2,$$
$$10^{-3} = 0.001, \qquad \log 0.001 = -3.$$

24. Characteristic and mantissa

Any number can be written as an integer plus a nonnegative† decimal fraction. For example, the number 2.43176 is the same as $2 + 0.43176$; the number 5 can be written as $5 + 0.00000$; and the number -3.64712 can be written as $-4 + 0.35288$. In the same way, a number which is a logarithm can be written as an integer plus a nonnegative decimal fraction. When a *common* logarithm is written in this manner, the integer is called the *characteristic*, and it may be positive, negative, or zero. The nonnegative decimal fraction is called the *mantissa*. In tables of common logarithms, the decimal part is *always* the mantissa.

Since a common logarithm is the exponent that must be applied to 10 to obtain a given number, it follows that:

(1) The logarithm of an integral power of 10 has its mantissa zero, and its characteristic is equal to the exponent attached to the 10.

---

* See § 72 for a graphical representation of $y = \log_{10} x$.

† A nonnegative number is a number which is either positive or zero.

Example 1:

(a) $\log (10^4) = 4$; the characteristic is 4, and the mantissa is zero.

(b) $\log (10^{-3}) = -3$; the characteristic is -3, and the mantissa is zero.

(2) The logarithm of a number greater than 1 is positive. As already indicated, the integral part is the characteristic and the decimal part is the mantissa.

Example 2:

If we know $\log 30 = 1.47712$, the characteristic is 1, and the mantissa is .47712, to five significant figures.

(3) The logarithm of a number less than 1 is negative. However, as has been stated, we can write this so that the decimal part is positive. For applications, where tables are to be used, this is necessary, since the tables list only positive mantissas.

Example 3:

$\log \frac{1}{30} = \log 1 - \log 30$. In the previous example we have given that $\log 30 = 1.47712$ and we know $\log 1 = 0$. Hence it follows that $\log \frac{1}{30} = -1.47712$, which is the same as $-1 - .47712$. However, if 1 is added to and then subtracted from this value, it is determined that $\log \frac{1}{30} = 0.52288 - 2$. Hence the mantissa of $\log \frac{1}{30}$ is .52288, and the characteristic is -2.

In the discussion that follows we shall see why it is advantageous to write a logarithm as a characteristic plus a mantissa which is always positive.

If we know $\log 3 = 0.47712$ and want to find $\log 300$ we proceed as follows:

$$\log 300 = \log 3 + \log 100 = \log 3 + \log (10^2)$$
$$= 0.47712 + 2.$$

In an analogous manner

$$\log 0.03 = \log 3 + \log 0.01 = \log 3 + \log (10^{-2})$$
$$= 0.47712 - 2.$$

$$\log 0.3 = \log 3 + \log 0.1 = \log 3 + \log (10^{-1})$$
$$= 0.47712 - 1.$$
$$\log 30 = \log 3 + \log 10 = \log 3 + \log (10^{1})$$
$$= 0.47712 + 1.$$
$$\log 3000 = \log 3 + \log 1000 = \log 3 + \log (10^{3})$$
$$= 0.47712 + 3.$$

These examples illustrate the following statement: *The mantissas of the logarithms of all numbers that differ from each other only in the location of the decimal point are the same.* The proof of the statement is very simple. Any two numbers that differ from each other only in the location of the decimal point can be written as the same number between 1 and 10 times an integral power of ten. Since the logarithm of an integral power of 10 is an integer, it follows that the logarithms of the two numbers in question must differ only in the integral part, *i.e., in the characteristic.* Hence the mantissa remains unchanged.

To determine the mantissa of the logarithm of a number we use a table of logarithms.*

To determine the characteristic of the logarithm of a number, we write the number as a product of an integral power of 10 times a number between 1 and 10 having the same set of significant figures as the original number. (See § 15.)   The exponent attached to 10 is the characteristic.   Why?

Example 4:
Since $2148.6 = 2.1486 \times 10^{3}$, the characteristic of log 2148.6 is 3.

* Although the tables are compiled by the use of advanced mathematics, it is possible to give an illustration of a method of obtaining a mantissa that may at least partly satisfy the curiosity of the student:
Let us find $\log_{10}2$. If we let $\log_{10}2 = x$, we have $2 = 10^{x}$. For $x = 0$, $10^{0} = 1$, and for $x = 1$, $10^{1} = 10$, hence x lies between 0 and 1. Next we investigate what k_{1} must be if $10^{\frac{k_{1}}{10}} = 2$ or if $10^{k_{1}} = 2^{10}$. Since $2^{10} = 1024$ and $10^{3} = 1000$, it follows that k_{1} lies between 3 and 4. So we know that $x = 0.3 +$. Obviously a continuation of this method of approximation becomes too cumbersome for practical application.

Example 5:

Since 2.193 = 2.193 × 10⁰, the characteristic of log 2.193 is 0.

Example 6:

Since 0.01468 = 1.468 × 10⁻², the characteristic of log 0.01468 is −2.

In practice it is generally convenient to write a negative characteristic in terms of a positive number minus ten. Using this convention, the characteristic of log 0.01468 would be written 8 − 10; of log 0.9836 would be written 9 − 10; of log 0.003164 would be written 7 − 10.

EXERCISES

Find the characteristics of the logarithms of the following numbers:

1. 3.1416.	**7.** 0.007216.	**13.** 2.1947.
2. 100,600.	**8.** 89.34.	**14.** 2,340.6.
3. 0.0132.	**9.** 0.021.	**15.** 0.4931.
4. 1,325.	**10.** 0.2498.	**16.** 1.6722.
5. 0.0000671.	**11.** 1.3974.	**17.** 22,314.6.
6. 7,726.49.	**12.** 0.0002369.	**18.** 0.00000123.

25. Numerical computations

In the previous section we learned what a characteristic and a mantissa are and how to determine the characteristic. Now we shall learn how to find the mantissa by using a table of logarithms. In our examples we shall use a five-place table of logarithms.

Example 1:

Find log 53.94.

First we write 53.94 as 5.394 × 10¹, and this tells us that the characteristic is 1. To determine the mantissa we turn to the table entitled "Five-place Logarithms." The column headed by *N*, at the left of each page, contains the first three figures of any number; the figure in the fourth place is found as a column heading at the top of the page. We look for the page that contains 539 in column N. The figures 539 in column N lie in a specific row. In this row and in the column headed by 4 we find the mantissa .73191.

Hence　　　　　log 53.94 = 1.73191.

Example 2:

Find log 0.0005628.

As before, the figures 562 in column N lie in a specific row of the table. In this row and in the column headed by 8 we read the mantissa .75035. The characteristic is $6 - 10$, since $0.0005628 = 5.628 \times 10^{-4}$.

Hence　　　　　log 0.0005628 = 6.75035 − 10.

NOTE: If more accurate results for the logarithms are desired, it is possible to obtain tables which contain the mantissas expanded to six or more places.

26. Antilogarithms

If $\log N = x$, then N may be described as the antilogarithm of x.

Example 1:

Find the antilogarithm of 2.82099.

This means that $\log N = 2.82099$, where N is the antilogarithm. The characteristic is 2 and the mantissa is .82099. We look for .82099 among the mantissas in the five-place table of logarithms. It is in the row to the right of 662 in the N-column and in the column headed by 2.

Hence　　　　　$\log (6.622 \times 10^2) = 2.82099$, or
　　　　　　　　　$\log 662.2 = 2.82099$.

Therefore　　　　$N = 662.2$

Example 2:

Find the antilogarithm of $8.39898 - 10$.

The characteristic is -2 and the mantissa is .39898. We find .39898 in the row and column of 2506.

Hence　　　　　$\log (2.506 \times 10^{-2}) = 8.39898 - 10$,

so the antilogarithm is 0.02506.

27. Interpolation

To find the mantissa of the logarithm of a number it is often necessary to interpolate. The following examples will illustrate.

Example 1:

Find log 729.84.

The characteristic is 2. Since log N increases with N, we know that log 729.80 < log 729.84 < log 729.90. Hence log 729.84 = log 729.80 + x, where we find x as follows:

$$10\left\{\begin{array}{l} \log\ 729.90\ =\ 2.86326 \\ 4\left\{\begin{array}{l} \log\ 729.84\ =\ 2.86320\ +\ x \\ \log\ 729.80\ =\ 2.86320 \end{array}\right\}x \end{array}\right\}0.00006$$

Assuming that the change in the numbers is proportional to the change in the logarithms, we have

$$\frac{4}{10} = \frac{x}{0.00006},\ \text{or}\ x = 0.00002.$$

Therefore   log 729.84 = 2.86322.

The error made as a consequence of the assumption is negligible for small differences. (See § 19 for a more complete explanation of the method used above.)

Interpolation can be facilitated by the use of the proportional parts that appear in the *five-place tables* on the right-hand side of each page. Each tabular difference occurring in the tables has been multiplied by 0.1, 0.2, . . . 0.9, and the results have been placed in columns headed by the tabular difference. The fifth figure of any number appears in the column upon the left of each table of proportional parts.

Using the proportional parts in the example just solved, we find the tabular difference for the two numbers between which 729.84 lies to be 6. In the column of the proportional parts headed by 6 and to the right of the fifth figure 4, we read 2.4, which may be approximated to the integral value 2.

This means that we should add 0.00002 to 0.86320, the mantissa of log 729.80.

Hence, we have log 729.84 = 2.86322.

Example 2:

Given that log N = 0.53729, find N.

The characteristic is 0. We find, in the *columns of the mantissas* in the table, the mantissas between which .53729 lies and then proceed to find N as follows:

$$0.0010 \left\{ \begin{array}{l} \log 3.4460 = 0.53732 \\ x \left\{ \begin{array}{l} (\log (3.4450 + x) = 0.53729 \\ \log 3.4450 = 0.53719 \end{array} \right\} 0.00010 \end{array} \right\} 0.00013$$

and $$\frac{x}{0.0010} = \frac{0.00010}{0.00013}, \text{ or } x = 0.0008.$$

Therefore $N = 3.4458.$

Using proportional parts, we look, under the tabular difference column headed by 13, for 10. The closest number to this is 10.4 and to the left of this is 8; this is the desired fifth figure. Hence

$$N = 3.4458.$$

Example 3:

Evaluate $N = 2.134/16.28$.

Since the logarithm of a quotient is the difference of the logarithms, it follows that

$$\log N = \log 2.134 - \log 16.28.$$
$$\log 2.134 = 0.32919$$
$$\log 16.28 = \underline{1.21165}$$
$$\log N = \quad ?$$

In order that the difference between the two logarithms have a positive mantissa, and in order to write the characteristic as an integer minus ten, we rewrite 0.32919 as 10.32919 − 10. Then we have

$$\log 2.134 = 10.32919 - 10$$
$$\log 16.28 = \underline{1.21165}$$
$$\log N = \quad 9.11754 - 10.$$

The characteristic is -1 and the mantissa is .11754. After interpolating, we obtain $N = 1.3108 \times 10^{-1} = 0.13108$, or $N = 0.1311$, to four significant figures.

Example 4:

Evaluate $N = \dfrac{2.0140 \times 0.0032700}{0.062730}$.

NOTE: The student should observe that the zeros upon the right of the decimals are significant figures.

Since the logarithm of a product is the sum of the logarithms, and the logarithm of a quotient is the difference of the logarithms, we have

$$\log N = \log 2.0140 + \log 0.0032700 - \log 0.062730.$$

Since $0.0032700 = 3.2700 \times 10^{-3}$, and $0.06273 = 6.2730 \times 10^{-2}$, the characteristic of $\log 0.0032700$ is -3 and the characteristic of $\log 0.062730$ is -2. To find N, we proceed as follows:*

$$
\begin{aligned}
\log 2.0140 &= 0.30406 \\
\log 0.0032700 &= \underline{7.51455 - 10} \\
\log 2.0140 + \log 0.0032700 &= 7.81861 - 10 \\
\log 0.062730 &= \underline{8.79748 - 10} \\
\log N &= \quad ?
\end{aligned}
$$

Since our difference would give us a negative decimal, we write $7.81861 - 10$ as $17.81861 - 20$. So now we have

$$
\begin{aligned}
\log 2.0140 + \log 0.0032700 &= 17.81861 - 20 \\
\log 0.062730 &= \underline{8.79748 - 10} \\
\log N &= 9.02113 - 10, \text{ and} \\
N &= 1.0499 \times 10^{-1}, \text{ or} \\
N &= 0.10499.
\end{aligned}
$$

Example 5:

Evaluate $N = \sqrt[3]{0.04236}$.

By Theorem 5 of § 22, $\log N^k = K \log N$. Hence $\log (0.04236)^{\frac{1}{3}} = \frac{1}{3} \log 0.04236$. From the tables we find $\log 0.04236 = 8.62696 - 10$, so $\frac{1}{3} \log 0.04236 = (8.62696 - 10)/3$. In order

---

* A very important element leading to accuracy in arithmetical computation is a systematic arrangement of the work. Whenever possible put numbers that are to be added or subtracted in columns.

to write this quotient as a number minus *ten*, we write $8.62696 - 10$ as $28.62696 - 30$, and thereby obtain

$$\tfrac{1}{3} \log 0.04236 = \frac{28.62696 - 30}{3} = 9.54232 - 10.$$

Consequently

$$N = 3.4860 \times 10^{-1} = 0.34860, \text{ or}$$
$$0.3486, \text{ to four significant figures.}$$

Example 6:

Find $\log_3 0.6.$*

Since $\log_a N = \log_b N / \log_b a$, we have

$$\log_3 0.6 = \frac{\log 0.6}{\log 3} = \frac{9.7782 - 10}{0.4771} = \frac{-0.2218}{0.4771} = -0.4649, \text{ or}$$

$\log_3 0.6 = -.5$, to one significant figure.

The student should take particular notice that in this example it was necessary to write $\log 0.6$ explicitly as a *negative* decimal.

Example 7:

Evaluate $K = \dfrac{\sqrt[3]{-31.426}\ (-2.364)^2}{\sqrt{0.003460}\ (643.24)^3}.$

Because we do not consider the logarithm of a negative number, we must determine the sign of the result by inspection. Since $\sqrt[3]{-a} = -\sqrt[3]{a}$, and $(-b)^2 = b^2$, it follows that K is negative. Let $N = -K$, then

$$N = \frac{\sqrt[3]{31.426}\ (2.364)^2}{\sqrt{0.003460}\ (643.24)^3}.$$

$\log N = \tfrac{1}{3} \log 31.426 + 2 \log 2.364 - \tfrac{1}{2} \log 0.003460 - 3 \log 643.24.$

$\log 31.426 = 1.49729$

$\tfrac{1}{3} \log 31.426 \qquad\qquad = 0.49910$

$\log\ \ 2.364 = 0.37365$

$\underline{2 \log\ \ 2.364 \qquad\qquad = 0.74730}$

$\tfrac{1}{3} \log 31.426 + 2 \log 2.364 \quad = 1.24640 \qquad\qquad = 11.24640 - 10$

$\log 0.003460 = 17.53908 - 20$

$\tfrac{1}{2} \log 0.003460 \qquad\qquad = 8.76954 - 10$

---

* In Example 6, a table of four-place logarithms was used.

$\log 643.24 \quad = \quad 2.80837$

$3 \log 643.24 \qquad\qquad\qquad = \quad \underline{8.42511}$

$\frac{1}{2} \log 0.003460 + 3 \log 643.24 = 17.19465 - 10 = \quad 7.19465$

Hence $\qquad\qquad\qquad\qquad\qquad \log N = \quad \overline{4.05175 - 10}$

and $\qquad\qquad\qquad N = 0.0000011266.$

Therefore

$\qquad K = -0.000001127$, to four significant figures.

A more convenient form in which to express this result is

$$K = -1.127 \times 10^{-6}$$

EXERCISES

1. Find the logarithms of the following:

(a) 283.95.　　　　(c) 0.64137.　　　　(e) 0.0053418.

(b) 0.098432.　　　(d) 7.3214.　　　　 (f) 0.37466.

2. Find the antilogarithms of the following:

(a) 3.46217.　　　 (c) 0.72368.　　　 (e) − 2.31457

(b) 9.17236 − 10.　(d) 8.42314 − 10.　(f) − 4.27316

3. Evaluate each of the following to the proper number of significant figures:

(a) $0.00986 \times 1.43.$

(b) $\dfrac{38.267}{9.4320}.$

(c) $\dfrac{1.67 \times 2.98}{3.47}.$

(d) $\sqrt{1.9420} \times 6.1930.$

(e) $\dfrac{0.04920}{\sqrt{0.1920}}.$

(f) $\sqrt[3]{-0.0043000}$

(g) $\dfrac{\sqrt{47.820}}{\sqrt[3]{9.2160}}.$

(h) $\sqrt[5]{0.090000} \times \sqrt{1.8600}.$

(i) $\dfrac{\sqrt{2.3467} \times 0.00034000}{(-0.014600)^{\frac{1}{3}}(-243.67)}.$

(j) $3.216 \times (1.4235)^4 \times (-618).$

(k) $\sqrt[7]{-0.09876}.$

(l) $\dfrac{\sqrt[3]{0.1942} \times \sqrt{6.933}}{(-0.2134)^2}.$

(m) $\pi^2 \times 9.1400 \times 0.0032641.$

(n) $\dfrac{0.1523 \times (11.467)^{\frac{1}{4}}}{(2.9)^3 \times (934.61) \times \sqrt[4]{16.325}}$

28. Cologarithms*

The cologarithm of a number is the logarithm of the reciprocal of the number. Thus if N is the number, we have

* May be omitted for a brief course.

$$\text{colog } N = \log \frac{1}{N} = \log 1 - \log N = -\log N.$$

Example 1:

$$\text{colog } 32.64 = \log \frac{1}{32.64} = -\log 32.64 = -1.51375.$$

By adding and subtracting 10 we are able to write the cologarithm so that the decimal fraction is positive. To illustrate, colog $32.64 = -1.51375 = (10 - 1.51375) - 10 = 8.48625 - 10.$ Hence the mantissa is .48625 and the characteristic is -2. Whenever log N is known it is possible to write down colog N by inspection. Starting from the left of the mantissa of log N, we subtract each digit in succession from 9 until we come to the last significant figure, which we subtract from 10. The characteristic of colog N is found by subtracting the characteristic of log N from $9 - 10$. Hence colog N is positive if log N is negative, and colog N is negative if log N is positive.

When we find the logarithm of a quotient, the use of cologarithms enables us to add the cologarithm of the denominator to the logarithm of the numerator instead of subtracting the logarithm of the denominator from the logarithm of the numerator. The following example will illustrate.

Example 2:

$$N = \frac{13.46 \times 2.936}{21.65 \times 1.242}. \text{ Find } N.$$

Solution 1 (without using cologarithms):

$$\log 13.46 = 1.12905$$
$$\log 2.936 = 0.46776$$
$$\log 13.46 + \log 2.936 = 1.59681$$
$$\log 21.65 = 1.33546$$
$$\log 1.242 = 0.09412$$
$$\log 21.65 + \log 1.242 = 1.42958$$
$$\log N = 0.16723$$
$$N = 1.470, \text{ to four significant}$$
$$\text{figures.}$$

Solution 2 (using cologarithms):

$$\begin{aligned}
\log 13.46 &= 1.12905 \\
\log 2.936 &= 0.46776 \\
\text{colog } 21.65 &= 8.66454 - 10 \\
\text{colog } 1.242 &= \underline{9.90588 - 10} \\
\log N &= 20.16723 - 20 = 0.16723 \\
N &= 1.470, \text{ to four significant figures.}
\end{aligned}$$

EXERCISES

1. Find the cologarithms, given the following logarithms:

(a) 3.19465.	(h) 1.34621.	(o) 8.16754 − 10.
(b) 5.34671.	(i) 0.96517.	(p) 1.98342.
(c) 0.98116.	(j) 3.67412	(q) 9.46120 − 10.
(d) 2.55263.	(k) 6.10425 − 10.	(r) 2.36411.
(e) 1.59428.	(l) 7.96112 − 10.	(s) 8.43215 − 10.
(f) 9.81946 − 10.	(m) 3.40565.	(t) 0.11935.
(g) 8.01233 − 10.	(n) 0.25369.	

2. Solve (using cologarithms): $N = \dfrac{1194.0}{\sqrt[3]{2280.0}}$.

3. Solve (using cologarithms): $N = \dfrac{19.467 \times \sqrt{2.3145}}{2.6143 \times 0.096522}$.

29. Logarithms of trigonometric functions

Since the trigonometric functions of a given angle are numbers, the method of finding the logarithms of the trigonometric functions is no different from that discussed in the preceding section. In evaluating $\log \sin 31° 28'$, however, it is not necessary to compute $\sin 31° 28'$ and then the logarithm of this result, since special tables have been prepared which give the logarithm of the sine of this angle immediately. Turning to the table of the *logarithms of trigonometric functions*, we find $\log \sin 31° 28' = 9.71767 - 10$.

This table differs from the other logarithm table in that the characteristic is given as well as the mantissa with the understanding that we subtract 10 from each characteristic. There are two exceptions: for log tangent of an angle greater than 45° and for log cotangent of an angle less than 45°, the logarithm appears directly in the table.

The method of interpolation is the same as that previously explained. The following examples illustrate the process.

Example 1:

Find log cos 53° 17′ 33″.

$$\begin{aligned}
\log \cos 53° 18′ &= 9.77643 - 10 \\
\log \cos 53° 17′ 33″ &= (9.77660 - 10) - y \\
\log \cos 53° 17′ &= 9.77660 - 10
\end{aligned}$$

Interpolating, we have

$$\frac{33}{60} = \frac{y}{0.00017}, \text{ so } y = 0.00009.$$

Therefore   log cos 53° 17′ 33″ = 9.77651 − 10.

Here, too, we can use the proportional-parts columns to advantage. The seconds are to the left of the columns that are headed by the tabular difference *17*, and opposite 30″ we read 8.5, opposite 3″ we read 0.8. Hence 33″ corresponds to 8.5 + 0.8 or 9.3; this value is then approximated to the nearest integer, 9. Since log cos θ diminishes as θ increases, we subtract 0.00009 from 0.77660, thereby obtaining

$$\log \cos 53° 17′ 33″ = 9.77651 - 10.$$

Example 2:

Solve the equation log sin θ = 9.92321 − 10 for all positive values of $\theta < 360°$.

From the table we find that log sin 56° 55′ = 9.92318 − 10 and log sin 56° 56′ = 9.92326 − 10. Obviously, therefore, the given value of log sin θ indicates that one value of θ is between 56° 55′ and 56° 56′. In planning to use proportional parts, we observe that the tabular difference of the two logarithms between which 9.92321 − 10 lies is 8. In the proportional-parts column headed by 8 we look for 3, the tabular difference between 9.92321 − 10 and 9.92318 − 10. The number closest to 3 appearing in the column is 2.7, opposite 20″ but above this in the same column is 0.3, opposite 2″, and the sum of 2.7 and 0.3 is 3. Therefore the required number of seconds is $20'' + 2'' = 22''$. So, in summary, one value of θ is $56° 55' 22''$.

Since sin θ is also *positive* in quadrant II, the second possible value of θ is $180° - 56° 55' 22''$ or $123° 4' 38''$.

EXERCISES

1. Find the values of the following:

(a) log sin $32° 18' 43''$.   (e) log sin $127° 34' 22''$.
(b) log cos $47° 31' 27''$.   (f) log cos $312° 12' 35''$.
(c) log tan $212° 19' 20''$.   (g) log tan $59° 15' 40''$.
(d) log cot $73° 50' 14''$.   (h) log cot $235° 51' 25''$.

2. Solve the following equations for all positive values of $\theta < 360°$:

(a) log sin $\theta = 9.81234 - 10$.   (e) log sin $\theta = 9.74312 - 10$.
(b) log cos $\theta = 9.65721 - 10$.   (f) log cos $\theta = 9.86194 - 10$.
(c) log tan $\theta = 0.14649$.   (g) log tan $\theta = 9.91788 - 10$.
(d) log cot $\theta = 9.98723 - 10$.   (h) log cot $\theta = 0.14217$.

30. The slide rule*

It is possible to multiply, divide, extract square roots, and perform other mathematical operations by means of the slide rule. In general the operations may be performed rapidly and accurately to at least two significant figures. The slide rule is a valuable tool for anyone whose work requires extensive numerical computation, and results can often be obtained accurately to three significant figures. With every slide rule there is included a good booklet of instructions, and hence it is not necessary to repeat them here. The construction of the slide rule is based on the theory of logarithms, and the student should be conscious of this as he attempts to understand its use.

It is essential, first of all, to master the reading of the scales. This is most important, since some of the small intervals count as 1 unit, some as 2 units, and still others as 5 units, and it is very easy to become confused. At least an

* May be omitted for a brief course.

hour can well be spent in reading the scales, looking up sines and tangents, and reading logarithms of numbers to three significant figures. Then, with the instruction book, at least another hour should be used in learning to do multiplication, division, squaring of numbers, and extraction of square root. In the next chapter we shall discuss the use of the rule in solving triangles.

EXERCISES

Using the slide rule, evaluate the following:
1. 0.00729×2.36.
2. 84700×0.913.
3. $1.46 \div 0.00725$.
4. $0.0913 \div 0.642$.
5. $\sqrt{26.7}$.
6. $\sqrt{0.00400}$.
7. $\sqrt{0.0920}$.
8. $\sqrt{1.06}$.
9. $(43.3)^2$.
10. $(0.0634)^2$.
11. $\dfrac{0.0630 \times 2.17 \times 0.00852}{0.000934 \times 0.542 \times 0.0476}$.
12. $\dfrac{31.6 \times 0.0072 \times 0.645}{0.000378 \times 9.40 \times 0.00521}$.
13. $\sqrt{0.0640} \times 2.13$.
14. $0.014 \times \pi \times (0.004)^{\frac{1}{2}}$.

EXERCISES: CHAPTER IV

1. Find the value of each of the following:
   (a) $\log \sin 29° 17' 20''$.
   (b) $\log \tan 53° 21' 43''$.
   (c) $\log \cos 16° 40' 24''$.
   (d) $\log \sin 48° 10' 11''$.
   (e) $\log \cos 68° 55' 40''$.
   (f) $\log \sin 912° 37' 19''$.
   (g) $\log \tan 214° 43' 30''$.
   (h) $\log \cot 195° 20' 36''$.
   (i) $\log \cos 310° 30' 20''$.
   (j) $\log \cos (-20° 30' 43'')$.
   (k) $(324.75)^4$.
   (l) $(1.1674)^{\frac{3}{8}}$.
   (m) $\log (3951)^2$.
   (n) $(\log 3951)^2$.
   (o) $\log \dfrac{6.3217}{5.9714}$.
   (p) $\dfrac{\log 6.3217}{\log 5.9714}$.

(q) $\sqrt[8]{123.46}$.

(t) $\dfrac{(1.3146)^{\frac{2}{3}}\ \sqrt[3]{39.462}}{\sqrt{0.019462}}$.

(r) $\dfrac{(23.465)^3}{(4.6329)^4}$.

(u) $(29.346)^5$.

(v) $(28.192)^3 \times \pi^2 \times \sqrt[4]{0.196}$.

(s) $\dfrac{21.483 \times 0.091463}{134.62 \times 1.8743}$.

(w) $\dfrac{\sqrt[3]{0.01934} \times \sin 214° \ 29'\ 32''}{(0.00942)^2}$

(x) $\dfrac{(29.471)^2 \times \sin 222° \ 30'\ 43'' \times \sqrt{193.46}}{(-9.4765)^3 \times \cos 146° \ 12'\ 35'' \times \sqrt[3]{29.438}}$.

(y) $\dfrac{3.642 \times 31.49 \times \cos 19° \ 28''}{\sqrt{16.42} \times \tan 43° \ 14'\ 30''}$.

(z) $\dfrac{\sqrt[3]{-24.367} \times \sqrt[5]{0.8319} \times \sin 62° \ 11'\ 20''}{(-0.1427)^2 \times \cos 43° \ 29'\ 51'' \times \sqrt{143}}$.

(aa) $\dfrac{\sqrt{11.28} \times \sqrt[3]{-0.01852}}{(0.92683)^2}$. (Use cologarithms.)

2. Solve the following equations for x:

(a) $\sqrt[3]{8^{x-1}} = 64$.

(h) $\log x = 6.96547 - 10$.

(b) $27^{2x+3} = 9^{3-2x}$.

(i) $\log \cos \ x = 9.63415 - 10$.

(c) $2^{3x+1} = 50$.

(j) $\log \tan x = 8.73132 - 10$.

(d) $3^{x-2} = 9^{2x+2}$.

(k) $\log \tan x = 10.27573 - 10$.

(e) $\log x = 4.71936$.

(l) $\log \sin \ x = 9.90800 - 10$.

(f) $\log x = 8.39764 - 10$.

(m) $\log \sin \ x = 9.36748 - 10$.

(g) $\log x = 0.31497$.

(n) $\log \cos \ x = 9.63478 - 10$.

3. Find the antilogarithms of the following:

(a) $6.53729 - 10$.

(d) 0.73184.

(b) 2.31473.

(e) 3.61279.

(c) $9.54617 - 10$.

(f) $7.64122 - 10$.

4. Solve for x, given:

(a) $3.11^x = 17.4$.

(c) $\log_5 3 = x$.

(b) $0.15^x = 6.1$.

(d) $\log_{0.3} 4 = x$.

5. Find the area of a circle if the radius is 9.3147 feet.

6. The volume of a sphere is $V = \frac{4}{3}\pi r^3$. Find the volume of a sphere if the radius is 31.46 inches.

7. The volume of a right circular cone is given by the formula $V = \frac{1}{3}\pi r^2 h$, where r is the radius of the base and h is the altitude. Find V if $r = 2.194$ feet and $h = 6.019$ feet.

8. The volume of a right circular cylinder is $V = \pi r^2 h$. Find V if $r = 1.986$ feet and $h = 7.813$ feet.

Chapter V

THE RIGHT TRIANGLE

31. Introduction

Many problems that require the application of trigonometry involve the solution of a right triangle. In fact the word trigonometry comes from two Greek words meaning *triangle* and *measurement*. In this chapter we shall illustrate with examples and exercises the importance of its application to the right triangle.

As is well known, the acute angles, A and B, of a right triangle are related by the equation

$$A + B = 90°;$$

and the sides a, b, and hypotenuse c are related by the equation

$$c^2 = a^2 + b^2.$$

This last relation is known as the Pythagorean theorem.

From the above relations it follows that if an acute angle and a side, or two sides, are known, the triangle may be constructed and is unique.

We have already seen in § 11 that the trigonometric functions of an acute angle may be defined in terms of the ratios of the sides of a right triangle. The functions of A in Figure 35 are

$$\sin A = a/c, \cos A = b/c, \tan A = a/b,$$
$$\csc A = c/a, \sec A = c/b, \cot A = b/a.$$

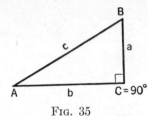

Fig. 35

Also, since A and B are acute angles of a right triangle, we have the important relations

$$\sin A = \cos B, \tan A = \cot B, \sec A = \csc B.$$

32. Solving the right triangle

Whenever we know an acute angle and a side, or two sides, of a right triangle, we can solve for the remaining parts. By solving the right triangle we mean finding the unknown parts.

Example 1:

Given $A = 28° 30'$ and $b = 18.3$, find a, c, and angle B.

(1) $B = 90° - A = 90° - 28° 30' = 61° 30'$.

(2) To find side a, we have

$$a/18.3 = \tan 28° 30', \text{ or}$$
$$a = 18.3 \tan 28° 30'.$$
$$\log a = \log 18.3 + \log \tan 28° 30'.$$
$$\log 18.3 = 1.26245$$
$$\log \tan 28° 30' = \underline{9.73476 - 10}$$
$$\log a = 10.99721 - 10.$$
$$a = 9.9360, \text{ or}$$
$$a = 9.94, \text{ to three signifi-}$$
cant figures.

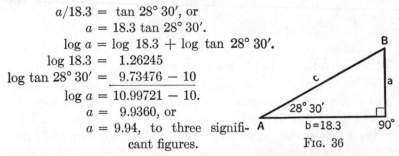

Fig. 36

Note: In solving a problem use, whenever possible, information that has been given rather than information that has been found, thus eliminating the danger of using incorrect results to obtain unknown parts.

(3) To find side c, we have

$$\cos 28° 30' = 18.3/c, \text{ or}$$
$$c = 18.3/\cos 28° 30'.$$
$$\log c = \log 18.3 - \log \cos 28° 30'.$$
$$\log 18.3 = 11.26245 - 10$$
$$\log \cos 28° 30' = \underline{9.94390 - 10}$$
$$\log c = 1.31855.$$
$$c = 20.823, \text{ or}$$
$$c = 20.8, \text{ to three significant figures.}$$

The unknown parts of the triangle are, therefore, $a = 9.94$, $c = 20.8$, and $B = 61° 30'$.

Use the Pythagorean theorem to check the values of a and c.

Example 2:

Given $b = 25.4$ and $c = 39.2$, find angles A and B and side a.

(1) To find A, we have

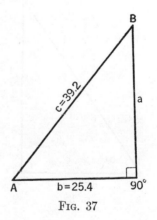

$$\cos A = b/c = 25.4/39.2.$$
$$\log \cos A = \log 25.4 - \log 39.2.$$
$$\log 25.4 = 11.40483 - 10$$
$$\log 39.2 = \underline{1.59329}$$
$$\log \cos A = 9.81154 - 10.$$
$$A = 49° 36' 18'', \text{ or}$$
$$A = 49° 37', \text{ to the closest minute.}$$

Fig. 37

(2) To find B, we have

$$B = 90° - A = 40° 23' 12'', \text{ or}$$
$$B = 40° 23', \text{ to the closest minute.}$$

Check the value obtained for B by seeing if $\log \sin B = 9.81154 - 10$.

(3) We shall now determine a.

Since $a^2 = c^2 - b^2 = (c - b)(c + b)$, we have

$$\log a^2 = 2 \log a = \log (c - b) + \log (c + b).$$

Since $c - b = 13.8$ and $c + b = 64.6$, we have

$$2 \log a = \log 13.8 + \log 64.6.$$
$$\log 13.8 = 1.13988$$
$$\log 64.6 = \underline{1.81023}$$
$$2 \log a = 2.95011,$$
$$\log a = 1.47506$$
$$a = 29.858, \text{ or}$$
$$a = 29.9, \text{ to three significant figures.}$$

The unknown parts of the triangle are $A = 49° 37'$, $B = 40° 23'$, and $a = 29.9$.

Example 3:

Given $a = 19.3$ and $b = 27.2$, find angles A and B, and side c.

(1) To find B, we have

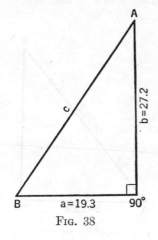

$$\tan B = 27.2/19.3.$$
$$\log \tan B = \log 27.2 - \log 19.3.$$
$$\log 27.2 = 1.43457$$
$$\log 19.3 = \underline{1.28556}$$
$$\log \tan B = 0.14901.$$
$$B = 54° 38' 31'' \text{ or,}$$

F̳ɪ̳ɢ̳. 38

rounded off to the closest minute,

$$B = 54° 39'.$$

(2) To find A, we have

$$A = 90° - 54° 38' 31'' = 35° 21' 29'',$$

or, to the closest minute,

$$A = 35° 21'.$$

(3) To find c we write

$$\sin 35°\, 21'\, 29'' = 19.3/c, \text{ or}$$
$$c = 19.3/\sin 35°\, 21'\, 29''.$$
$$\log c = \log 19.3 - \log \sin 35°\, 21'\, 29''.$$

$$\begin{aligned}\log 19.3 &= 11.28556 - 10\\ \log \sin 35°\, 21'\, 29'' &= \underline{9.76244 - 10}\\ \log c &= 1.52312.\\ c &= 33.352, \text{ or}\\ c &= 33.4,\end{aligned}$$

when rounded off to three significant figures.

The unknown parts of the triangle, therefore, are $B = 54°\, 39'$, $A = 35°\, 21'$ and $c = 33.4$.

NOTE: In this example it was *necessary* to use parts obtained by solution in order to obtain one of the unknown parts.

EXERCISES

Solve for all the remaining parts of the triangle, given $C = 90°$, and:

1. $B = 25°\, 15'$, $a = 150.0$.
2. $a = 1120$, $b = 2133$.
3. $A = 83°\, 45'\, 18''$, $b = 15.321$.
4. $b = 12.593$, $c = 24.685$.
5. $B = 46°\, 28'$, $b = 12.460$.
6. $a = 32.81$, $A = 28°\, 30'\, 15''$.
7. $B = 43°\, 16'$, $c = 9.1460$.
8. $b = 0.9048$, $a = 1.365$.
9. $a = 347.4$, $c = 624.8$.
10. $A = 30°\, 10'\, 25''$, $b = 14.26$.
11. $a = 4.63$, $c = 9.27$.

12. $A = 42°\, 28'$, $c = 196.3$.
13. $a = 2.465$, $c = 6.398$.
14. $B = 20°\, 34'$, $b = 1034$.
15. $A = 32°\, 16'$, $a = 94.670$.
16. $b = 9.410$, $c = 13.62$.
17. $B = 62°\, 15.6'$, $b = 2941.7$.
18. $c = 16923$, $A = 75.18°$.
19. $b = 2.631$, $c = 6.194$.
20. $B = 28.193°$, $c = 48.261$.
21. $A = 28°\, 45'$, $c = 10.360$.
22. $A = 43°\, 18'$, $b = 2.37$.

33. Solving the right triangle with the slide rule*

After the student has learned to read sines and tangents on his slide rule he is ready to use it to solve the right triangle. Four possible cases may occur, and each is discussed by

---

* May be omitted for a brief course. The explanation as given on the following pages pertains to the K & E Polyphase and Mannheim slide rules. Some slide rules read the sine and tangent from the same scale.

means of an example.   The student is referred to his slide-rule instruction book for a more detailed study.   Before discussing numerical examples, consider any right triangle with sides a, b, c, and angles A, B, 90°.   (See Fig. 35.)   Since $\sin A = a/c$ and $\sin 90° = 1$, it follows that $\sin A/\sin 90° = a/c$, or

(1) $\sin A/a = \sin 90°/c$.

In the same way, $\sin B = b/c$ and $\sin B/\sin 90° = b/c$, or

(2) $\sin B/b = \sin 90°/c$.

Putting (1) and (2) together into one relationship, we obtain

$$(3) \qquad \frac{\sin A}{a} = \frac{\sin B}{b} = \frac{\sin 90°}{c}.$$

This is a special case of a law known as the law of sines; the law is applicable to any triangle and will be discussed more fully in the chapter on the general triangle.   The relation is very useful for solving some triangles with the slide rule, as will be seen from the following examples.

Example 1:

To solve a right triangle if an acute angle and the hypotenuse are given.   Let us suppose that we are given $A = 33.6°$ and $c = 16.8$.

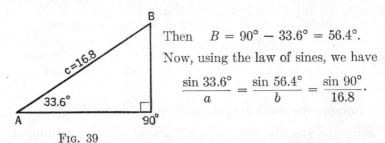

Then $B = 90° - 33.6° = 56.4°$.

Now, using the law of sines, we have

$$\frac{\sin 33.6°}{a} = \frac{\sin 56.4°}{b} = \frac{\sin 90°}{16.8}.$$

Fig. 39

To solve for a and b, we use the S- and A-scales.   Adjust the slide so that 90° on the S-scale is aligned with 16.8 on the A-scale. Move the indicator until the hairline coincides with 33.6 on the S-scale, and read the value of side a on the A-scale to be 9.31.

Keeping the scales in the same relative position, move the indicator until the hairline coincides with 56.4 on the S-scale and read on the A-scale, $b = 14.0$.

NOTE: If when 90° is aligned with 16.8, the indicator goes off the scale as we attempt to align the hairline with 33.6, we readjust the slide so that the left-hand index of the S-scale coincides with 16.8 and proceed as before.

The results may be checked by the Pythagorean theorem, using the slide rule to evaluate the squares.

Example 2:

To solve a right triangle if an acute angle and a side (not the hypotenuse) are given. Let us suppose that we are given $A = 47° 20'$ and side $b = 34.2$.

First, we find

$$B = 90° - 47° 20' = 42° 40'.$$

Then, using the law of sines, we have

$$\frac{\sin 47° 20'}{a} = \frac{\sin 42° 40'}{34.2} = \frac{\sin 90°}{c}.$$

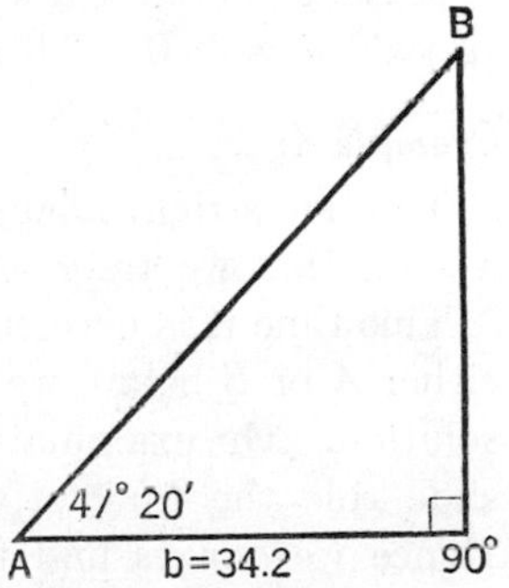

FIG. 40

Align $42° 40'$ on the S-scale with 34.2 on the A-scale. Moving the indicator until the hairline coincides with $47° 20'$, we read on the A-scale, $a = 37.2$ Finally, moving the indicator until the hairline coincides with 90°, we read on the A-scale, $c = 50.5$. The check may be performed as suggested in the previous example.

Example 3:

To solve a right triangle if the hypotenuse and one of the legs are given. Let us suppose that we are given $a = 21.4$ and $c = 43.6$. Using the law of sines, we have

$$\frac{\sin A}{21.4} = \frac{\sin B}{b} = \frac{\sin 90°}{43.6}.$$

Align 90° on the S-scale with 43.6 on the A-scale. Move the indicator to 21.4 on the A-scale and read on the S-scale, $A = 29° 23'$. Hence

$$B = 90° - 29° 23' = 60° 37'.$$

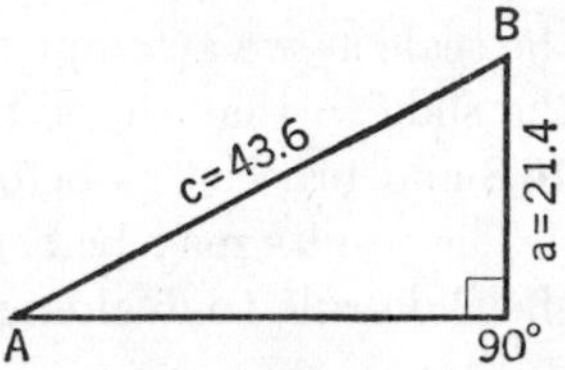

B

c=43.6

a=21.4

A   90°

FIG. 41

NOTE: Here we found it necessary to use a result which had been obtained by solution in order to find B. Read again the first note in § 32.

Moving the indicator to 60° 37' on the S-scale, we read on the A-scale, $b = 38.0$. Check the results.

Example 4:

To solve a right triangle if the legs a and b are given. We shall assume that we are given $a = 23.4$ and $b = 47.3$.

This time it is necessary to use the T- and D-scales and find either A or B before we can use the law of sines and complete the solution. On examination we find we can read *directly* from the slide rule the tangent of any angle equal to or less than 45°. Hence we *always* find the *smaller* of the two acute angles first. In our example, since $a < b$, we know that $A < B$. Also, since $\tan 45° = 1$, we can write

$$\frac{\tan A}{\tan 45°} = \frac{a}{b} = \frac{23.4}{47.3}, \text{ and}$$

$$\frac{\tan A}{23.4} = \frac{\tan 45°}{47.3}.$$

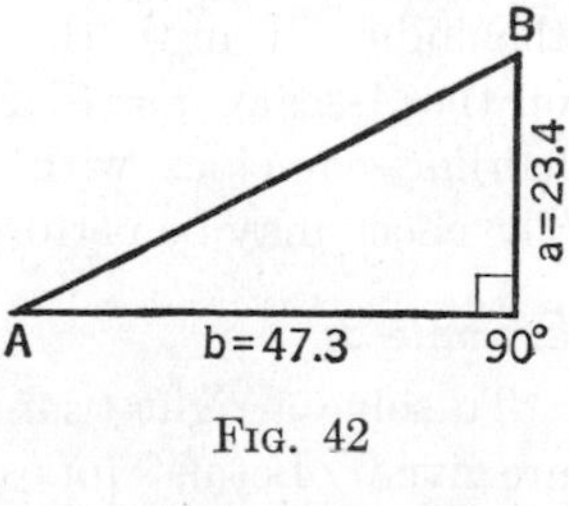

B

a=23.4

A   b=47.3   90°

FIG. 42

Align 45° on the T-scale with 47.3 on the D-scale. Moving the indicator to 23.4 on the D-scale, we read on the T-scale, $A = 26° 20'$.

NOTE: If the indicator goes off the scale as we attempt to find angle A, we must align the left-hand index of the T-scale with a on the D-scale and proceed as before. Knowing A, we find $B = 90° - A$. So $B = 90° - 26° 20' = 63° 40'$. Then

$$\frac{\sin 26° 20'}{23.4} = \frac{\sin B}{47.3} = \frac{\sin 90°}{c}.$$

Align $26° 20'$ on the S-scale with 23.4 on the A-scale. Move the indicator to $90°$ on the S-scale and read on the A-scale, $c = 52.8$. Although we have already found B, we can use the law of sines to check our result.

EXERCISES

Solve the following triangles with the slide rule:

1. $A = 34°$, $c = 46.7$.
2. $B = 65°$, $a = 13.8$.
3. $a = 27.8$, $c = 51.4$.
4. $b = 14.9$, $c = 34.6$.
5. $a = 51.0$, $b = 30.4$.
6. $A = 27.5°$, $a = 42.6$.
7. $b = 31.4$, $a = 22.3$.
8. $B = 27° 20'$, $c = 63.4$.

34. Geometrical applications

a. Rectilinear figures. — A figure is said to be rectilinear if it is composed of straight lines. Sometimes, by applying repeatedly the method of solving right triangles, we can find all the parts of a given rectilinear figure when some of the parts are known.

Example:

Suppose that in Figure 43 we are given $\sin A = \frac{5}{13}$, $p = 24.0$, $\tan B = \frac{4}{3}$, and $\cos C = \frac{1}{2}$, and wish to find s, w, t, and z.

(1) In the right triangle that contains A, we are given $\sin A$ and side p and, hence, can find s as follows:

Since $\sin A = \frac{5}{13}$, it follows that $\cos A = \frac{12}{13}$ and $\sec A = \frac{13}{12}$. Why? Now $s/p = \sec A$ and, therefore,

$$s = p \sec A = 24.0 \times \tfrac{13}{12} \doteq 26.0$$

(2) Next we turn to the triangle that contains B, and again we know an angle and a side.

Since $\tan B = \frac{4}{3}$, we have $\sin B = \frac{4}{5}$. Why? Now $w/s = \sin B$ and, therefore,

$$w = s \sin B = 26.0 \times \tfrac{4}{5} = 20.8.$$

(3) Finally, in the triangle that contains C, we know $\cos C$ and side w.

Since $\cos C = \frac{1}{2}$, we have $\sin C = \sqrt{3}/2$. In view of the fact that $z/w = \cos C$, it follows that

$$z = 20.8 \times \tfrac{1}{2} = 10.4.$$

Also $t/w = \sin C$, so we have

$$t = w \sin C = 20.8 \times \frac{\sqrt{3}}{2} = 10.4 \times \sqrt{3},$$

or

$t = 18.0$, to three significant figures.

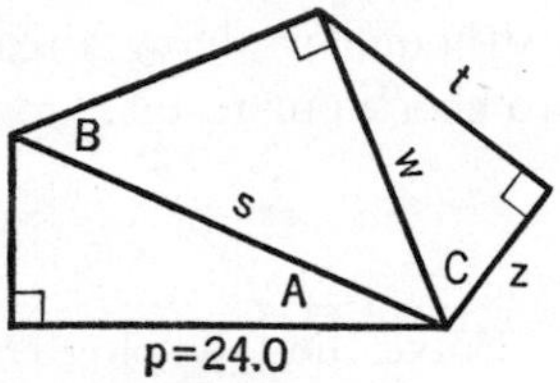

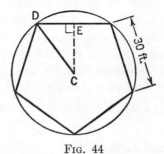

p=24.0

Fig. 43

b. Isosceles triangles. — If a perpendicular is dropped from the vertex angle of an isosceles triangle to the opposite side, the triangle is divided into two equal right triangles. This principle may be applied frequently, as illustrated by the following example.

Example:

A regular pentagon is inscribed in a circle. If the perimeter of the pentagon is 150 feet, what is the radius of the circle?

Since a regular pentagon is a five-sided figure whose sides all have the same length, it follows that the length of each side is $150/5 = 30.0$ feet. Also, each side subtends a central angle of

Fig. 44

$360°/5 = 72°$ and is the base of an isosceles triangle having its equal sides equal to the radius r of the circle. If we draw a perpendicular from C, the center of the circle, to E, the midpoint of a side of the pentagon, we have a right triangle with r as hypotenuse. (See Fig. 44.) Since $DE = 15.0$ feet and $\angle DCE = 36°$, we have

$$r = 15/\sin 36°.$$
$$\log r = \log 15 - \log \sin 36°.$$
$$\log 15 = 11.17609 - 10$$
$$\log \sin 36° = \underline{9.76922 - 10}$$
$$\log r = 1.40687$$

After interpolating, we obtain

$$r = 25.5 \text{ feet},$$

to three significant figures.

*c. The general triangle.** — It is possible, although not always the best or quickest method, to solve a general triangle by dividing it into right triangles. A detailed study of the general triangle is contained in Chapter VII.

Example 1:

Find the remaining parts of the triangle in which $B = 120°$, $a = 27.0$, and $b = 43.0$.

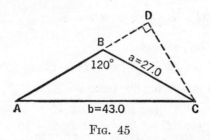

FIG. 45

Draw the altitude from C to side AB extended to D. Then in right triangle ADC, we have $DC/27 = \sin 60°$, or $DC = 27 \sin 60°$.

---

* Part c may be omitted until Chapter VII.

Hence

$$\log DC = \log 27 + \log \sin 60°.$$
$$\log 27 = 1.43136$$
$$\log \sin 60° = \underline{9.93753 - 10}$$
$$\log DC = 11.36889 - 10.$$

We shall not actually solve for DC, since its logarithm is sufficient to enable us to obtain angle A. In fact, we have

$$\sin A = DC/43, \text{ and}$$
$$\log \sin A = \log DC - \log 43.$$
$$\log DC = 11.36889 - 10$$
$$\log 43 = \underline{1.63347}$$
$$\log \sin A = 9.73542 - 10.$$

There are two angles A that satisfy this equation. After interpolating we find these angles to be $A_1 = 32° 56' 3''$ and $A_2 = 147° 3' 57''$. So it appears that there may be two triangles which satisfy the given conditions. We shall see however, that in this example there is only one solution. Since the sum of the angles of any triangle is 180°, it follows that:

$$C_1 = 180° - (A_1 + B) = 180° - 152° 56'3'' = 27° 35' 7''.$$

However, if A_2 is used, we find that $A_2 + B$ is greater than 180°, and this is impossible. Why?

To find c, we must first find AD and BD; then $c = AD - BD$. Using triangle BDC, we have

$$BD/27 = \cos 60°, \text{ or } BD = 27 \times \frac{1}{2} = 13.5.$$

Using triangle ADC, we have

$$AD/43 = \cos 32° 56' 3'', \text{ or } AD = 43 \cos 32° 56' 3''.$$

Hence, $\log AD = \log 43 + \log \cos 32° 56' 3''.$

$$\log 43 = 1.63347$$
$$\log \cos 32° 56' 3'' = \underline{9.92392 - 10}$$
$$\log AD = 11.55739 - 10.$$
$$AD = 36.090.$$

Consequently, $c = 36.090 - 13.5 = 22.590,$ or

$$c = 22.6, \text{ to three significant figures.}$$

So the solution of the triangle provides

$A = 32° 56'$ and $C = 27° 4'$, to the nearest minute,

and $c = 22.6$, to three significant figures.

Example 2:

Solve the triangle in which $A = 30°$, $a = 10$, and $c = 15$.

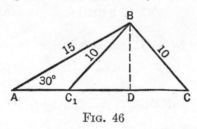

FIG. 46

Dropping a perpendicular from B to AC at D in the triangle ABC, we have

$$BD/15 = \sin 30°, \text{ or } BD = 15 \times \frac{1}{2} = 7.5.$$

Now, using triangle BDC, we have

$$\sin C = 7.5/10 = 0.75000.$$

There are two angles $C < 360°$ that satisfy this equation and, using the table of natural functions, we obtain

$$C = 48° 35' 25'' \text{ or } C_1 = 131° 24' 35''.$$

For this example it follows that both angles are possible; hence there are two solutions to the triangle.

(1) Using $C = 48° 35' 25''$, we have

$$B = 180° - (30° + 48° 35' 25'') = 101° 24' 35''.$$

Now we have $b = AD + DC$. Using triangle ABD, we see that

$$AD/15 = \cos 30°, \text{ or } AD = 15 \cos 30°.$$
$$\log AD = \log 15 + \log \cos 30°.$$
$$\log 15 = \quad 1.17609$$
$$\log \cos 30° = \quad 9.93753 - 10$$
$$\log AD = 11.11362 - 10$$
$$AD = 12.990.$$

In the same way, using triangle BDC, we have

$$DC/10 = \cos 48° 35' 25'', \text{ or } DC = 10 \cos 48° 35' 25''.$$

$$
\begin{array}{rl}
\log DC = & \log 10 + \log \cos 48° 35' 25''. \\
\log 10 = & 1.00000 \\
\log \cos 48° 35' 25'' = & \underline{9.82061 - 10} \\
\log DC = & 10.82061 - 10. \\
DC = & 6.6161.
\end{array}
$$

Hence, $AD + DC = 12.990 + 6.6161 = 19.6061$, or

$$b = 20, \text{ to two significant figures.}$$

(2) Using $C_1 = 131° 24' 35''$, which is angle AC_1B in the figure, we note that

$$B_1 = 180° - (30° + 131° 24' 35'') = 18° 35' 25''.$$

This time we have $AC_1 = AD - C_1D$. Since $C_1D = DC$ (why?), we have

$$AC_1 = 12.990 - 6.6161 = 6.3739, \text{ or}$$

$$b_1 = 6.4, \text{ to two significant figures.}$$

Example 3:

Solve the triangle wherein $A = 30°$, $c = 15$, and $a = 5$ are given:

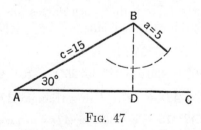

FIG. 47

In this example, we have $BD = 15 \sin 30° = 7.5$. Since BD is the shortest distance from B to side AC and yet it is more than the side of the triangle from B to C, it follows that there is no triangle satisfying the given conditions.

Example 4:

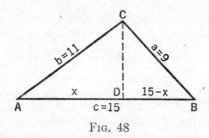

Fig. 48

Given $a = 9$, $b = 11$, and $c = 15$, find the angles of the triangle. Drop a perpendicular from C to D on AB. (See Fig. 48.) Then, applying the Pythagorean theorem to each of the two triangles formed, we have

(1) $121 = x^2 + h^2$ $=$ $x^2 + h^2$

(2) $81 = (15 - x)^2 + h^2 = 225 - 30x + x^2 + h^2$.

Subtracting the members of equation (2) from those of (1), we obtain

(3) $40 = -225 + 30x$, or $30x = 265$.

Consequently, $x = 8.83$ and $15 - x = 6.17$, to three significant figures.

Now, using the right triangle ACD, we have $\cos A = 8.83/11$.

Hence, $\log \cos A = \log 8.83 - \log 11$.

$\log 8.83 = 10.94596 - 10$

$\log 11 = \underline{\quad 1.04139 \quad}$

$\log \cos A = \quad 9.90457 - 10$.

$A = 36° 36' 3''$ or $323° 23' 57''$.

Since the second angle is already greater than 180°, it is not part of the solution.

In the same way, we find

$\cos B = 6.17/9$, and $\log \cos B = \log 6.17 - \log 9$.

$\log 6.17 = 10.79029 - 10$

$\log 9 = \underline{\quad 0.95424 \quad}$

$\log \cos B = \quad 9.83605 - 10$.

100   *THE RIGHT TRIANGLE*

Again we interpolate and find

$$B = 46° 43' 13''.$$

Since the sum of the angles of any triangle is 180°, we have

$$C = 180° - (A + B) = 180° - 83° 19' 16'' = 96° 40' 44''.$$

Hence, to the nearest minute, the angles of the triangle are

$$A = 36° 36', B = 46° 43', \text{ and } C = 96° 41'.$$

Verify the results of Example 4 by dropping a perpendicular from B to AC in Figure 48 and finding A and C again.

EXERCISES

1. Find the length of AB if $AD = 20.0$, $\cos p = \frac{3}{5}$, $\sin q = \frac{5}{8}$, and $B = 45° 0'$.

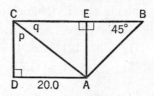

2. Given $\sin p = \frac{5}{8}$, $AC = 16.8$, and $\tan q = \frac{3}{2}$, find BD.

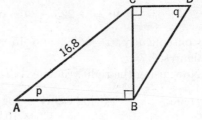

3. Given $\tan p = \frac{3}{5}$, $BC = 6.0$, $\cos q = \frac{2}{3}$, find AD and DC.

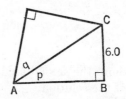

4. Solve the following isosceles triangles, where $B = C$ are the base angles:

(a) $A = 64° 24'$ and $b = 14.6$ feet.
(b) $B = 34° 46'$ and $a = 212$ feet.
(c) $a = 448$ inches and $c = 613$ inches.

(d) Perimeter = 824 feet and b = 248 feet.
(e) Area = 144 square feet and altitude = 48.0 feet.
(f) $B = \pi/6$ radians, c = 46.0 yards.
(g) A = 1.6 radians, altitude = 18 inches.

5. Solve the following general triangles:
   (a) $A = 48°\ 21'$, $B = 32°\ 16'$, and $b - 122$ feet.
   (b) $A = 3\pi/4$ radians, a = 116 feet and b = 90.4 feet.
   (c) $C = \pi/4$ radians, a = 48.2 inches and b = 76.7 inches.
   (d) $B = 130°\ 16'$, a = 1.26 feet and c = 2.45 feet.
   (e) $A = 63°\ 24'$, $C = 46°\ 42'$, and b = 0.264 miles.
   (f) $C = 59.8°$, c = 9.70 inches and a = 14.2 inches.

6. If the length of a side of a regular hexagon is 18.0 inches, what are the radii of the inscribed and circumscribed circles?

7. A circle is inscribed in an equilateral triangle. If the length of a side of the triangle is 3.8 inches, what is the radius of the circle?

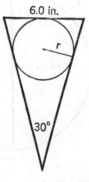

8. A circle is inscribed in an isosceles triangle of base 6.0 inches. If the vertical angle is 30°, what is the radius of the circle?

9. Find y in the diagram.

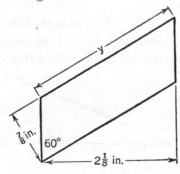

10. Five holes, $\frac{5}{8}$ inches in diameter, are to be drilled equally spaced along the circumference of a circle. The diameter of the circle containing the centers of the circular holes is 4.32 inches. Find the distances x and y shown in the figure.

11. Determine θ as shown in the figure.

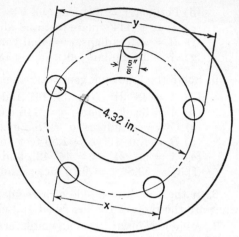

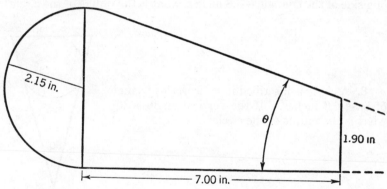

35. Definitions of special angles employed in surveying and navigation

a. Angle of elevation. — If an observer at A looks upward to an object at C, then the angle that his line of sight AC makes with the horizontal AB is called the *angle of elevation.* (See Fig. 49.)

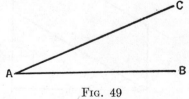

Fig. 49

b. Angle of depression. — If an observer at A looks downward to an object at C, then the angle that his line of sight makes with the horizontal is called the *angle of depression.* (See Fig. 50.)

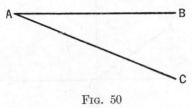

Fig. 50

c. Bearing. — When the direction of a segment OA is given by means of the clockwise angle that the segment makes with the ray ON, pointing north, we call this direction the *compass bearing* of A with respect to O.

In Figure 51, the compass bearing of OA is 237°. When given this way it is understood that the angle is clockwise and a negative sign is not necessary.

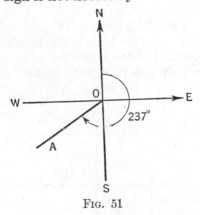

Fig. 51

The bearing of A with respect to O is often given in terms of the *acute* angle that OA makes with the north axis ON or with the south axis OS. When this method is used, letters indicating whether the direction is north or south and east or west are included with the angle. It is traditional that the N or S letter is given first, then the acute angle, and, finally, the E or W letter.   In Figure 52, the bearing of OA is 55° west of north.   This is written N 55° W.

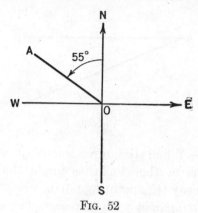

FIG. 52

Example 1:

A ship is sailing with a compass bearing of 218°.   If it leaves port O at 6 A.M. and sails at 15 knots,* what is its position at 9 A.M. with relation to the port.   (See Fig. 53.)

Since the ship travels for 3 hours at 15 knots, it has gone 45 nautical miles by 9 A.M.   The acute-angle bearing of the ship is S 38° W.   Let A and B be the respective projections of P on the N-S axis and the E-W axis through O, where P is the position of

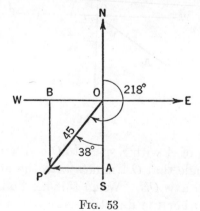

FIG. 53

* A knot is a speed of one nautical mile per hour.

the ship at 9 A.M. Then $|AP|/|OP| = \sin 38°$, and $|AP|$ $= |OP|\sin 38° = 45 \sin 38°$.

$$\log |AP| = \log 45 + \log \sin 38°.$$

$$\begin{aligned} \log 45 &= 1.65321 \\ \log \sin 38° &= \underline{9.78934 - 10} \\ \log |AP| &= 11.44255 - 10. \end{aligned}$$

After interpolating, we find

$$|AP| = 27.7 \text{ miles,}$$

to three significant figures.

In the same way, $|BP| = 45 \cos 38°$.

$$\log |BP| = \log 45 + \log \cos 38°.$$

$$\begin{aligned} \log 45 &= 1.65321 \\ \log \cos 38° &= \underline{9.89653 - 10} \\ \log |BP| &= 11.54974 - 10. \end{aligned}$$

Interpolating, we find

$$|BP| = 35.5 \text{ miles,}$$

to three significant figures.

So at 9 A.M. the position of the ship is 27.7 miles west of O and 35.5 miles south of O.

Example 2:

A flagpole 50 feet high can be seen by an observer from a point A on a level with the foot of the flagpole. He finds the angle of elevation to the top of the flagpole to be 25°. (See Fig. 54.) How far is A from C, the base of the flagpole?

We have $AC/50 = \cot 25°$, or $AC = 50 \cot 25°$. Therefore

$$\begin{aligned} \log AC &= \log 50 + \log \cot 25°. \\ \log 50 &= 1.69897 \\ \log \cot 25° &= \underline{0.33123} \\ \log AC &= 2.03020. \end{aligned}$$

So, $AC = 107$ feet, to three significant figures.

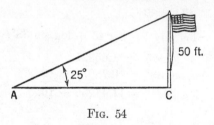

FIG. 54

EXERCISES

1. From a cliff 63 feet high, a soldier sights an enemy tank. If the angle of depression of the tank is 12° and if it is moving directly toward the observer along a straight road perpendicular to the cliff, how far was the tank from the base of the cliff at the instant that it was sighted?

2. The angle of elevation of a flagpole measured from a point 200 feet from the base of the pole is 18.6°. How high is the pole?

3. A ship sails a course of 135°. After it has sailed for 128.0 miles, what is its location with respect to its original position?

4. A pilot in an airplane 2000 feet above the sea sights a cruiser. If the angle of depression is 48.3°, what is the distance between the plane and the ship?

5. A ship sails N 72° W for 143 miles. How far west is the ship from its original position? Is it north or south of its original position and how much?

6. A right triangle is inscribed in a circle. If the sides are 26.0 inches and 37.0 inches, respectively, what is the radius of the circle?

7. A guy wire is to be attached to a telephone pole 20 feet above the ground. If the other end is to be fastened to the ground 20 feet from the base of the pole, if 1 foot is needed for fastening it to the ground, and if 3 feet are needed for fastening it to the pole, how much wire is needed for the entire operation and what angle will the wire make with the horizontal?

8. An observer in an airplane 2800 feet above sea level sights two ships and notes their angles of depression to be 62° and 54°, respectively. If the airplane is between the ships and in the same vertical plane with them, what is the distance between them?

9. A surveyor wishes to find the distance across a swamp. From his position C, he finds the angle subtended by AB to be 90°.

If A and B are on opposite sides of the swamp, if CA is 243 yards and CB is 315 yards, find the distance across the swamp from A to B.

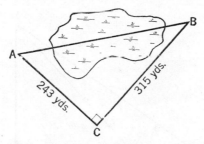

10. A regular octagon (eight sides) is inscribed in a circle of radius 17 inches; what is the length of a side? What is the radius of the circle which may be inscribed in the octagon?

11. The angle of elevation of the top of a tower, the base of which is 220 feet from the point of observation, is 49° 23'. Find the height of the tower.

12. To find the distance across a lake from P_1 to P_2, a line was run along one shore from P_1 to P_3 perpendicular to P_1P_2 and 275 feet in length. The angle $P_1P_3P_2$ was found to be 47° 25' 18". Find the distance P_1P_2.

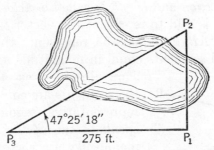

13. From the deck of a ship 38 feet above water level the angle of depression of a rock on the shore at the water's edge is 10°. How far away is the rock from the observer?

14. A man in a balloon observes that two objects 1 mile apart subtend an angle of 57° 25'. If he is exactly above the middle point between the objects, how high is he above the ground?

15. A ladder 30.0 feet long placed against a wall makes an angle of 53° 27' with the horizontal. Find to what height the ladder reaches on the wall and how far it is from the foot of the wall.

16. From a point A the angle of elevation of a building is 35°. From a point B, 100 feet closer, the angle of elevation is 47°. How high is the building?

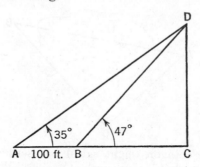

36. Vectors

We represent a directed line segment geometrically by means of a segment with an arrowhead to indicate direction. We read this as "the line segment from A to B." The length of the segment represents the absolute distance from A to B. Considered as an entity, the *collection* of all segments having the same *direction* and *length* is called a *vector*. Any one of the segments is said to represent the vector. For example, the segment AB in Figure 55 represents the vector that consists of all segments equal in magnitude and having the

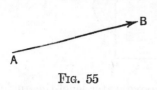

FIG. 55

same direction as AB. Since all the segments are equal and AB is a representative segment, we shall speak of the vector AB. By the magnitude of a vector we mean the length of a representative segment. So the magnitude of the vector AB is represented by $|AB|$. It is very important to note that *direction* is as important as *length*, and that if we change the direction of the segment it no longer represents the same vector.

For example, in Figure 56, AB, CD, and EF are all representative segments of the same vector, whereas HG and PQ

are each representative segments of different vectors. Force, velocity, and acceleration are examples of quantities which may be represented by vectors. The magnitude of the velocity is called speed.

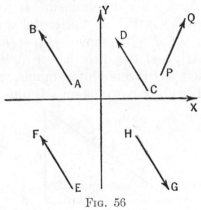

FIG. 56

It is a well-known principle of physics that two forces F_1 and F_2 acting on a body at the same point may be replaced by a single force F which will have the same effect on the body as F_1 and F_2 combined. As indicated in Figure 57, the vector representing F is the diagonal of a parallelogram having F_1 and F_2 as adjacent sides. We speak of this as a *parallelogram of forces*. F is called the *resultant* force, and F_1 and F_2 are called the *components* of F.

Another convenient method of illustrating the resultant force in terms of its components is by means of a triangle. This is illustrated in Figure 57 if we look at only one-half of the parallelogram. This is called a *triangle of forces*. (See Fig. 58.)

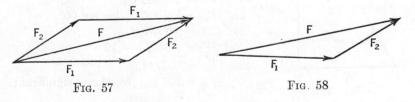

FIG. 57   FIG. 58

Many of the applications of vectors involve right triangles. We shall represent the horizontal and vertical components of a vector F by F_h and F_v, respectively. When F is known, F_h and F_v are uniquely determined; likewise, when F_h and F_v are known, F is uniquely determined. If we let α be the angle that F makes with the horizontal and let $|F|$ be the magnitude of F, we have $|F_h| = |F| \, |\cos \alpha|$ and $|F_v| = |F| \, |\sin \alpha|$, and the direction of F_h is either to the right or to the left as $\cos \alpha$ is plus or minus, while the direction of F_v is either up or down as $\sin \alpha$ is plus or minus.

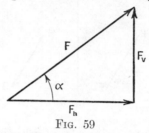

Fig. 59

If F_h and F_v are known, then $|F| = \sqrt{|F_h|^2 + |F_v|^2}$; and $\tan \alpha = |F_v| / |F_h|$ if F_v and F_h are *both* directed positively or negatively, while $\tan \alpha = -|F_v| / |F_h|$ if F_v and F_h are directed so that one is positive when the other is negative.

Example 1:

A force of magnitude 123 pounds at an angle of 60° with the horizontal is exerted on an object. What are the magnitudes of its horizontal and vertical components?

$$|F_h| = 123 \cos 60° = 123 \left(\tfrac{1}{2}\right)$$
$$= 61.5 \text{ lb., to three significant figures.}$$
$$|F_v| = 123 \sin 60°.$$
$$\log |F_v| = \log 123 + \log \sin 60°.$$
$$\log 123 = 2.08991$$
$$\log \sin 60° = \underline{9.93753 - 10}$$
$$\log |F_v| = 2.02744.$$
$$|F_v| = 107 \text{ lb., to three significant figures.}$$

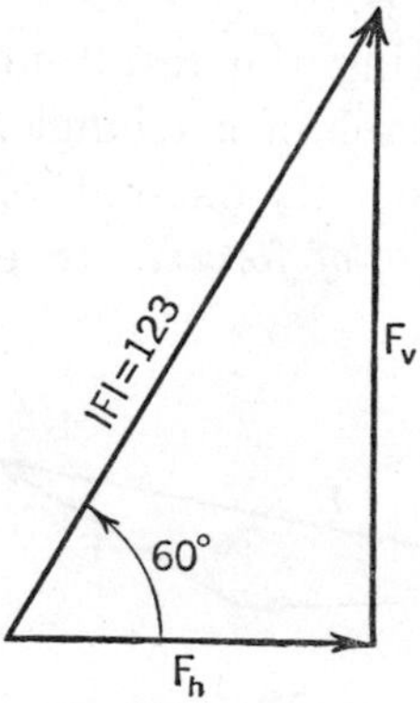

Fig. 60

Example 2:

A man has a motor boat which will travel at the rate of 12 miles an hour. If he heads the boat directly across a stream that is flowing at the rate of 8.0 miles an hour, in what direction and at what rate will his boat move? If the stream is 134 yards wide, at what point on the opposite shore will he land and how far does he travel?

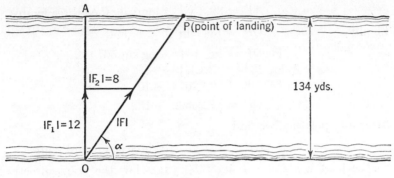

Fig. 61

The resultant velocity vector F shown in Figure 61 gives the direction and speed of the boat. If α denotes the angle that the direction of the boat makes with the flow of the stream, we have

$$\tan \alpha = \tfrac{12}{8} = \tfrac{3}{2} = 1.500.$$

Using the four-place tables of natural functions, we find $\alpha = 56°\ 19'$, to the nearest minute. To find the rate at which the boat will move, we have

$$|F| = 12/\sin 56°\ 19'.$$

Then $\log |F| = \log 12 - \log \sin 56°\ 19'.$

$$\log 12 = 11.07918 - 10$$
$$\log \sin 56°\ 19' = \underline{\quad 9.92018 - 10}$$
$$\log |F| = \quad 1.15900.$$

So $|F| = 14.4$ miles per hour,

to three significant figures.

To find how far the boat will travel and at what point on the opposite bank it will land we use a triangle similar to the force triangle. (See Fig. 61.)

We have $\qquad\qquad AP = 134 \cot 56° 19'.$

Hence $\qquad\qquad \log AP = \log 134 + \log \cot 56° 19'.$

$$\begin{array}{rl} \log 134 = & 2.12710 \\ \log \cot 56° 19' = & \underline{9.82380 - 10} \\ \log AP = & 11.95090 - 10. \end{array}$$

Interpolating, we obtain

$\qquad\qquad AP = 89.3$ yd., rounded off to three figures.

Finally, $\qquad\qquad OP = 134/\sin 56° 19',$ and

$$\begin{array}{rl} \log OP = & \log 134 - \log \sin 56° 19'. \\ \log 134 = & 2.12710 \\ \log \sin 56° 19' = & \underline{9.92018 - 10} \\ \log OP = & 12.20692 - 10. \end{array}$$

After interpolating, we find

$\qquad\qquad OP = 161$ yd., to three significant figures.

So the boat lands at a point 89.3 yd. below the point directly opposite the starting place, and the boat travels 161 yd.

EXERCISES

1. A force F makes an acute angle with the horizontal. If the magnitude of its horizontal component is 327 pounds and the magnitude of its vertical component is 163 pounds, what is F?

2. A force F makes an acute angle with the horizontal, and $|F| = 716$ pounds. If $|F_h| = 298$ pounds, find the direction of F and the magnitude of F_v.

3. A force F_1 of magnitude 143 pounds is required to keep an object weighing 226 pounds from sliding down an inclined plane.

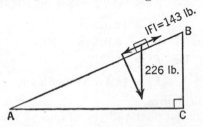

What is the inclination of the plane with the horizontal and what is the force due to friction? *Hint:* The object exerts a force of

magnitude 143 pounds down the plane.   The triangle of forces is
similar to the triangle ABC in the diagram.

4. A boat is moving at 16 knots in a direction perpendicular to
the current of the water in a channel which is flowing at 5.0 knots.
If the channel is 30 miles wide and the boat is being steered directly
across, where will it land and how far will the boat have gone?

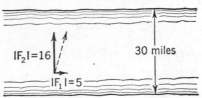

5. A swimmer wants to reach a point on the opposite shore of
a river that is 526 yards wide.   If he knows that the current is
flowing at the rate of 2 miles an hour, and he can swim at the rate
of 3 miles an hour, in what direction should be swim in order to
reach the point just opposite him on the other shore?   How long
will it take him to reach his destination?   *Hint:* Find the actual
rate of the swimmer, and divide this into the width of the river.

6. A shell is fired at an angle of elevation of 28° and with a
velocity of magnitude 1600 feet per second.   Find the magnitudes
of its initial horizontal and vertical velocities.

7. An airplane is flying due south with a speed of 182 miles per
hour.   An east wind is blowing at 36.0 miles per hour.   At the
end of 45 minutes how far has the plane flown?

8. A vessel has sailed 128 miles southwest.   What is the compass bearing of the ship and how far south and west is it from
its original position?

9. A shell is fired at an angle of elevation of 45° and with an
initial horizontal speed of 1400 feet per second.   Find the muzzle
speed of the shell and its vertical speed.

10. A plane flies N 32° E for 314 miles and then flies S 58° E for
217 miles.   What is its final position with relation to its starting
place?

EXERCISES: CHAPTER V

1. Solve the following right triangles:
   (a) $A = 45°\ 20'$, $c = 135.00$.
   (b) $B = 22°\ 30'$, $a = 420.37$.
   (c) $b = 1.1500$, $c = 3.2500$.
   (d) $a = 25.214$, $b = 75.116$.

(e) $c = 110.00$, $a = 45.000$.

(f) $a = 146.72$, $A = 60° 30' 20''$.

(g) $b = 1.8000$, $B = \dfrac{\pi}{3}$ radians.

(h) $A = \dfrac{\pi}{4}$ radians, $b = 11.256$.

(i) $c = 304.00$, $B = \dfrac{\pi}{6}$ radians.

(j) $B = 0.8$ radians, $c = 283.14$.

2. Solve the following isosceles triangles:

(a) Altitude is 10.357, one equal side is 14.396.

(b) Vertex angle is 64° 28′, base is 12.382.

(c) Perimeter is 428.3, base is 108.7.

(d) Base is 2.436, one equal side is 6.924.

(e) Base angle is 60° 30′ 28″, area is 300.24.

(f) Base angle is 44° 10′ 16″, one equal side is 24.280.

(g) Perimeter is 324.66, one equal side is 134.21.

(h) Altitude is 4.963, base is 6.252.

(i) A central angle of 120° 20′ 36″ is subtended by a chord of a circle. If the radius of the circle is 8.942 inches, what is the length of the chord?

3. A man 6 feet 1 inch tall casts a shadow 8 feet 4 inches long. What is the angle of elevation of the sun?

4. Two straight roads intersect at an angle of 32° 25′ 30″. A gasoline station is on one of the roads 3192 yards from the intersection. How far is the gasoline station from the other road?

5. At a point 219.62 feet away from the base of a tree, the angle of elevation of the top is 16° 35′ 40″. How tall is the tree?

6. The angle of elevation of the top of a hill is 62° 20′ 35″. After one walks 500 yards directly toward the hill, one finds the angle of elevation to be 50° 10′ 20″. How high is the hill and how far away is the top from the first point of observation?

7. A tower stands on a hill. The hill makes an angle of 15° 20′ 25″ with the horizontal. The angle of depression from the top of the tower to a point 200 yards down the hill from the base of the tower is 44° 25′ 15″. What is the height of the tower?

8. From the top of a cliff 634 feet high the angles of depression of two large stones lying in a straight line with the foot of the cliff are 42° 20′ and 30° 30′ respectively. What is the distance between the two stones?

9. Find the magnitudes of the horizontal and vertical components of a force of 83.79 pounds inclined at 32° 18′ with the horizontal.

10. A force of magnitude 165 pounds is required to keep a weight of 203 pounds from sliding down an inclined plane. What is the inclination of the plane?

11. A weight of 1893 pounds, resting on an inclined plane, is held in place by a cable. If the inclined plane makes an angle of 28° 47′ with the horizontal, what is the tension in the cable?

12. Find the magnitude of the force necessary to draw a wagon weighing 1192 pounds up a plane inclined at 26° 34′.

13. A man leaves a certain city and drives along a straight road for 4 hours at the rate of 35 miles per hour. At the end of this time he turns upon another straight road making an angle of 25° 30′ with an extension of the original road and drives for 2 hours to his final destination at the rate of 32 miles per hour. How far has he driven and how far is he from the first road?

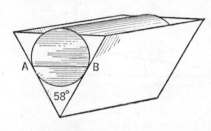

14. A cylinder 4 feet in diameter rests in a trough, the sides of which make an angle of 58° with each other. (See figure.) If A and B are points directly opposite each other at which the cylinder touches the trough, what is the length of AB?

15. A weight is hung from a steel ring which is suspended midway between two vertical walls by three wires. Two of the wires are attached to one wall at points 6.00 feet above the ring. These wires are equal in length and the points to which they are attached to the wall are 10.0 feet apart. (See figure.) If the distance between walls is 24.0 feet,

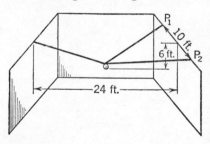

what is the length of each of the two wires and what is the angle between them?

16. A large water tank is supported by three legs each 30 feet long. The upper ends of the legs are at the vertexes of an equilateral triangle 12 feet on a side. The lower ends are on the

vertexes of an equilateral triangle 24 feet on a side. How high
are the upper ends of the supporting legs?

17. A cardboard rectangle, 7 by 9 inches, is held so that the
9-inch side is horizontal. The rectangle is then folded, the upper
right corner being brought to a point on the lower side, 3 inches
over from the lower left corner. (See figure.) How long is the
crease and what angle does it make with the top edge?

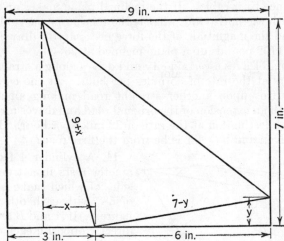

Chapter VI

IDENTITIES

37. The fundamental identities

An equation is said to be an identity provided it is satisfied by *every value* of the variable or variables for which the functions involved in the equation are defined. For example, $(x - y)^2 \equiv x^2 - 2xy + y^2$ is an identity. The symbol $\equiv$ means "identically equal to." Test the identity by substituting for x and y the following values: $(-1,2)$, $(3,-2)$, $(\frac{1}{2},\frac{1}{3})$, $(\sqrt{2},-\frac{1}{2})$, $(\sqrt{3},\sqrt{5})$. On the other hand, the equation $x^2 - 2xy + y^2 = 0$ is not an identity since *at least one* pair of numbers, $(1,0)$, does not satisfy it. In the following sections we shall be interested in trigonometric identities. The trigonometric identities are equations involving the *trigonometric functions* that are satisfied by all values of the *angle*, or *angles*, for which the functions are defined. All the equations of § 12 and § 13 are identities. There are eight identities that are so useful and common that they are sometimes called the fundamental identities. In § 8 we discussed three of these identities — the reciprocal relations:

(1) $\sin \theta \equiv \dfrac{1}{\csc \theta}$; (2) $\cos \theta \equiv \dfrac{1}{\sec \theta}$; (3) $\tan \theta \equiv \dfrac{1}{\cot \theta}$.

If we turn back to § 9 we see that in each figure $MP^2 + OM^2 = 1$, $1 + AT^2 = OT^2$, and $1 + BS^2 = OS^2$.
Hence, we have

(4) $\sin^2 \theta + \cos^2 \theta \equiv 1$; (5) $1 + \tan^2 \theta \equiv \sec^2 \theta$;
(6) $1 + \cot^2 \theta \equiv \csc^2 \theta$.

Also from § 9, we have $\tan \theta = \dfrac{MP}{OM}$ and $\cot \theta = \dfrac{OM}{MP}$.

Thus it follows that

(7) $\tan \theta \equiv \dfrac{\sin \theta}{\cos \theta}$ (8) $\cot \theta \equiv \dfrac{\cos \theta}{\sin \theta}$

These eight fundamental identities are so important that they should be memorized.

EXERCISES

1. Test each of the eight identities by substituting for θ the values 0°, 30°, 45°, 60°, and 90°.

2. Why does a test of the identities fail in some cases when $\theta = 0°$, 90°, 180°, or 360°?

3. Write each of the eight identities in two other ways. *Hint:* (1) may be written:

$$\csc \theta \equiv \frac{1}{\sin \theta}, \text{ or } \sin \theta \csc \theta \equiv 1.$$

It is suggested that when the student proves the following identities, in this and later sections, he should do so by reducing only one side of the identity to the other side. Also it is advisable to start with the more complicated side, if there is one, or with the side that seems to offer the most working opportunities. If functions other than sines and cosines occur in the identity, it is sometimes helpful to change the terms on one side to sines or cosines before proceeding. The following examples illustrate the process.

Example 1:

Prove that the equation $\tan x \csc x \equiv \sec x$ is an identity.

We shall work with the left side. Expressing everything in terms of sines and cosines, we have

$$\frac{\sin x}{\cos x} \frac{1}{\sin x} \equiv \frac{1}{\cos x} \equiv \sec x,$$

so the left member is equivalent to the right member and the identity is established.

Example 2:

$$(\sin \alpha + \cos \alpha)^2 \equiv 1 + 2 \sin \alpha \cos \alpha.$$

Expanding the left side and using relation (4) we have

$$\sin^2 \alpha + 2 \sin \alpha \cos \alpha + \cos^2 \alpha \equiv 1 + 2 \sin \alpha \cos \alpha.$$

Example 3:

$$\left| \sqrt{\frac{1 - \sin A}{1 + \sin A}} \right| \equiv |\sec A - \tan A|.$$

The absolute values are taken in order to eliminate the ambiguity of *sign* that otherwise would exist since for A in the second or third quadrants $\sec A - \tan A$ is negative.

Working with the *left* side, we rationalize it by multiplying numerator and denominator by $1 - \sin A$. So we have

$$\left| \sqrt{\frac{(1 - \sin A)(1 - \sin A)}{(1 + \sin A)(1 - \sin A)}} \right| \equiv \left| \frac{1 - \sin A}{\cos A} \right| \equiv \left| \frac{1}{\cos A} - \frac{\sin A}{\cos A} \right|$$
$$\equiv |\sec A - \tan A|.$$

Example 4:

$$\frac{\sec^2 x + \csc^2 x}{\cot^2 x} \equiv (1 + \tan^2 x)^2.$$

Again working with the left side, and recalling relations (5) and (6), we have

$$\tan^2 x (1 + \tan^2 x + 1 + \cot^2 x) \equiv \tan^2 x + \tan^4 x + \tan^2 x + 1$$
$$\equiv \tan^4 x + 2 \tan^2 x + 1$$
$$\equiv (1 + \tan^2 x)^2.$$

Example 5:

$$\sec \theta - \cos \theta \equiv \cos \theta \tan^2 \theta.$$

Working with the right side, we have

$$\cos \theta \tan^2 \theta \equiv \cos \theta (\sec^2 \theta - 1)$$
$$\equiv \cos \theta \sec^2 \theta - \cos \theta$$
$$\equiv \sec \theta - \cos \theta.$$

EXERCISES

1. Write the six trigonometric functions in terms of the sine of the angle.

2. Write the six trigonometric functions in terms of the cosine of the angle.

3. Prove the following identities:
   (a) $\tan x \cos x \equiv \sin x$.
   (b) $1 - \sin^2 x \equiv \cos^2 x$.
   (c) $(\sin \beta + \cos \beta)(\sin \beta - \cos \beta) \equiv 1 - 2 \cos^2 \beta$.
   (d) $(\sec \beta + \tan \beta)(\sec \beta - \tan \beta) \equiv 1$.
   (e) $\sec x (1 + \cos x) \equiv 1 + \sec x$.
   (f) $\sin x \tan^2 x \cot^3 x \equiv \cos x$.
   (g) $\tan y + \cot y \equiv \sec y \csc y$.
   (h) $\sin x \cos x \tan x + \cos x \sin x \cot x \equiv 1$.
   (i) $(\sin x + \cos x)(\tan x + \cot x) \equiv \sec x + \csc x$.
   (j) $\cos \alpha - \sec \alpha \equiv -\tan \alpha \sin \alpha$.
   (k) $\cos^2 u - \sin^2 u \equiv \cos^2 u (\sec^2 u - 2 \tan^2 u)$.
   (l) $\dfrac{1 + \cos x}{1 - \cos x} \equiv \dfrac{\sec x + 1}{\sec x - 1}$.

   (m) $\sec \beta - 2 \sin \beta \equiv \dfrac{(\sin \beta - \cos \beta)^2}{\cos \beta}$.

   (n) $\dfrac{\sec^2 \theta + \csc^2 \theta}{\sec^2 \theta - \csc^2 \theta} \equiv \dfrac{\tan^2 \theta + 1}{\tan^2 \theta - 1}$.

   (o) $\tan^2 y + 2(1 - \sec y) \equiv (\tan^2 y + 1)(1 - \cos y)^2$.
   (p) $\sin (180° + \theta) \equiv \cos (270° - \theta)$.
   (q) $\tan^4 x + \tan^2 x \equiv \sec^4 x - \sec^2 x$.

   (r) $2(\sin x + \sin x \cos x) \equiv \dfrac{2 \sin^3 x}{1 - \cos x}$.

   (s) $\dfrac{\sin x + 2 \sin x \cos x}{2 + \cos x - 2 \sin^2 x} \equiv \tan x$.

   (t) $\dfrac{1}{\cot y + \tan y} \equiv \sin y \cos y$.

   (u) $\sec^2 x + \csc^2 x \equiv \sec^2 x \csc^2 x$.
   (v) $\sin^2 \theta \csc^3 \theta \tan \theta \equiv \sec \theta$.

   (w) $\dfrac{\sin x}{\cos x} + \dfrac{\sec x}{\csc x} \equiv 2 \tan x$.

   (x) $\dfrac{1 + \cos y}{1 - \cos y} \equiv \dfrac{\sin^2 y}{(1 - \cos y)^2}$.

   (y) $(\sin x - \cos x)^2 + (\sin x + \cos x)^2 \equiv 2$.
   (z) $(1 - \sec x)^2 - \tan^2 x \equiv 2(1 - \sec x)$.
   (aa) $1 - \tan^4 \theta \equiv 2 \sec^2 \theta - \sec^4 \theta$.

(ab) $\cos^2 B \, (1 + \tan^2 B) + \sin^2 B \, (1 + \cot^2 B) \equiv 2.$

(ac) $\dfrac{\csc x}{\csc x - 1} + \dfrac{\csc x}{\csc x + 1} \equiv 2 \sec^2 x.$

(ad) $\dfrac{\tan \theta + 1}{\sin \theta + \cos \theta} \equiv \sec \theta.$

(ae) $\cot y \cos y + \sin y \equiv \csc y.$

(af) $\left| \sqrt{\dfrac{1 - \cos y}{1 + \cos y}} \right| \equiv | \csc y - \cot y |.$

(ag) $\tan \theta \cot \theta + \sin \theta \csc \theta \equiv 2(\sin^2 \theta + \cos^2 \theta).$

(ah) $\dfrac{\cot A \cos A}{\cot A - \cos A} \equiv \dfrac{\cos A}{1 - \sin A}.$

(ai) $\dfrac{1}{1 + \cos x} + \dfrac{1}{1 - \cos x} \equiv 2 \csc^2 x.$

(aj) $\sin \theta \, (\cot \theta + 1) \equiv \sin \theta + \cos \theta.$

(ak) $\sec^4 y - 1 \equiv 2 \tan^2 y + \tan^4 y.$

(al) $\dfrac{\sin x + \cot x}{\sin x - \cot x} \equiv \dfrac{\tan^2 x + \sec x}{\tan^2 x - \sec x}.$

(am) $\dfrac{\cos^2 A \csc^2 A + 1}{1 + \cot^2 A} \equiv 1.$

(an) $\dfrac{(\sin \theta + \cos \theta)^2}{\cos^2 \theta \tan^2 \theta} \equiv (1 + \cot \theta)^2.$

(ao) $(\sin x + \cos x)(\sec x + \csc x) - 2 \equiv \sec x \csc x.$

(ap) $(1 - \cos^2 y + \sin^2 y)^2 + 4 \sin^2 y \cos^2 y \equiv 4 \sin^2 y.$

(aq) $(\cos^2 \theta - \sin^2 \theta)^2 + 4 \sin^2 \theta \cos^2 \theta \equiv 1.$

(ar) $(\cos^2 x + \sin^2 x)^3 - (\tan^2 x - \sec^2 x) \equiv 2.$

38. Addition formulas

A striking property of the trigonometric functions is that a function of the difference or of the sum of two angles can be expressed in terms of the trigonometric functions of the individual angles. Let us find an identity for $\cos (\alpha - \beta)$ in terms of the sine and cosine of α and β.

Construct a *unit* circle and place α and β in standard position. Then P_1 and P_2, the points where the terminal sides of β and α intersect the unit circle, have the co-ordinates

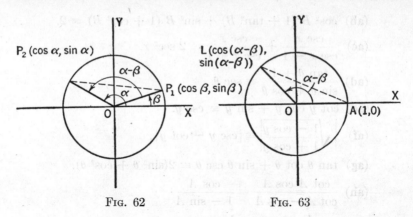

Fig. 62   Fig. 63

$(\cos \beta, \sin \beta)$ and $(\cos \alpha, \sin \alpha)$, respectively. Why? (See Fig. 62).

Using the distance formula (§ 5), we have

$$(P_1P_2)^2 = (\cos \alpha - \cos \beta)^2 + (\sin \alpha - \sin \beta)^2.$$

Expanding and rearranging our terms, we have

$$(P_1P_2)^2 = \cos^2 \alpha + \sin^2 \alpha + \cos^2 \beta + \sin^2 \beta$$
$$- 2(\cos \alpha \cos \beta + \sin \alpha \sin \beta)$$
$$= 2 - 2(\cos \alpha \cos \beta + \sin \alpha \sin \beta).$$

Now place $\alpha - \beta$ in standard position by rotating the entire axis system so that A coincides with P_1 and $\angle AOL$ is $\alpha - \beta$.* (See Fig. 63.) Again using the distance formula, we have

$$(AL)^2 = [\cos (\alpha - \beta) - 1]^2 + \sin^2 (\alpha - \beta)$$
$$= \cos^2 (\alpha - \beta) + \sin^2 (\alpha - \beta) + 1 - 2 \cos (\alpha - \beta)$$
$$= 2 - 2 \cos (\alpha - \beta).$$

But $|P_1P_2| = |AL|$; hence,

$$2 - 2 \cos (\alpha - \beta) = 2 - 2(\cos \alpha \cos \beta + \sin \alpha \sin \beta).$$

So, $\cos (\alpha - \beta) = \cos \alpha \cos \beta + \sin \alpha \sin \beta.$

* $\angle AOL$ may be $360° - (\alpha - \beta)$. For example, consider α a negative angle in quadrant IV and β a positive angle in quadrant II. However, L now has for its co-ordinates $[\cos (\alpha - \beta), - \sin (\alpha - \beta)]$. Why?

Since α and β have been selected arbitrarily, we have established the important identity:

(9) $\qquad \cos(\alpha - \beta) \equiv \cos \alpha \cos \beta + \sin \alpha \sin \beta.$

Example 1:

Evaluate $\cos 15°$ by the use of identity (9).

$$\begin{aligned}\cos 15° &= \cos(45° - 30°)\\ &= \cos 45° \cos 30° + \sin 45° \sin 30°\\ &= \frac{\sqrt{2}}{2} \times \frac{\sqrt{3}}{2} + \frac{\sqrt{2}}{2} \times \frac{1}{2}\\ &= \sqrt{2}(\sqrt{3} + 1)/4.\end{aligned}$$

Example 2:

Show that $\cos(\pi - \alpha) \equiv -\cos \alpha.$

From (9) we have

$$\begin{aligned}\cos(\pi - \alpha) &\equiv \cos \pi \cos \alpha + \sin \pi \sin \alpha\\ &\equiv -1(\cos \alpha) + 0(\sin \alpha)\\ &\equiv -\cos \alpha.\end{aligned}$$

39. The relations between β and $(90° - \beta)$

We have already studied the relations between β and $(90° - \beta)$ for the special case where β is a positive acute angle. (See § 14.) Now we are ready to establish the relations when β is any angle.

Replacing α by $90°$ in identity (9), we have

$$\begin{aligned}\cos(90° - \beta) &\equiv \cos 90° \cos \beta + \sin 90° \sin \beta\\ &\equiv (0) \cos \beta + (1) \sin \beta\\ &\equiv \sin \beta.\end{aligned}$$

Hence we have established the identity,

(10) $\qquad \cos(90° - \beta) \equiv \sin \beta$, **for any angle β.**

Now let β be the angle $90° - \alpha$, and we have from relation (10)

$$\begin{aligned}\cos[90° - (90° - \alpha)] &\equiv \sin(90° - \alpha), \text{ or}\\ \cos \alpha &\equiv \sin(90° - \alpha).\end{aligned}$$

Since it makes no difference what we call our angle, let us replace α by β to be consistent with the symbolism employed in (10); then we have

(11) $\sin (90° - \beta) \equiv \cos \beta.$

Using relations (7), (10) and (11), we can write

$$\tan (90° - \beta) \equiv \sin (90° - \beta)/\cos (90° - \beta)$$
$$\equiv \cos \beta/\sin \beta \equiv \cot \beta.$$

By employing the reciprocal relations and these last conclusions we immediately obtain the formulas,

$$\cot (90° - \beta) \equiv \tan \beta,$$
$$\sec (90° - \beta) \equiv \csc \beta,$$
and $$\csc (90° - \beta) \equiv \sec \beta.$$

40. The relations between $\sin (\alpha - \beta)$, $\sin (\alpha + \beta)$, $\cos (\alpha + \beta)$, and the sine and cosine of α and β

We have already seen in § 13 that $\sin (-\theta) \equiv -\sin \theta$ and that $\cos (-\theta) \equiv \cos \theta$. After replacing β in (9) by $-\beta$, we have

$$\cos [\alpha - (-\beta)] \equiv \cos \alpha \cos (-\beta) + \sin \alpha \sin (-\beta).$$

After simplification, we then have the fundamental relation,

(12) $\cos (\alpha + \beta) \equiv \cos \alpha \cos \beta - \sin \alpha \sin \beta.$

Since α is any angle, we may replace α in (12) by $90° - \alpha$; this leads to

(a) $\cos (90° - \alpha + \beta) \equiv \cos [90° - (\alpha - \beta)]$
$$\equiv \sin (\alpha - \beta).$$

Using relations (12), (10), and (11), we have

(b) $\cos (90° - \alpha + \beta) \equiv \cos [(90° - \alpha) + \beta]$
$$\equiv \cos (90° - \alpha) \cos \beta - \sin (90° - \alpha) \sin \beta,$$
$$\equiv \sin \alpha \cos \beta -- \cos \alpha \sin \beta.$$

By combining the results in relations **(a)** and **(b)**, we obtain

(13) $\sin (\alpha - \beta) \equiv \sin \alpha \cos \beta - \cos \alpha \sin \beta.$

Finally, if we replace β by $-\beta$ in identity (13); we have

$\sin (\alpha - (-\beta)) \equiv \sin \alpha \cos (-\beta) - \cos \alpha \sin (-\beta),$ or

(14) $\sin (\alpha + \beta) \equiv \sin \alpha \cos \beta + \cos \alpha \sin \beta.$

Example 1:

If $\sin \alpha = \frac{1}{2}$, $\cos \beta = -\frac{3}{4}$, and α and β are in the same quadrant, find $\sin (\alpha + \beta)$, $\cos (\alpha + \beta)$, $\sin (\alpha - \beta)$, and $\cos (\alpha - \beta)$.

Since the sine is positive and the cosine is negative only in the second quadrant, α and β are in this quadrant. So we have

$\sin \alpha = \frac{1}{2}, \cos \alpha = -\dfrac{\sqrt{3}}{2}$ and $\sin \beta = \dfrac{\sqrt{7}}{4}, \cos \beta = -\frac{3}{4}.$

Using identities (9), (12), (13), and (14), we have

$$\sin (\alpha + \beta) = \sin \alpha \cos \beta + \cos \alpha \sin \beta$$
$$= \left(\frac{1}{2}\right)\left(-\frac{3}{4}\right) + \left(-\frac{\sqrt{3}}{2}\right)\left(\frac{\sqrt{7}}{4}\right)$$
$$= -\left(\frac{\sqrt{3}}{8}\right)(\sqrt{3} + \sqrt{7}).$$

$$\sin (\alpha - \beta) = \sin \alpha \cos \beta - \cos \alpha \sin \beta$$
$$= \left(\frac{1}{2}\right)\left(-\frac{3}{4}\right) - \left(-\frac{\sqrt{3}}{2}\right)\left(\frac{\sqrt{7}}{4}\right)$$
$$= -\left(\frac{\sqrt{3}}{8}\right)(\sqrt{3} - \sqrt{7}).$$

$$\cos (\alpha + \beta) = \cos \alpha \cos \beta - \sin \alpha \sin \beta$$
$$= \left(-\frac{\sqrt{3}}{2}\right)\left(-\frac{3}{4}\right) - \left(\frac{1}{2}\right)\left(\frac{\sqrt{7}}{4}\right)$$
$$= \left(\frac{1}{8}\right)(3\sqrt{3} - \sqrt{7}).$$

$$\cos (\alpha - \beta) = \cos \alpha \cos \beta + \sin \alpha \sin \beta$$
$$= \left(-\frac{\sqrt{3}}{2}\right)\left(-\frac{3}{4}\right) + \left(\frac{1}{2}\right)\left(\frac{\sqrt{7}}{4}\right)$$
$$= \left(\frac{1}{8}\right)(3\sqrt{3} + \sqrt{7}).$$

Example 2:

Expand cos (270° + α).

Using (12), we have

$$\cos(270° + α) = \cos 270° \cos α - \sin 270° \sin α$$
$$= (0) \cos α - (-1) \sin α$$
$$= \sin α.$$

Example 3:

Find cos 75°.

$$\cos 75° = \cos(30° + 45°) = \cos 30° \cos 45° - \sin 30° \sin 45°,$$
$$= \frac{\sqrt{3}}{2}\frac{\sqrt{2}}{2} - \frac{1}{2}\frac{\sqrt{2}}{2} = \frac{(\sqrt{3} - 1)\sqrt{2}}{4}.$$

Therefore

$$\cos 75° = \frac{(\sqrt{3} - 1)\sqrt{2}}{4}.$$

EXERCISES

1. Find sin 75°.

2. Find cos 105°, sin 105°, sin 255°, and cos 255°.

3. Given sin α = 1/2, cos β = √3/2, and the terminal sides of α and β in different quadrants; find sin (α + β) and cos (α + β). Is there more than one solution?

4. Given cos α = −√2/2, cos β = 1/2, with the terminal side of α in quadrant III, and the terminal side of β in quadrant IV; find sin (α + β) and cos (α + β).

5. Find sin (90° + α) as a trigonometric function of α. Repeat the problem for cos (90° + α).

6. Evaluate sin 15°, cos 15°, sin 165°, and cos 165°.

7. Given sin α = √3/2, cos β = −3/5, and the terminal sides of α and β in the same quadrant; find sin (α + β) and cos (α + β).

8. Given sin α = −√3/2, cos β = −1/√2, and the terminal sides of α and β in the same quadrant; find cos (α + β) and sin (α + β).

9. If sin α = 1/2, cos β = −(√3/2), and the terminal sides of α and β are in different quadrants, find sin (α − β) and cos (α − β).

10. If sin β = $\frac{3}{5}$, cos α = $\frac{1}{3}$, and α and β are in different quadrants, find sin (α − β), cos (α − β), sin (α + β), and cos (α + β).

11. Prove the following identities:

(a) $\cos (x + 30°) - \cos (x - 30°) \equiv -\sin x.$

(b) $\cos (45° + x) - \cos (45° - x) \equiv -\sqrt{2} \sin x.$

(c) $\sin (x + 30°) + \sin (x - 30°) \equiv \sqrt{3} \sin x.$

(d) $\sin (x + 30°) + \cos (x + 60°) \equiv \cos x.$

(e) $\sin (\alpha + \beta + \gamma) \equiv \sin \alpha \cos \beta \cos \gamma + \cos \alpha \sin \beta \cos \gamma$
$+ \cos \alpha \cos \beta \sin \gamma - \sin \alpha \sin \beta \sin \gamma.$

12. Expand the following:

(a) $\sin (180° - \alpha); \quad \cos (180° - \alpha).$

(b) $\sin (270° - \alpha); \quad \cos (270° - \alpha).$

(c) $\sin (270° + \alpha); \quad \cos (270° + \alpha).$

(d) $\sin (360° - \alpha); \quad \cos (360° - \alpha).$

41. Tan $(\alpha - \beta)$ and tan $(\alpha + \beta)$

Using identities **(7)**, **(9)**, and **(13)**, we immediately obtain

$$\tan (\alpha - \beta) \equiv \frac{\sin (\alpha - \beta)}{\cos (\alpha - \beta)}$$
$$\equiv \frac{\sin \alpha \cos \beta - \cos \alpha \sin \beta}{\cos \alpha \cos \beta + \sin \alpha \sin \beta}.$$

Dividing each term of the numerator and the denominator on the right by $\cos \alpha \cos \beta$, we obtain, after simple reductions,

(15)
$$\tan (\alpha - \beta) \equiv \frac{\tan \alpha - \tan \beta}{1 + \tan \alpha \tan \beta}.$$

If in **(15)** we replace β by $-\beta$, we obtain

(16)
$$\tan (\alpha + \beta) \equiv \frac{\tan \alpha + \tan \beta}{1 - \tan \alpha \tan \beta}.$$

Example:

Expand $\tan (\pi - \alpha)$.

$$\tan (\pi - \alpha) = \frac{(\tan \pi - \tan \alpha)}{(1 + \tan \pi \tan \alpha)}$$
$$= -\tan \alpha, \text{ since } \tan \pi = 0.$$

EXERCISES

1. Verify **(15)** and **(16)** by carrying out all the operations and necessary simplifications.

2. Find $\tan 75°$, $\tan 105°$, and $\tan 255°$.

3. Derive in two ways the identity for $\cot (\alpha + \beta)$ in terms of the cotangents of α and β.

4. Find $\tan (\alpha + \beta)$ and $\cot (\alpha + \beta)$ under the following conditions:

(a) $\sin \alpha = 1/2$, $\cos \beta = \sqrt{2}/2$, and the terminal sides of α and β are in different quadrants.

(b) $\cos \alpha = - \sqrt{2}/2$, $\cos \beta = 1/2$, the terminal side of α is in quadrant III, and the terminal side of β is in quadrant IV.

(c) $\sin \alpha = \sqrt{3}/2$, $\cos \beta = -3/5$, and the terminal sides of α and β are in the same quadrant.

(d) $\sin \alpha = - \sqrt{3}/2$, $\cos \beta = -1/\sqrt{2}$, and the terminal sides of α and β are in the same quadrant.

5. Find $\tan 15°$, $\tan 165°$, and $\cot (-15°)$.

6. If $\tan \alpha = \sqrt{3}$ and $\tan \beta = \frac{1}{2}$, find $\tan (\alpha - \beta)$ and $\cot (\alpha - \beta)$.

7. If $\tan \alpha = 1/\sqrt{3}$ and $\tan \beta = 2$, find $\tan (\alpha - \beta)$ and $\cot (\alpha - \beta)$.

8. Prove the following identities:

(a) $\dfrac{\tan (45° + x)}{\tan (45° - x)} \equiv \dfrac{(1 + \tan x)^2}{(1 - \tan x)^2}$.

(b) $\tan (x + 45°) + \cot (x - 45°) \equiv 0$.

(c) $\tan (\pi + \alpha) \equiv \tan \alpha$.

(d) $\tan (\alpha - 2\pi) \equiv \tan \alpha$.

(e) $\dfrac{(1 - \tan \alpha)}{(1 + \tan \alpha)} \equiv \tan (45° - \alpha)$.

42. The double-angle formulas

If $\alpha = \beta$, identities (**14**), (**12**), and (**16**) become, respectively,

$$(17) \qquad \sin 2\alpha \equiv 2 \sin \alpha \cos \alpha,$$

$$(18) \qquad \cos 2\alpha \equiv \cos^2 \alpha - \sin^2 \alpha,$$

$$(19) \qquad \tan 2\alpha \equiv \frac{2 \tan \alpha}{1 - \tan^2 \alpha}.$$

As a consequence of (4), relation (18) may be written in either of the following forms:

(18′) $$\cos 2\alpha \equiv 1 - 2 \sin^2 \alpha,$$

(18″) $$\cos 2\alpha \equiv 2 \cos^2 \alpha - 1.$$

EXERCISES

1. Using (17), (18), and (19), find $\sin 90°$, $\cos 90°$, and $\tan 90°$.

2. Derive an identity for $\cot 2\alpha$, $\sec 2\alpha$, and $\csc 2\alpha$ in terms of $\cot \alpha$, $\sec \alpha$, and $\csc \alpha$, respectively.

3. Let $2\alpha = \theta$ and rewrite (17), (18), and (19) in terms of the angle θ. What right have we to do this?

4. Using the double-angle formulas, find the sine, cosine, and tangent of 120°.

5. If $\sin \theta = \frac{3}{4}$, find $\sin 2\theta$. How many solutions are there?

6. If $\sin \theta = -\frac{3}{4}$, find $\cos 2\theta$. How many solutions are there?

7. Find $\sin 4\theta$, $\cos 4\theta$, and $\tan 4\theta$ in terms of the functions of θ. *Hint:* Let $\alpha = 2\theta$ in formulas (17), (18), and (19).

8. Find $\sin 2\theta$, $\cos 2\theta$, and $\tan 2\theta$, if $\sin \theta = -\frac{7}{25}$.

9. Find $\sin 2\theta$, $\cos 2\theta$, and $\tan 2\theta$, if $\cos \theta = \frac{3}{5}$ and $\sin \theta$ is negative.

10. Prove the following identities:

(a) $\cos 2x \equiv \dfrac{\cot^2 x - 1}{\cot^2 x + 1}.$

(b) $1 + \tan^2 y \equiv 2 \tan y \csc 2y.$

(c) $\dfrac{1 - \cos 2\theta}{1 + \cos 2\theta} \equiv \sec^2 \theta - 1.$

(d) $\sin (x + y) \cos (x - y) + \cos (x + y) \sin (x - y)$
$$\equiv \sin 2x.$$

(e) $\cos (x + y) \cos (x - y) + \sin (x + y) \sin (x - y)$
$$\equiv \cos 2y.$$

43. The half-angle formulas

Solving for $\sin^2 \alpha$ in formula (18′), we have

$$\sin^2 \alpha \equiv \frac{1 - \cos 2\alpha}{2},$$

or $$\sin \alpha \equiv \pm\sqrt{\frac{1 - \cos 2\alpha}{2}}.$$

Replacing α by $A/2$, we obtain

(20) $\sin^2 \dfrac{A}{2} \equiv \dfrac{1 - \cos A}{2}$, or $\sin \dfrac{A}{2} \equiv \pm \sqrt{\dfrac{1 - \cos A}{2}}$.

Here the plus sign precedes the radical when $A/2$ falls in quadrants I or II, and the minus sign precedes the radical when $A/2$ falls in quadrants III or IV.

Solving for $\cos^2 \alpha$ in (18''), we have $\cos^2 \alpha \equiv \dfrac{1 + \cos 2\alpha}{2}$,

or $\cos \alpha \equiv \pm \sqrt{\dfrac{1 + \cos 2\alpha}{2}}$ and, by the same substitution as before, we have

(21) $\cos^2 \dfrac{A}{2} \equiv \dfrac{1 + \cos A}{2}$, or $\cos \dfrac{A}{2} \equiv \pm \sqrt{\dfrac{1 + \cos A}{2}}$.

From results (20) and (21), we obtain

(22) $\tan \dfrac{A}{2} \equiv \pm \sqrt{\dfrac{1 - \cos A}{1 + \cos A}}$.

In both (21) and (22) the sign in front of the radical is determined by the magnitude of the angle $A/2$. Give a detailed explanation of the proper choice of sign as was done for (20).

It is often convenient to write (22) without the radical. To do this we proceed as follows:

$$\left| \tan \dfrac{A}{2} \right| \equiv \left| \sqrt{\dfrac{1 - \cos A}{1 + \cos A}} \right|$$

$$\equiv \left| \sqrt{\dfrac{1 - \cos A}{1 + \cos A} \times \dfrac{1 - \cos A}{1 - \cos A}} \right|$$

$$\equiv \left| \dfrac{1 - \cos A}{\sin A} \right|.$$

For $0° < \dfrac{A}{2} < 90°$ and $180° < \dfrac{A}{2} < 270°$, $\tan \dfrac{A}{2}$ and

$\sin A$ are positive; and for $90° < \dfrac{A}{2} < 180°$ and $270° < \dfrac{A}{2}$

$< 360°$, $\tan \dfrac{A}{2}$ and $\sin A$ are negative. Therefore, since

$1 - \cos A$ is always positive or zero, and since $\tan \dfrac{A}{2}$ is positive or negative as $\sin A$ is positive or negative, the signs indicating absolute value are not needed and we have

$$\tan \frac{A}{2} \equiv \frac{1 - \cos A}{\sin A}.$$

See problem 3 in the following exercises for another form for $\tan \dfrac{A}{2}$.

EXERCISES

1. Evaluate the following without using the tables:

(a) $\sin 15°$.

(b) $\cos 15°$.

(c) $\tan 15°$.

(d) $\cot 15°$.

(e) $\sin 22\frac{1}{2}°$.

(f) $\cos 22\frac{1}{2}°$.

(g) $\tan 22\frac{1}{2}°$.

(h) $\cot 22\frac{1}{2}°$.

(i) $\sin 67\frac{1}{2}°$.

(j) $\cos 67\frac{1}{2}°$.

(k) $\tan 67\frac{1}{2}°$.

(l) $\sin (-22\frac{1}{2}°)$.

(m) $\cos (-22\frac{1}{2}°)$.

(n) $\tan (-15°)$.

(o) $\sin (-15°)$.

2. Derive an identity for $\cot \dfrac{A}{2}$ in terms of $\cos A$.

3. Prove $\tan \dfrac{A}{2} \equiv \dfrac{\sin A}{1 + \cos A} \equiv \dfrac{1 - \cos A}{\sin A}$.

4. Given $\cos \theta = -\dfrac{1}{3}$; find $\sin \dfrac{\theta}{2}$, $\cos \dfrac{\theta}{2}$, $\tan \dfrac{\theta}{2}$, and $\cot \dfrac{\theta}{2}$.

5. Given $\sin \theta = \dfrac{3}{5}$; find $\sin \dfrac{\theta}{2}$, $\cos \dfrac{\theta}{2}$, $\tan \dfrac{\theta}{2}$, and $\cot \dfrac{\theta}{2}$.

6. Given $\tan \theta = 2$ and $\sin \theta$ negative; find the values of the six functions of $\theta/2$.

7. Given $\sin \theta = \dfrac{24}{25}$, find $\sin \dfrac{\theta}{2}$, $\cos \dfrac{\theta}{2}$, $\tan \dfrac{\theta}{2}$, and $\cot \dfrac{\theta}{2}$.

8. Prove the following identities:

(a) $\cot \dfrac{A}{2} \equiv \dfrac{1 + \cos A}{\sin A}$.

(b) $(\sec A - 1) \csc A \equiv \tan \dfrac{A}{2} \sec A$.

(c) $\sin^2 \dfrac{\theta}{2} + \cos^2 \dfrac{\theta}{2} \equiv 1.$

(d) $\cos \theta \equiv 2 \cos^2 \dfrac{\theta}{2} - 1 \equiv 1 - 2 \sin^2 \dfrac{\theta}{2}.$

(e) $\dfrac{1 + \sin A}{\cos A} \equiv \dfrac{1 + \tan \dfrac{A}{2}}{1 - \tan \dfrac{A}{2}}.$

(f) $4 \sin^2 \dfrac{x}{2} \cos^2 \dfrac{x}{2} \equiv 1 - \cos^2 x.$

(g) $\dfrac{2 \tan \dfrac{y}{2}}{1 + \tan^2 \dfrac{y}{2}} \equiv \sin y.$

44. Sums and differences of the sines and cosines of two angles

By adding and subtracting respectively relations (**13**) and (**14**), we obtain

(23) $2 \sin \alpha \cos \beta \equiv \sin (\alpha + \beta) + \sin (\alpha - \beta),$

(24) $2 \cos \alpha \sin \beta \equiv \sin (\alpha + \beta) - \sin (\alpha - \beta).$

In the same way, by adding and subtracting respectively relations (**9**) and (**12**), we obtain

(25) $2 \cos \alpha \cos \beta \equiv \cos (\alpha + \beta) + \cos (\alpha - \beta),$

(26) $- 2 \sin \alpha \sin \beta \equiv \cos (\alpha + \beta) - \cos (\alpha - \beta).$

If $\alpha + \beta$ is designated by A and $\alpha - \beta$ by B, then

$$\alpha = \frac{A + B}{2} \text{ and } \beta = \frac{A - B}{2}.$$

Substituting these values of α and β in the above relations, we obtain the following important set of formulas:

(27) $\sin A + \sin B \equiv 2 \sin \left(\dfrac{A + B}{2} \right) \cos \left(\dfrac{A - B}{2} \right),$

(28) $\sin A - \sin B \equiv 2 \cos \left(\dfrac{A+B}{2}\right) \sin \left(\dfrac{A-B}{2}\right),$

(29) $\cos A + \cos B \equiv 2 \cos \left(\dfrac{A+B}{2}\right) \cos \left(\dfrac{A-B}{2}\right),$

(30) $\cos A - \cos B \equiv -2 \sin \left(\dfrac{A+B}{2}\right) \sin \left(\dfrac{A-B}{2}\right).$

EXERCISES

1. Show that $\sin 25° - \sin 15° = 2 \cos 20° \sin 5°$.
2. Show that $2 \sin 34° \cos 10° = \sin 44° + \sin 24°$.
3. In identity (27) replace B by $-B$, and obtain (28).
4. Replace B by $180° - B$ in (29) and obtain (30).
5. Replace A by $90° - \theta$ and B by $90° - \phi$ in identities (27) and (28) and obtain relations for $\cos \theta + \cos \phi$ and $\cos \theta - \cos \phi$.

6. Express as a product:

(a) $\sin 40° + \sin 20°$.   (i) $\sin 15° - \sin 75°$.
(b) $\sin 40° - \sin 20°$.   (j) $\sin 2x + \sin x$.
(c) $\cos 40° + \cos 20°$.   (k) $\cos 3x - \cos 5x$.
(d) $\cos (-40°) - \cos (-20°)$.   (l) $\sin 80° + \sin 20°$.
(e) $\sin 50° + \sin 10°$.   (m) $\sin 35° - \sin 25°$.
(f) $\cos 75° - \cos 15°$.   (n) $\cos 10x + \cos 2x$.
(g) $\sin 15° + \sin 45°$.   (o) $\sin 6x + \sin 2x$.
(h) $\sin 45° - \sin 15°$.   (p) $\cos 54° - \cos 36°$.

7. Express as a sum or difference:

(a) $\cos 15° \cos 35°$.   (f) $\cos \dfrac{5x}{2} \cos \dfrac{x}{2}$.

(b) $\sin 30° \sin 40°$.   (g) $\sin 2x \cos 4x$.
(c) $\sin 35° \cos 11°$.   (h) $\cos 50° \cos 40°$.
(d) $\cos 24° \sin 10°$.   (i) $\sin 2x \cos x$.
(e) $\sin 40° \sin 20°$.   (j) $\cos 4x \sin 2x$.

8. Show that $\dfrac{\sin 50° - \sin 10°}{\cos 50° - \cos 10°} = -\sqrt{3}$.

9. Evaluate:

(a) $\dfrac{\sin 80° - \sin 10°}{\sin 80° + \sin 10°}$.

(b) $\dfrac{\cos 80° - \cos 10°}{\cos 80° + \cos 10°}$.

(c) $\dfrac{\sin 130° + \sin 20°}{\cos 130° + \cos 20°}$.

10. Prove that $\dfrac{\sin \alpha - \sin \beta}{\sin \alpha + \sin \beta} \equiv \dfrac{\cot\left(\dfrac{\alpha + \beta}{2}\right)}{\cot\left(\dfrac{\alpha - \beta}{2}\right)}$.

11. Find an equivalent expression for $\dfrac{\sin \alpha + \sin \beta}{\sin \alpha - \sin \beta}$.

12. Find an equivalent expression for $\dfrac{\cos \alpha - \cos \beta}{\cos \alpha + \cos \beta}$.

13. Prove the following identities.:

(a) $\dfrac{\sin 2x + \sin x}{\cos 2x + \cos x} \equiv \tan \dfrac{3x}{2}$.

(b) $2 \sin (45° + \theta) \sin (45° - \theta) \equiv \dfrac{1}{\sec 2\theta}$

(c) $\dfrac{\tan \dfrac{\theta + \phi}{2}}{\cot \dfrac{\theta - \phi}{2}} \equiv \dfrac{\cos \phi - \cos \theta}{\cos \phi + \cos \theta}$.

(d) $\dfrac{\sin A - \sin 3A}{\cos A - \cos 3A} \equiv \tan 2A$.

(e) $\cot A - \tan B \equiv \cos (A + B) \csc A \sec B$.

(f) $\dfrac{\cot B - \tan B}{\cot B + \tan B} \equiv \cos 2B$.

45. Summary

For convenient reference, the identities derived in this chapter have been listed below. It is most important that the student be able to use them. Especially is this true for those students who intend to continue with the study of analytic geometry and the calculus.

(1) $\sin \theta \csc \theta \equiv 1$.

(2) $\cos \theta \sec \theta \equiv 1$.

(3) $\tan \theta \cot \theta \equiv 1$.

(4) $\sin^2 \theta + \cos^2 \theta \equiv 1$.

(5) $\sec^2 \theta - \tan^2 \theta \equiv 1$.

(6) $\csc^2 \theta - \cot^2 \theta \equiv 1$.

(7) $\tan \theta \equiv \dfrac{\sin \theta}{\cos \theta}.$

(8) $\cot \theta \equiv \dfrac{\cos \theta}{\sin \theta}.$

(9) $\cos (\alpha - \beta) \equiv \cos \alpha \cos \beta + \sin \alpha \sin \beta.$

(10) $\cos (90° - \beta) \equiv \sin \beta.$

(11) $\sin (90° - \beta) \equiv \cos \beta.$

(12) $\cos (\alpha + \beta) \equiv \cos \alpha \cos \beta - \sin \alpha \sin \beta.$

(13) $\sin (\alpha - \beta) \equiv \sin \alpha \cos \beta - \cos \alpha \sin \beta.$

(14) $\sin (\alpha + \beta) \equiv \sin \alpha \cos \beta + \cos \alpha \sin \beta.$

(15) $\tan (\alpha - \beta) \equiv \dfrac{\tan \alpha - \tan \beta}{1 + \tan \alpha \tan \beta}.$

(16) $\tan (\alpha + \beta) \equiv \dfrac{\tan \alpha + \tan \beta}{1 - \tan \alpha \tan \beta}.$

(17) $\sin 2\alpha \equiv 2 \sin \alpha \cos \alpha.$

(18) $\cos 2\alpha \equiv \cos^2 \alpha - \sin^2 \alpha.$

(18′) $\cos 2\alpha \equiv 1 - 2 \sin^2 \alpha.$

(18″) $\cos 2\alpha \equiv 2 \cos^2 \alpha - 1.$

(19) $\tan 2\alpha \equiv \dfrac{2 \tan \alpha}{1 - \tan^2 \alpha}.$

(20) $\sin \dfrac{A}{2} \equiv \pm \sqrt{\dfrac{1 - \cos A}{2}}.$

(21) $\cos \dfrac{A}{2} \equiv \pm \sqrt{\dfrac{1 + \cos A}{2}}.$

(22) $\tan \dfrac{A}{2} \equiv \pm \sqrt{\dfrac{1 - \cos A}{1 + \cos A}}.$

(23) $2 \sin \alpha \cos \beta \equiv \sin (\alpha + \beta) + \sin (\alpha - \beta).$

(24) $2 \cos \alpha \sin \beta \equiv \sin (\alpha + \beta) - \sin (\alpha - \beta).$

(25) $2 \cos \alpha \cos \beta \equiv \cos (\alpha + \beta) + \cos (\alpha - \beta).$

(26) $-2 \sin \alpha \sin \beta \equiv \cos (\alpha + \beta) - \cos (\alpha - \beta).$

(27) $\sin A + \sin B \equiv 2 \sin \left(\dfrac{A + B}{2}\right) \cos \left(\dfrac{A - B}{2}\right).$

(28) $\sin A - \sin B \equiv 2 \cos \left(\dfrac{A + B}{2}\right) \sin \left(\dfrac{A - B}{2}\right).$

(**29**) $\cos A + \cos B \equiv 2 \cos \left(\dfrac{A + B}{2} \right) \cos \left(\dfrac{A - B}{2} \right).$

(**30**) $\cos A - \cos B \equiv -2 \sin \left(\dfrac{A + B}{2} \right) \sin \left(\dfrac{A - B}{2} \right).$

EXERCISES: CHAPTER VI

1. Express each of the trigonometric functions in terms of the tangent.

2. Express each of the trigonometric functions in terms of the cotangent.

3. Express each of the trigonometric functions in terms of the secant.

4. Express each of the trigonometric functions in terms of the cosecant.

5. Expand the following:

(**a**) $\sin (\pi/4 + \theta)$.   (**e**) $\tan (\pi/6 - \theta)$.
(**b**) $\cos (\pi/4 + \theta)$.   (**f**) $\cos (\pi/3 - \theta)$.
(**c**) $\sin (\pi/6 - \theta)$.   (**g**) $\tan (\pi/4 + \theta)$.
(**d**) $\cos (\pi/3 + \theta)$.   (**h**) $\cot (\pi/6 - \theta)$.

6. If $\sin \theta = \frac{1}{4}$ and $\cos \phi = -\frac{3}{4}$, and θ and ϕ are in the same quadrant, find $\sin (\theta + \phi)$ and $\cos (\theta - \phi)$.

7. If $\cos \theta = \frac{3}{5}$, $\sin \phi = -\frac{4}{5}$, and θ and ϕ are in different quadrants, find $\cos (\theta + \phi)$ and $\sin (\theta - \phi)$.

8. Show that $\sin 40° + \sin 20° = \sin 80°$.

9. Show that $\cos 40° + \cos 20° = \sqrt{3} \sin 80°$.

10. Show that $\sin 60° - \sin (-30°) = \dfrac{\sqrt{3} + 1}{2}$.

11. Show that $\cos 30° - \cos (-60°) = \dfrac{\sqrt{3} - 1}{2}$.

12. Given $\tan 2\alpha = \frac{7}{24}$, find $\sin \alpha$ and $\cos \alpha$.

13. Given $\sin 2\alpha = \frac{3}{5}$, find $\sin \alpha$ and $\cos \alpha$.

14. Given $\sin \alpha = \frac{3}{5}$, with $\cos \alpha$ negative, find $\sin 2\alpha$, $\cos 2\alpha$, and $\tan 2\alpha$.

15. Given $\sin \alpha = \frac{4}{5}$, with $\cos \alpha$ positive, find $\sin 2\alpha$, $\cos 2\alpha$, and $\tan 2\alpha$.

16. Given $\sin \alpha = \frac{3}{5}$, $\cos \beta = \frac{3}{5}$, and α and β in the same quadrant, find:

(**a**) $\sin (\alpha - \beta)$.   (**c**) $\sin (\alpha + \beta)$.   (**e**) $\tan (\alpha - \beta)$.
(**b**) $\cos (\alpha - \beta)$.   (**d**) $\cos (\alpha + \beta)$.   (**f**) $\cot (\alpha - \beta)$.

17. Prove that $\sin 3\theta \equiv 3 \sin \theta - 4 \sin^3 \theta$.

18. Derive a formula for $\cos 3\theta$ in terms of $\cos \theta$.

19. Find an identity for $\tan 3\alpha$ in terms of $\tan \alpha$.

20. Derive formulas for $\sin 4\theta$ and $\cos 4\theta$ in terms of $\sin \theta$ and $\cos \theta$, respectively.

21. Prove the following identities:

(a) $\cos^4 \alpha - \sin^4 \alpha \equiv 1 - 2 \sin^2 \alpha$.

(b) $\sin^6 \alpha + \cos^6 \alpha \equiv 1 - 3 \cos^2 \alpha \sin^2 \alpha$.

(c) $\dfrac{\sin (\theta - \phi)}{\sin (\theta + \phi)} \equiv \dfrac{\tan \theta - \tan \phi}{\tan \theta + \tan \phi}$.

(d) $\sin 3x \sin 6x + \sin x \sin 2x \equiv \sin 4x \sin 5x$.

(e) $\cos 2\theta \equiv \dfrac{1 - \tan^2 \theta}{1 + \tan^2 \theta}$.

(f) $\sin 2\theta \equiv \dfrac{2 \tan \theta}{1 + \tan^2 \theta}$.

(g) $\cos (n + 1)x \cos x + \sin (n + 1)x \sin x \equiv \cos nx$.

(h) $\dfrac{1 + \sin A - \cos A}{1 + \sin A + \cos A} \equiv \tan \dfrac{A}{2}$.

(i) $\tan \dfrac{A + B}{2} - \tan \dfrac{A - B}{2} \equiv \dfrac{2 \sin B}{\cos A + \cos B}$.

(j) $\dfrac{\sin y + \sin 3y + \sin 5y + \sin 7y}{\cos y + \cos 3y + \cos 5y + \cos 7y} \equiv \tan 4y$.

(k) $\dfrac{\sec y \cot y - \csc y \tan y}{\cos y - \sin y} \equiv \csc y \sec y$.

(l) $\tan \left(\dfrac{\pi}{4} + A \right) \equiv \sec 2A + \tan 2A$.

(m) $(1 + \sin x + \cos x)^2 \equiv 2(1 + \sin x)(1 + \cos x)$.

(n) $\sin \left(\dfrac{\pi}{4} - \alpha \right) \equiv \dfrac{\cos \alpha - \sin \alpha}{\sqrt{2}}$.

(o) $\tan \left(\dfrac{\pi}{4} - \alpha \right) \equiv \dfrac{1 - \tan \alpha}{1 + \tan \alpha}$.

(p) $\cos (x + y) \cos (x - y) - \sin (x + y) \sin (x - y)$
$\equiv \cos 2x$.

(q) $\tan^2 \theta \equiv \dfrac{\sec 2\theta - 1}{\sec 2\theta + 1}$.

(r) $\dfrac{1 + \tan x}{1 - \tan x} \equiv \sec 2x \, (1 + \sin 2x)$.

(s) $\cot \dfrac{A}{2} \equiv \dfrac{\sin A}{1 - \cos A}.$

(t) $\dfrac{\sin 7x - \sin 5x}{\cos 7x + \cos 5x} \equiv \dfrac{1}{\cot x}.$

(u) $\sin^2 (7x) + 1 + \cos^2 (7x) \equiv 2.$

(v) $\cos^2 (5x) - \sin^2 (5x) \equiv \cos 10x.$

(w) $\dfrac{\sin 2x + \sin x}{1 + \cos x + \cos 2x} \equiv \tan x.$

(x) $\tan \theta + \tan \phi \equiv \dfrac{\sin (\theta + \phi)}{\cos \theta \cos \phi}.$

(y) $\csc 2\theta \equiv \cot 2\theta + \tan \theta.$

(z) $(1 + \tan \theta) \tan (45° - \theta) \equiv 1 - \tan \theta.$

(aa) $\tan \dfrac{A}{2} = \dfrac{\sin A}{1 + \cos A} \equiv \dfrac{1 - \cos A}{\sin A}.$

(ab) $\sin \left(x + \dfrac{\pi}{4} \right) + \sin \left(x + \dfrac{3\pi}{4} \right) \equiv \sqrt{2} \cos x.$

(ac) $\dfrac{\cos 5A - \cos 7A}{\sin 7A - \sin 5A} \equiv \tan 6A.$

(ad) $\sin (45° + x) \sin (45° - x) \equiv \tfrac{1}{2} \cos 2x.$

(ae) $4 \sin \alpha \cos (30° + \alpha) \cos (30° - \alpha) \equiv \sin 3\alpha.$

(af) $\dfrac{\tan \tfrac{1}{2}(\theta - \phi)}{\cot \tfrac{1}{2}(\theta + \phi)} \equiv \dfrac{\cos \phi - \cos \theta}{\cos \phi + \cos \theta}.$

(ag) $\cot x + \tan y \equiv \cos (x - y) \csc x \sec y.$

(ah) $\sin 5\theta \cos 5\theta \equiv \tfrac{1}{2} \sin 10\theta.$

(ai) $\cos^4 6x + 2 \sin^2 6x \cos^2 6x + \sin^4 6x \equiv 1.$

(aj) $\sin \alpha \equiv \dfrac{2 \tan \dfrac{\alpha}{2}}{1 + \tan^2 \dfrac{\alpha}{2}}.$

(ak) $\cos^2 3\theta - \sin^2 3\theta \equiv \cos 6\theta.$

(al) $\dfrac{\sec^2 2\theta + \csc^2 2\theta}{\sec^2 2\theta \csc^2 2\theta} \equiv 1.$

(am) $4 \sin (x+ 30°) \cos (x + 60°) \equiv 2 \cos 2x - 1.$

(an) $2 \cos (x + 45°) \cos (x - 45°) \equiv \cos 2x.$

(ao) $\cot \theta - 1 \equiv (1 - \tan \theta) \cot \theta.$

(ap) $\sin 3y + 2 \sin 5y + \sin 7y \equiv 4 \sin 5y \cos^2 y.$

22. Verify without reference to tables that:

(a) $\cos 20° + \cos 100° + \cos 140° = 0$.

(b) $\sin 70° + \sin 80° = \sin 10° + \sin 20° + \sin 40° + \sin 50°$.

23. If A and B are the acute angles of a right triangle and a, b, and c are the sides opposite A, B, and C, respectively, prove:

(a) $\sin 2A \equiv \dfrac{2ab}{c^2}$.

(b) $\cos 2A \equiv \dfrac{b^2 - a^2}{c^2}$.

(c) $\tan \dfrac{A}{2} \equiv \dfrac{a}{b + c}$.

24. If A, B, and C are the angles of any triangle, prove:

(a) $\sin A + \sin B + \sin C \equiv 4 \cos \dfrac{A}{2} \cos \dfrac{B}{2} \cos \dfrac{C}{2}$.

(b) $\tan A + \tan B + \tan C \equiv \tan A \tan B \tan C$.

(c) $\sin 2A + \sin 2B + \sin 2C \equiv 4 \sin A \sin B \sin C$.

(d) $\cos A + \cos B - \cos C = 4 \cos \dfrac{A}{2} \cos \dfrac{B}{2} \sin \dfrac{C}{2} - 1$.

(e) $\sin A + \sin B - \sin C \equiv 4 \sin \dfrac{A}{2} \sin \dfrac{B}{2} \cos \dfrac{C}{2}$.

(f) $\cos A + \cos B + \cos C \equiv 1 + 4 \sin \dfrac{A}{2} \sin \dfrac{B}{2} \sin \dfrac{C}{2}$.

Chapter VII

THE GENERAL TRIANGLE

46. Solution of the general triangle

If we are given three parts of a triangle, of which at least one is a side, we are able to obtain solutions for the remaining parts. We may be given:

1. *Two angles and a side*
2. *Two sides and an angle opposite one of the sides*
3. *Two sides and the included angle*
4. *Three sides.*

In the sections that follow we shall derive formulas that enable us to solve the triangle in each of the above four cases.

47. Law of sines

When two angles and a side or two sides and an angle *opposite* one of the sides are known, we may solve the triangle by means of the law of sines. This law states that *the sines of the angles of any triangle are proportional to the corresponding opposite sides.* It is particularly useful since it is adaptable to computation by logarithms and, therefore, to the slide rule.

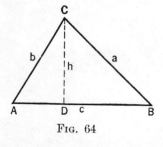

Fig. 64

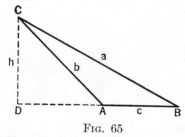

Fig. 65

The law of sines is derived as follows. In both Figures 64 and 65, A, B, and C represent the angles; a, b, and c represent the sides; and h represents the altitude on side c. In Figure 64 $\sin A = h/b$, and in Figure 65 $\sin A = \sin (180° - A) = h/b$, so in either figure $\sin A = h/b$ and $\sin B = h/a$.

Therefore $\qquad h = b \sin A = a \sin B,$

and

$$\frac{b}{\sin B} = \frac{a}{\sin A}.$$

In a similar way, by dropping a perpendicular from A upon side a, we have

$$\frac{b}{\sin B} = \frac{c}{\sin C}.$$

As a consequence, we obtain the *law of sines:*

$$\frac{a}{\sin A} = \frac{b}{\sin B} = \frac{c}{\sin C}.$$

We may also write this law in the form,

$$\frac{\sin A}{a} = \frac{\sin B}{b} = \frac{\sin C}{c}.$$

Case 1: *Given two angles and a side.* Given $A = 40° 27' 36''$, $C = 38° 41' 17''$, and $b = 16.392$, solve the triangle.

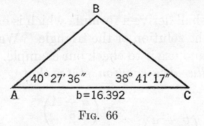

B

40° 27′ 36″   38° 41′ 17″

A   b=16.392   C

Fig. 66

Since $A + B + C = 180°$, and $A + C = 79° 8' 53''$, we have
$$B = 180° - 79° 8' 53'' = 100° 51' 7''.$$

From the law of sines we have

$$a = \frac{b \sin A}{\sin B} = \frac{16.392 \sin 40° 27' 36''}{\sin 100° 51' 7''},$$

and

$$\log a = \log 16.392 + \log \sin 40° 27' 36'' - \log \sin 100° 51' 7''.$$

$$
\begin{array}{rl}
\log 16.392 = & 1.21463 \\
\log \sin 40° 27' 36'' = & 9.81219 - 10 \\
\log 16.392 + \log \sin 40° 27' 36'' = & 11.02682 - 10 \\
\log \sin 100° 51' 7'' = & 9.99217 - 10 \\
\log a = & 1.03465.
\end{array}
$$

Therefore

$$a = 10.831.$$

To determine c, since b, B, and C are known, we use the relation,

$$\frac{c}{\sin C} = \frac{b}{\sin B}.$$

Hence

$$\log c = \log 16.392 + \log \sin 38° 41' 17'' - \log \sin 100° 51' 7''.$$

$$
\begin{array}{rl}
\log 16.39 = & 1.21463 \\
\log \sin 38° 41' 17'' = & 9.79594 - 10 \\
\log 16.392 + \log \sin 38° 41' 17'' = & 11.01057 - 10 \\
\log \sin 100° 58' 7'' = & 9.99217 - 10 \\
\log c = & 1.01840.
\end{array}
$$

Therefore

$$c = 10.433.$$

In § 52 we shall derive a formula which is extremely useful for checking the solution of the triangle. We shall state the formula here and use it to check our example. The formula, known as *Mollweide's equation*, states that

(1)
$$\left(\frac{b-a}{c}\right) = \frac{\sin\left(\dfrac{B-A}{2}\right)}{\cos\dfrac{C}{2}},$$

where a, b, and c are the sides and A, B, and C are the angles of the triangle. As will be observed, this formula is important as a check, since it relates all the parts of a triangle.

In the example just considered, we have
$$b - a = 5.561$$
$$\frac{(B - A)}{2} = 30° \, 11' \, 46''$$
$$\frac{C}{2} = 19° \, 20' \, 39''.$$

Hence, by Mollweide's equation, it follows that
$$\frac{5.561}{10.433} = \frac{\sin 30° \, 11' \, 46''}{\cos 19° \, 20' \, 39''}.$$

Taking logarithms of both sides, we have

$\log 5.561 - \log 10.433 = \log \sin 30° \, 11' \, 46'' - \log \cos 19° \, 20' \, 39''$,

or $0.74515 - 1.01841 = 9.70154 - 10 - (9.97476 - 10)$,

and $9.72674 - 10 = 9.72678 - 10$.

The difference in the fifth place is due to the interpolation. The fact that the difference is so small provides an excellent check upon the data previously obtained, since (1) is true only when a, b, and c are the sides of a triangle and A, B, and C are the corresponding opposite angles.

We shall work the same problem again, using the slide rule and evaluating the sides to three significant figures and the angles to minutes. We take $A = 40° \, 28'$, $C = 38° \, 41'$, and $b = 16.4$. Then $B = 180° - (40° \, 28' + 38° \, 41') = 100° \, 51'$. Now, using the law of sines, we have
$$\frac{\sin 40° \, 28'}{a} = \frac{\sin 100° \, 51'}{16.4} = \frac{\sin 38° \, 41'}{c}.$$

Since $\sin 100° \, 51' = \sin 79° \, 9'$, we line up $79° \, 9'$ on the S-scale with 16.4 on the A-scale. Then, moving the indicator until the hairline coincides with $40° \, 28'$ on the S-scale, we read from the A-scale $a = 10.8$. Now, moving the indicator to $38° \, 41'$ on the S-scale, we read from the A-scale $c = 10.4$.

Case **2**: *Given two sides and an angle opposite one of the sides.*

When two sides and an angle opposite one of the sides are given, it is possible to have one solution, two solutions, or no solution of

the triangle, depending upon the conditions given.   This is known
as the ambiguous case, and the situations that may arise are illustrated in the following diagrams.

Suppose we are given the angle A and the sides a and b.

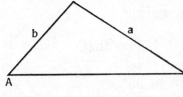

(1) If $A < 90°$ and $a \geqq b$,
there is one solution.

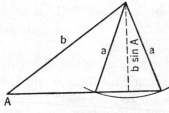

(2) If $A < 90°$ and $a = b \sin A$, there is one solution.

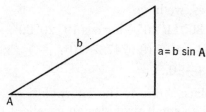

(3) If $A < 90°$ and $b \sin A < a < b$, there are two solutions.

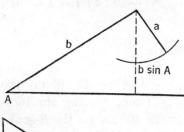

(4) If $A < 90°$ and $a < b \sin A$, there is no solution.

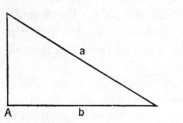

(5) If $A = 90°$ and $a > b$,
there is one solution.

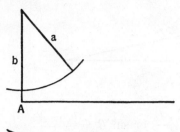

(6) If $A = 90°$ and $a \leqq b$, there is no solution.

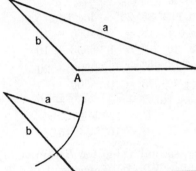

(7) If $A > 90°$ and $a > b$, there is one solution.

(8) If $A > 90°$ and $a < b$, there is no solution.

After a careful study of the different situations that may arise, we note that, if A, a, and b are the parts given, there is only one solution when a is greater than b; there is only one solution (a right triangle) when a is less than b and $\log \sin B = 0$; there are two solutions if a is less than b and $\log \sin B$ is negative; and there is no solution when $\log \sin B$ is positive. Explain the reasons for this statement.

Although it is often possible to note *by inspection* the number of solutions that the triangle will have, it is much more important to be able to determine from the nature of the computations whether there exists one triangle, two triangles, or no triangle satisfying the given conditions. The following examples serve to illustrate this statement.

Example 1:

Given $b = 0.43718$, $a = 1.9275$, and $A = 112° 35' 20''$; find the remaining parts.

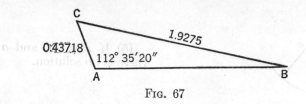

FIG. 67

From the law of sines, $\dfrac{\sin A}{a} = \dfrac{\sin B}{b}$, or $\sin B = \dfrac{b \sin A}{a}$.

$\log \sin B = \log 0.43718 + \log \sin 112° 35' 20'' - \log 1.9275.$

$$\begin{aligned}
\log 0.43718 &= 9.64066 - 10 \\
\log \sin 112° 35' 20'' &= 9.96533 - 10 \\
\log 0.43718 + \log \sin 112° 35' 20'' &= 19.60599 - 20 \\
\log 1.9275 &= 0.28500 \\
\log \sin B &= 9.32099 - 10 \\
\end{aligned}$$

and
$$B = 12° 5' 15'', \text{ or}$$
$$167° 54' 45''.$$

Since A is *obtuse*, however, the second value for B cannot be part of the solution for the triangle. Why? Knowing A and B, we have

$$C = 180° - (112° 35' 20'' + 12° 5' 15'') = 55° 19' 25''.$$

Finally, to obtain c, we use $c = \dfrac{a \sin C}{\sin A}$.

$\log c = \log 1.9275 + \log \sin 55° 19' 25'' - \log \sin 112° 35' 20''.$

$$\begin{aligned}
\log 1.9275 &= 0.28500 \\
\log \sin 55° 19' 25'' &= 9.91507 - 10 \\
\log 1.9275 + \log \sin 55° 19' 25'' &= 10.20007 - 10 \\
\log \sin 112° 35' 20'' &= 9.96533 - 10 \\
\log c &= 0.23474. \\
\end{aligned}$$

Therefore
$$c = 1.7167.$$

The student should check these results.

Solution by the slide rule:

S-scale	sin 67° 25′	sin B	sin C
A-scale	1.93	0.437	c

After 67° 25′ on the S-scale is lined up with 1.93 on the A-scale, the unknown parts are readily obtained as follows:

$$B = 12° 5′$$
$$C = 180° - (112° 35′ + 12° 5′) = 55° 20′$$
$$c = 1.72$$

Example 2:

Given $a = 11.60$, $b = 15.34$, and $A = 150°$, solve the triangle.

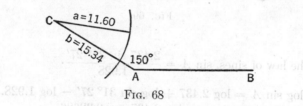

Fɪɢ. 68

By the law of sines, $\dfrac{\sin B}{15.34} = \dfrac{\sin 150°}{11.60}$.

$$\log \sin B = \log 15.34 + \log \sin 150° - \log 11.60.$$

$$
\begin{aligned}
\log 15.34 &= 1.18583\\
\log \sin 150° &= \underline{9.69897 - 10}\\
\log 15.34 + \log \sin 150° &= 10.88480 - 10\\
\log 11.60 &= \underline{1.06446}\\
\log \sin B &= 9.82034 - 10.
\end{aligned}
$$

and

$$B = 41° 23′ 30″.$$

Since $A + B = 191° 23′ 30″$, and since the sum of the angles of a triangle equals 180°, there exists *no* triangle corresponding to the parts assigned in the problem.

Example 3:

Given $a = 2.437$, $c = 1.928$, and $C = 31° 27′$, find the remaining parts.

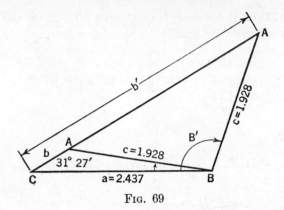

$$\text{Fig. 69}$$

By the law of sines, $\sin A = \dfrac{2.437 \sin 31° 27'}{1.928}.$

$\log \sin A = \log 2.437 + \log \sin 31° 27' - \log 1.928.$

$$
\begin{aligned}
\log 2.437 &= \ \ 0.38686 \\
\log \sin 31° 27' &= \ \ 9.71747 - 10 \\
\log 2.437 + \log \sin 31° 27' &= 10.10433 - 10 \\
\log 1.928 &= \ \ 0.28511 \\
\log \sin A &= \ \ 9.81922 - 10.
\end{aligned}
$$

and
$$
\begin{aligned}
A' &= \ \ 41° 15' 44'', \text{ or} \\
A &= 138° 44' 16''.
\end{aligned}
$$

Case (*a*): Considering $A' = 41° 15' 44''$, we have

$B' = 180° - (A' + C) = 180° - 72° 42' 44'' = 107° 17' 16''.$

By the law of sines, $b' = \dfrac{1.928 \sin 107° 17' 16''}{\sin 31° 27'}.$

$\log b' = \log \sin 107° 17' 16'' + \log 1.928 - \log \sin 31° 27'.$

$$
\begin{aligned}
\log \sin 107° 17' 16'' &= \ \ 9.97992 - 10 \\
\log 1.928 &= \ \ 0.28511 \\
\log \sin 107° 17' 16'' + \log 1.928 &= 10.26503 - 10 \\
\log \sin 31° 27' &= \ \ 9.71747 - 10 \\
\log b' &= \ \ 0.54756.
\end{aligned}
$$

and
$$b' = 3.5283.$$

So the solutions to case (a) are $a = 2.437$, $b' = 3.528$, and $c = 1.928$, to four significant figures, and $A' = 41° 16'$, $B' = 107° 17'$, and $C = 31° 27'$, to the nearest minute.

Case (b): Considering $A = 138° 44' 16''$, we have

$$B = 180° - (A + C) = 180° - 170° 11' 16'' = 9° 48' 44''.$$

and

$$b = \frac{1.928 \sin 9° 48' 44''}{\sin 31° 27'}.$$

$$\log b = \log \sin 9° 48' 44'' + \log 1.928 - \log \sin 31° 27'.$$

$$\begin{aligned}
\log \sin 9° 48' 44'' &= 9.23152 - 10 \\
\log 1.928 &= 10.28511 - 10 \\
\log \sin 9° 48' 44'' + \log 1.928 &= 19.51663 - 20 \\
\log \sin 31° 27' &= 9.71747 - 10 \\
\log b &= 9.79916 - 10
\end{aligned}$$

and

$$b = 0.62974.$$

The solutions to case (b) are $a = 2.437$, $b = 0.6297$, $c = 1.928$ to four significant figures, and $A = 138° 44'$, $B = 9° 49'$, and $C = 31° 27'$, to the nearest minute.

Check the results by means of Mollweide's equation.

If the slide rule is used, much time and space can be saved, as illustrated in the following slide-rule solution.

$$\frac{\sin A}{2.44} = \frac{\sin 31° 27'}{1.93} = \frac{\sin C}{c}$$

S-scale	$\sin A$	$\sin 31° 27'$	$\sin B$
A-scale	2.44	1.93	b

This gives $A = 41° 15'$, or $A = 138° 45'$.

(a) Using $A = 41° 15'$, we obtain

$$B = 180° - (31° 27' + 41° 15') = 107° 18'.$$

Moving the indicator to $72° 42'$, the supplement of $107° 18'$, we find $b = 3.53$.

(b) Using $A = 138° 45'$, we obtain

$$B = 180° - (31° 27' + 138° 45') = 9° 48'.$$

Moving the indicator to $9° 48'$, we find $b = 0.630$.

EXERCISES

1. Solve the following triangles and check the results:
   (a) $A = 28° 30'$, $B = 32° 15'$, $c = 123$.
   (b) $a = 23.47$, $B = 115° 30'$, $C = 20° 29'$.
   (c) $A = 43° 52'$, $a = 9.182$, $b = 6.322$.
   (d) $C = 35° 28'$, $b = 10.543$, $c = 8.6914$.
   (e) $B = 130° 15' 20''$, $b = 151.23$, $c = 120.38$.
   (f) $C = 115° 43' 40''$, $a = 0.88346$, $c = 0.56923$.
   (g) $c = 341.9$, $A = 60° 25'$, $C = 44° 20'$.
   (h) $b = 7.3412$, $B = 32° 29' 16''$, $c = 10.314$.
   (i) $a = 58.479$, $B = 64° 15'$, $b = 36.624$.
   (j) $a = 642.54$, $A = 55° 40' 20''$, $c = 982.86$.
   (k) $C = 42° 37' 21''$, $c = 1.9875$, $A = 100° 20' 51''$.
   (l) $a = 65.21$, $c = 43.84$, $C = 37° 46'$.
   (m) $B = 60° 20' 30''$, $a = 1.4360$, $b = 3.9150$.
   (n) $A = 122° 22' 43''$, $B = 18° 35' 16''$, $c = 0.0914$.
   (o) $C = 150° 30' 30''$, $c = 5.8314$, $a = 9.1212$.
   (p) $B = 87° 33' 34''$, $A = 29° 40' 20''$, $b = 31.425$.
   (q) $C = 114° 30' 20''$, $a = 9.426$, $c = 8.612$.
   (r) $C = 114° 30' 20''$, $a = 9.426$, $c = 12.348$.
   (s) $a = 271.60$, $b = 324.50$, $B = 25° 30' 30''$.
   (t) $B = 52° 12' 40''$, $c = 0.098364$, $b = 0.061129$.
   (u) $A = 31° 15' 24''$, $C = 62° 25' 20''$, $a = 1315$.
   (v) $b = 24.635$, $c = 32.138$, $B = 46° 18' 22''$.

2. Two observers, located at A and B, observe an enemy machine-gun nest at C. If $\angle BAC$ is $47° 0'$, $\angle ABC$ is $38° 0'$, and $AB = 325.0$ yards, how far is the enemy from both A and B?

3. A man drives a truck 12.3 miles on a straight road running $N\ 10° 40'\ E$. He then turns into another straight road, running $N\ 12° 10'\ W$, and drives for 8.5 miles. At the end of the drive how far is he from his original position?

4. A man on a cliff notes that the angles of depression of two objects in the road below are $63° 0'$ and $27° 0'$. If the cliff is 58.0 feet high and the road is perpendicular to the cliff, how far apart are the objects?

5. The distance from an observation post A to a gun position B is 620 yards. What is the distance from the gun to a target at C if angle $ABC = 36.7°$ and angle $BAC = 29.4°$?

6. Two cruisers leave the same port at the same time. One cruiser sails due west at 15 knots and the other cruiser sails faster in a constant direction $N\ 38° 0'\ W$. If they are 80 nautical miles apart after 5 hours, what is the speed of the second cruiser?

7. Two straight roads intersect at an angle of 37° 0′. An artillery unit has placed one of its guns on one of the roads at a point 2600 yards from the intersection of the roads. If the maximum range of the gun is 2000 yards, what section of the other road can be kept under the fire of the gun?

8. A piston travels in the horizontal line which contains the crank center. If the crank is r inches long, the connecting rod y inches long, and the angle the crank makes with the horizontal is θ, express the distance x between crank center and piston in terms of r, y, and θ. Assume $y > r$. (See diagram.)

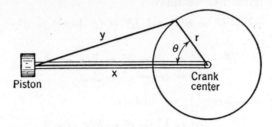

48. Law of cosines

When two sides and the included angle are given or when three sides are given we can solve the triangle by the law of cosines. This law states that in any triangle the square of any side is equal to the sum of the squares of the other two sides minus twice the product of these two sides and the cosine of their included angle.

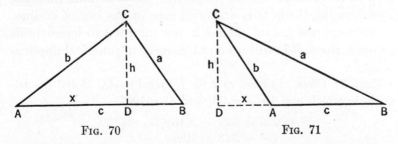

Fig. 70   Fig. 71

The law of cosines is derived as follows. After dropping a perpendicular from C to point D on side c represent the length of AD by x. Then in Figure 70 we have

$$x^2 + h^2 = b^2 \text{ and } h^2 + (c - x)^2 = a^2.$$

Eliminating h^2 between these two equations, we have

$$b^2 - x^2 = a^2 - c^2 + 2cx - x^2,$$

or $$b^2 = a^2 - c^2 + 2cx.$$

Since $x = b \cos A$, we have, upon making this substitution,

$$a^2 = b^2 + c^2 - 2bc \cos A.$$

Using Figure 71, we have

$$x^2 + h^2 = b^2, \text{ and } h^2 + (c + x)^2 = a^2.$$

Hence

$$b^2 - x^2 = a^2 - x^2 - 2cx - c^2,$$

or $$b^2 = a^2 - c^2 - 2cx.$$

Since $x = -b \cos A$, we obtain

$$a^2 = b^2 + c^2 - 2bc \cos A.$$

If we construct the altitudes from A to side a and from B to side b and repeat the previous argument in each case, we obtain

$$b^2 = a^2 + c^2 - 2ac \cos B,$$

and $$c^2 = a^2 + b^2 - 2ab \cos C.$$

The student should note that when $C = 90°$ the last equation is reduced to the Pythagorean theorem and that the Pythagorean theorem is a special case of the law of cosines.

Although the law of cosines is not adapted to logarithmic computations, it is still used extensively in practical applications.

Case 3: *Given two sides and the included angle.* Solve the triangle in which $a = 15$, $b = 23$, and $C = 120°$.

$$c^2 = 225 + 529 - 2(15)(23) \cos 120°$$
$$= 754 + 345 = 1099.$$

Hence, $\qquad c = 33$, to two significant figures.

To find angles A and C, we use the law of sines. The student should finish the example and check his results.

Case 4: *Given three sides.* Solve the triangle in which $a = 10$, $b = 12$, and $c = 17$. From the law of cosines, we have

$$\cos A = \frac{b^2 + c^2 - a^2}{2bc}.$$

Hence, $$\cos A = \frac{144 + 289 - 100}{2(12)(17)},$$

$$\cos A = \frac{333}{408} = \frac{111}{136}.$$

$$\log \cos A = \log 111 - \log 136.$$
$$\log 111 = 12.04532 - 10$$
$$\log 136 = \underline{2.13354}$$
$$\log \cos A = \overline{9.91178 - 10},$$

and $A = 35° \, 18'$, to the closest minute.

In the same way,

$$\cos B = \frac{a^2 + c^2 - b^2}{2ac},$$

$$\cos B = \frac{100 + 289 - 144}{2(10)(17)},$$

$$\cos B = \frac{245}{340} = \frac{49}{68}.$$

$$\log \cos B = \log 49 - \log 68.$$
$$\log 49 = 11.69020 - 10$$
$$\log 68 = \underline{1.83251}$$
$$\log \cos B = \overline{9.85769 - 10},$$

and $B = 43° \, 54'$, to the closest minute.

Finally,

$$\cos C = \frac{a^2 + b^2 - c^2}{2ab},$$

$$\cos C = \frac{100 + 144 - 289}{2(10)(12)},$$

$$\cos C = \frac{-45}{240} = \frac{-3}{16}.$$

Since $\cos C$ is negative, we know that C must be obtuse and so

we first find $180° - C$. We know that $\cos (180° - C) = \frac{3}{16}$.
Why? Hence, we have

$$\log \cos (180° - C) = \log 3 - \log 16.$$
$$\log 3 = 10.47712 - 10$$
$$\log 16 = \underline{1.20412}$$
$$\log \cos (180° - C) = \overline{9.27300 - 10,}$$

and $180° - C = 79° 11'$, to the closest minute.

Therefore $C = 100° 49'$, to the closest minute.

To check our results, we find

$$A + B + C = 35° 18' + 43° 54' + 100° 49' = 180° 1'.$$

Since the sum of the angles of a triangle should be $180°$, we see
that we have made an error of $1'$, which is due to the interpolation
and to the approximation of the angles to minutes.

EXERCISES

1. Solve the following triangles:
   (a) $a = 11$, $b = 8.0$, $C = 63° 18'$.
   (b) $b = 0.19$, $c = 0.27$, $A = 56° 10'$.
   (c) $b = 6.70$, $c = 11.4$, $A = 112° 0'$.
   (d) $a = 27$, $b = 36$, $C = 118° 35'$.
   (e) $a = 17$, $b = 21$, $c = 26$.
   (f) $a = 81.0$, $b = 67.0$, $c = 102$.
   (g) $a = 162$, $c = 243$, $B = 109° 24'$.
   (h) $a = 0.98$, $b = 0.83$, $c = 1.37$.

2. Two ships leave the same dock at the same time. One has
a bearing of $120°$ and the other a bearing of $247°$. If the first
sails with a speed of 16 knots and the second at a speed of 19 knots,
how far apart are they at the end of 4 hours?

3. Two straight roads intersect in an angle of $52°$. Town A
is located on one of the roads about 123 miles from the intersection
and town B is located on the other road 87 miles from the intersection. How far apart are the towns and how far is each town
from the other road?

4. Three pegs are driven into a vertical wall, peg A being set 1
foot to the left of and 3 feet below peg B and peg C being set 2 feet
to the right of and 1 foot below peg B. How much cord would be
necessary to connect A to B to C and back to A? What is the
angle at B?

5. A train leaves a station and travels at 65 miles per hour along a straight track. Another train leaves the same station an hour later on a straight track making an angle of 118° with the first track and travels at 53 miles per hour. How far apart are the trains after 3 hours?

6. An airplane flies due south at a speed of 183 miles per hour. A second plane flies at a speed of 171 miles per hour in a direction $N\ 60°\ W$. How far apart are the planes after 5 hours?

7. A ship leaves port and sails $S\ 32°\ E$ at 16 knots. After 3 hours it changes its direction to $S\ 14°\ E$ and sails at 18 knots for 6 hours. How far in nautical miles is the ship from the port?

8. Two forces act on an object. If the magnitude of one force F_1 is 67 pounds and the magnitude of the second force F_2 is 43 pounds, and if the angle between the forces is 32° 0′, find the magnitude of the resultant force.

9. A derrick is made up (in part) of two members pivoted to the same point on a base. The two members are 28 feet and 42 feet long, respectively, and lie in the same vertical plane on the same side of the fixed point on the base. (See figure.)

   (a) If the longer member makes an angle of 58° with the ground and the shorter member makes an angle of 76° with the ground, what is the distance x between the upper ends of the members?

   (b) If the upper ends are connected by a third member 24 feet long, what is the angle θ between the original two members?

   (c) If the upper ends of the members are 25 feet and 32 feet *above the ground*, what is the distance x between the ends?

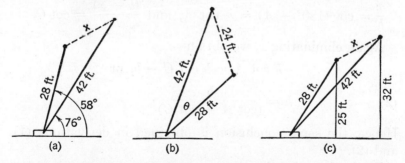

(a)   (b)   (c)

10. Two horses are hitched to a post so that the angle between them is 75°. If one horse pulls with a force of magnitude 300 pounds and the other with a force of magnitude 500 pounds, what is the resultant magnitude of the forces on the post?

49. Law of cotangents

In order to find an altitude of a triangle when the base upon which the altitude is dropped and the adjacent angles to this base are known, we use a formula known as the law of cotangents.

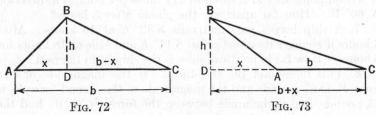

FIG. 72   FIG. 73

Given A, C, and side b, to find h.

Using Figure 72, we have

$$\frac{x}{h} = \cot A, \text{ and } \frac{(b - x)}{h} = \cot C.$$

Eliminating x between these equations, we have

$$h \cot A = b - h \cot C, \text{ or}$$

(1) $$h = \frac{b}{(\cot A + \cot C)}.$$

Using Figure 73, we have

$$\frac{x}{h} = \cot (180° - A) = -\cot A, \text{ and } \frac{(b + x)}{h} = \cot C.$$

Again eliminating x, we obtain

$$-h \cot A = h \cot C - b, \text{ or}$$

(2) $$h = \frac{b}{(\cot A + \cot C)}.$$

Hence, the same conclusion is obtained in derivations (1) and (2).

In the formula, A and C represent any two angles of a triangle, b is the side adjacent to both A and C, and h is the altitude on b. The formula can also be used to find b

when h and the angles A and C are known.   To do this we solve the equation for b, obtaining

$$b = h(\cot A + \cot C).$$

Example 1:

Find the altitude h of the triangle in Figure 74.

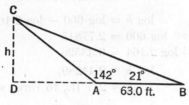

FIG. 74

By the law of cotangents,

$$h = \frac{63.0}{\cot 21° + \cot 142°} = \frac{63.0}{2.605 - 1.280} = \frac{63.0}{1.325}.$$

$$\log h = \log 63.0 - \log 1.325.$$
$$\log 63.0 = 1.79934$$
$$\log 1.325 = \underline{0.12222}$$
$$\log h = \overline{1.67712},$$

so $h = 47.6$ ft., to three significant figures.

Example 2:

An observer on a cliff notes that the angles of depression of two objects on a straight road perpendicular to the cliff are 16° 20′ and 10° 10′, respectively.   If the distance between the objects is known to be 600 feet, how high is the cliff?

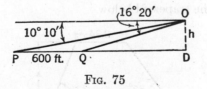

FIG. 75

In Figure 75 we observe that the base angles OPQ and OQP are 10° 10′ and 163° 40′, respectively.   Hence, we have

$$h = \frac{600}{\cot 10° \ 10' + \cot 163° \ 40'}.$$

So

$$h = \frac{600}{\cot 10° \ 10' - \cot 16° \ 20'}$$

$$= \frac{600}{5.576 - 3.412} = \frac{600}{2.164}.$$

$$\log h = \log 600 - \log 2.164$$
$$\log 600 = 2.77815$$
$$\log 2.164 = 0.33526$$
$$\overline{\log h = 2.44289,}$$

and $h = 277$ ft., to three significant figures.

EXERCISES

1. Find the altitude h on the side c if it is known that
(a) $A = 32° \ 15'$, $B = 47° \ 22'$, $c = 94.0$.
(b) $A = 58° \ 30'$, $B = 42° \ 15'$, $c = 113$.
(c) $A = 120°$, $B = 34°$, $c = 217$.
(d) $A = 112° \ 20'$, $B = 56°$, $c = 3.70$.

2. A man in a balloon 1000 feet above the ground notes the angles of depression of two buildings to be 63° 40′ and 48° 25′, respectively. If the balloonist is in the vertical plane with the buildings and if the buildings are on opposite sides of the balloon, how far apart are the buildings?

3. The keeper of a lighthouse notes the angle of depression of two ships to be 31° 42′ and 20° 10′. If he is in the same vertical plane as the ships and if the lighthouse is 135 feet high, how far apart are the ships?

4. Find x in the trapezoid below.

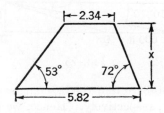

5. Find angles A and B in the quadrilateral below.

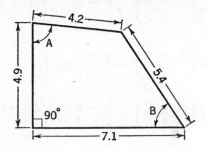

50. Law of tangents*

In order to solve case 3 of § 47 with the aid of logarithms, we frequently make use of a formula known as the law of tangents. This law states that *the difference of any two sides of a triangle is to their sum as the tangent of one-half the difference of the respective opposite angles is to the tangent of one-half the sum of these angles.*

The law of tangents is derived as follows. By the law of sines we have $\dfrac{a}{\sin A} = \dfrac{b}{\sin B} = \dfrac{c}{\sin C} = k$, where k is a constant of proportionality. Hence $a = k \sin A$, $b = k \sin B$, $c = k \sin C$, and

$$\frac{a-b}{a+b} = \frac{k \sin A - k \sin B}{k \sin A + k \sin B} = \frac{\sin A - \sin B}{\sin A + \sin B}.$$

From identities **(27)** and **(28)** in Chapter VI, we have

$$\frac{a-b}{a+b} = \frac{2 \cos\left(\dfrac{A+B}{2}\right) \sin\left(\dfrac{A-B}{2}\right)}{2 \sin\left(\dfrac{A+B}{2}\right) \cos\left(\dfrac{A-B}{2}\right)} = \frac{\tan\left(\dfrac{A-B}{2}\right)}{\tan\left(\dfrac{A+B}{2}\right)}.$$

* May be omitted for a brief course.

Therefore

$$\tan\left(\frac{A - B}{2}\right) = \frac{a - b}{a + b}\tan\left(\frac{A + B}{2}\right).^*$$

Similarly

$$\tan\left(\frac{A - C}{2}\right) = \frac{a - c}{a + c}\tan\left(\frac{A + C}{2}\right),$$

and

$$\tan\left(\frac{B - C}{2}\right) = \frac{b - c}{b + c}\tan\left(\frac{B + C}{2}\right).$$

Example :

Given $a = 4.3617$, $c = 2.0725$, and $B = 83° 15' 28''$; solve the triangle.

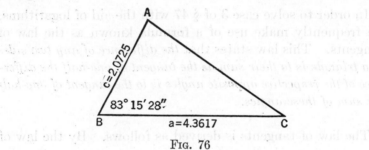

FIG. 76

By the law of tangents,

$$\tan\left(\frac{A - C}{2}\right) = \frac{a - c}{a + c}\tan\left(\frac{A + C}{2}\right).$$

Hence

$$\log\tan\left(\frac{A - C}{2}\right) = \log (a - c) + \log\tan\left(\frac{A + C}{2}\right) - \log (a + c).$$

First we obtain $a - c = 2.2892$, $a + c = 6.4342$, and

$$\frac{A + C}{2} = \frac{180° - B}{2} = \frac{96° 44' 32''}{2} = 48° 22' 16''.$$

Then

$$\log\tan\left(\frac{A - C}{2}\right) = \log 2.2892 + \log\tan 48° 22' 16'' - \log 6.4342.$$

* If $b > a$, then $B > A$, and we write
$$\tan\left(\frac{B - A}{2}\right) = \frac{b - a}{b + a}\tan\left(\frac{B + A}{2}\right).$$

$$\log 2.2892 = 0.35969$$
$$\log \tan 48° 22' 16'' = \underline{0.05123}$$
$$\log 2.2892 + \log \tan 48° 22' 16'' = 10.41092 - 10$$
$$\log 6.4342 = \underline{0.80849}$$
$$\log \tan \left(\frac{A - C}{2}\right) = 9.60243 - 10.$$

Therefore

$$\frac{A - C}{2} = 21° 49' 5''.$$

We already know that $\dfrac{A + C}{2} = 48° 22' 16''.$

Adding and subtracting, respectively, these two equations we have
$$A = 70° 11' 21''$$
and
$$C = 26° 33' 11''.$$

Now, using the value of C just obtained and the law of sines, we find b.

$$\log b = \log 2.0725 + \log \sin 83° 15' 28'' - \log \sin 26° 33' 11''.$$
$$\log 2.0725 = 0.31650$$
$$\log \sin 83° 15' 28'' = \underline{9.99698 - 10}$$
$$\log 2.0725 + \log \sin 83° 15'28'' = 10.31348 - 10$$
$$\log \sin 26° 33' 11'' = \underline{9.65034 - 10}$$
$$\log b = 0.66314$$

Therefore

$$b = 4.604.$$

Check these results by means of Mollweide's equation.

EXERCISES

Solve the following triangles:

1. $a = 21.46$, $b = 46.28$, $C = 32° 28' 30''$.
2. $A = 60° 38'$, $b = 6.9345$, $c = 8.1126$.
3. $c = 216.45$, $a = 186.20$, $B = 114° 14' 42''$.
4. $C = 100° 38' 29''$, $a = 0.09432$, $b = 0.1247$.
5. $b = 6129$, $A = 125° 30' 30''$, $c = 4326$.
6. $a = 3.2641$, $b = 6.0094$, $c = 109° 29' 50''$.
7. $b = 28.440$, $c = 43.250$, $A = 45° 18' 0''$.

8. $c = 19436$, $a = 32118$, $B = 102°\ 21'\ 11''$.
9. $a = 0.2843$, $b = 0.6817$, $C = 29°\ 42'$.
10. $B = 76°\ 23'\ 50''$, $c = 111.43$, $a = 202.65$.

51. The half-angle formulas*

We may solve case 4 of § 47 with the aid of logarithms by using a set of formulas known as the *half-angle formulas*. From identities (**20**) and (**21**) in Chapter VI and from the law of cosines, we have

$$\sin\frac{A}{2} = \sqrt{\frac{1 - \cos A}{2}} = \sqrt{\frac{1}{2} - \frac{b^2 + c^2 - a^2}{4bc}}$$

$$= \sqrt{\frac{2bc - b^2 - c^2 + a^2}{4bc}}$$

$$= \sqrt{\frac{a^2 - (b - c)^2}{4bc}} = \sqrt{\frac{(a - b + c)(a + b - c)}{4bc}},$$

$$= \sqrt{\frac{(s - b)(s - c)}{bc}}, \text{ where } s = \frac{a + b + c}{2}.$$

Also,

$$\cos\frac{A}{2} = \sqrt{\frac{1 + \cos A}{2}} = \sqrt{\frac{1}{2} + \frac{b^2 + c^2 - a^2}{4bc}}$$

$$= \sqrt{\frac{2bc + b^2 + c^2 - a^2}{4bc}}$$

$$= \sqrt{\frac{(b + c)^2 - a^2}{4bc}} = \sqrt{\frac{(a + b + c)(b + c - a)}{4bc}},$$

$$= \sqrt{\frac{s(s - a)}{bc}}, \text{ where, again, } s \text{ is one half the}$$

perimeter.

By recalling that $\tan\dfrac{A}{2} = \dfrac{\sin\dfrac{A}{2}}{\cos\dfrac{A}{2}}$, we readily obtain the

---

* May be omitted for a brief course.

formulas for the tangent of the half angle, namely,

$$\tan\frac{A}{2} = \sqrt{\frac{(s-b)(s-c)}{s(s-a)}} = \frac{1}{s-a}\sqrt{\frac{(s-a)(s-b)(s-c)}{s}}.$$

Similarly,

$$\tan\frac{B}{2} = \sqrt{\frac{(s-a)(s-c)}{s(s-b)}} = \frac{1}{s-b}\sqrt{\frac{(s-a)(s-b)(s-c)}{s}}.$$

$$\tan\frac{C}{2} = \sqrt{\frac{(s-a)(s-b)}{s(s-c)}} = \frac{1}{s-c}\sqrt{\frac{(s-a)(s-b)(s-c)}{s}}.$$

In § 54 it will be shown that the radius r of the inscribed circle of any triangle may be expressed in terms of the sides by the formula

$$r = \sqrt{\frac{(s-a)(s-b)(s-c)}{s}}.$$

In terms of r, therefore, the half-angle formulas become:

$$\tan\frac{A}{2} = \frac{r}{s-a},$$

$$\tan\frac{B}{2} = \frac{r}{s-b},$$

$$\tan\frac{C}{2} = \frac{r}{s-c}.$$

In the actual solution of a problem, one finds colog s, $\log(s-a)$, $\log(s-b)$, $\log(s-c)$, $\log\sqrt{\dfrac{(s-a)(s-b)(s-c)}{s}}$ or $\log r$; then the solution of the triangle is readily obtained.

Example:

Given $a = 32.467, b = 17.391, c = 29.845$; solve the triangle.

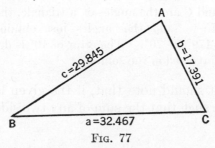

Fig. 77

$s = 39.852$, $s - a = 7.385$, $s - b = 22.461$, $s - c = 10.007$.

$$
\begin{aligned}
\text{colog } s &= \text{colog } 39.852 = & 8.39955 - 10 \\
\log (s - a) &= \log \ 7.385 = & 0.86835 \\
\log (s - b) &= \log 22.461 = & 1.35143 \\
\log (s - c) &= \log 10.007 = & \underline{1.00030}
\end{aligned}
$$

$$\log \frac{(s - a)(s - b)(s - c)}{s} = 11.61963 - 10.$$

So
$$\log r = \frac{1.61963}{2} = 0.80982.$$

$$\log \tan \frac{A}{2} = \log r - \log (s - a)$$

$$= (10.80982 - 10) - 0.86835 = 9.94147 - 10,$$

and $\dfrac{A}{2} = 41° \ 9' \ 3''$.

Therefore $\quad A = 82° \ 18' \ 6''$.

$$\log \tan \frac{B}{2} = \log r - \log (s - b)$$

$$= (10.80982 - 10) - 1.35143 = 9.45839 - 10,$$

and $\dfrac{B}{2} = 16° \ 1' \ 52''$.

Therefore $\quad B = 32° \ 3' \ 44''$.

$$\log \tan \frac{C}{2} = \log r - \log (s - c)$$

$$= (10.80982 - 10) - 1.00030 = 9.80952 - 10,$$

and $\qquad \dfrac{C}{2} = 32° \ 49' \ 10''$.

Therefore $\quad C = 65° \ 38' \ 20''$.

Since A, B, and C are the angles of a triangle, their sum should equal 180°. If we add the angles just obtained we obtain $A + B + C = 179° \ 59' \ 70''$. The error of 10'' is due to the slight approximation involved in the solution.

The student should note that, if the given lengths of the three sides are such that the sum of any two sides is less than the third side, no triangle can exist. This is also apparent from the numerical calculations, for if $a + b < c$, $s - c$ is negative and since the square root of a negative number is imaginary, real values of the functions do not exist.

52. Check formulas for the general triangle*

It is most important to check the results obtained in the solution of a triangle. Any method is satisfactory provided it has not already been used in obtaining the solution.

If we are given the three sides of a triangle, the simplest check is to show that

(1) $$A + B + C = 180°.$$

For the other three cases we use Mollweide's equation:

(2) $$\frac{a - b}{c} = \frac{\sin\left(\dfrac{A - B}{2}\right)}{\cos\dfrac{C}{2}}.$$

If $b > a$, and, hence, $B > A$, we write this formula,

(2') $$\frac{b - a}{c} = \frac{\sin\left(\dfrac{B - A}{2}\right)}{\cos\dfrac{C}{2}}.$$

The formula is derived as follows:
From the law of sines,

$$\frac{a}{\sin A} = \frac{b}{\sin B} = \frac{c}{\sin C} = k,$$

we have $a = k \sin A$, $b = k \sin B$, $c = k \sin C$.
Therefore

$$\frac{a - b}{c} = \frac{\sin A - \sin B}{\sin C}$$

* May be omitted for a brief course.

Now, by identity (**27**) in Chapter VI, it follows that

$$\sin A - \sin B \equiv 2 \cos\left(\frac{A+B}{2}\right) \sin\left(\frac{A-B}{2}\right),$$

and by identity (**17**) in Chapter VI, we have

$$\sin C \equiv 2 \sin\frac{C}{2} \cos\frac{C}{2}.$$

Hence

$$\frac{a-b}{c} = \frac{2 \cos\left(\dfrac{A+B}{2}\right) \sin\left(\dfrac{A-B}{2}\right)}{2 \sin\dfrac{C}{2} \cos\dfrac{C}{2}}$$

But $C = 180° - (A + B)$; hence

$$\sin\frac{C}{2} = \sin\left(90° - \frac{A+B}{2}\right) = \cos\left(\frac{A+B}{2}\right).$$

Therefore

$$\frac{a-b}{c} = \frac{\sin\left(\dfrac{A-B}{2}\right)}{\cos\dfrac{C}{2}}.$$

Derive the alternate check formula,

$$\frac{a+b}{c} = \frac{\cos\left(\dfrac{A-B}{2}\right)}{\sin\dfrac{C}{2}},$$

where a, b, and c are the sides and A, B, and C are the angles of a triangle. NOTE: Either of the two check formulas may be used.

EXERCISES

Solve the following triangles for the remaining parts and check the results:

   1. $A = 115° \; 15' \; 27''$, $b = 1.2984$, $c = 3.4617$.
   2. $C = 73° \; 21' \; 43''$, $a = 4.6920$, $b = 8.3142$.
   3. $a = 439.3$, $b = 591.7$, $c = 723.9$.

4. $a = 8.6427$, $b = 6.2758$, $c = 5.3922$.
5. $B = 18°\ 53'\ 31''$, $a = 1.1942$, $b = 3.6215$.
6. $a = 0.12973$, $b = 0.29173$, $c = 0.28134$.
7. $A = 47°\ 33'\ 21''$, $B = 63°\ 14'\ 53''$, $c = 294.68$.
8. $a = 314.51$, $b = 395.62$, $c = 458.27$.
9. $A = 145°\ 30'\ 0''$, $c = 4.0190$, $a = 6.3840$.
10. $A = 37°\ 10'\ 21''$, $C = 124°\ 24'\ 33''$, $b = 2.0213$.
11. $C = 100°\ 19'\ 47''$, $a = 5.9210$, $c = 6.1860$.
12. $B = 109°\ 12'\ 52''$, $b = 6.6291$, $c = 8.7126$.
13. $b = 4459.2$, $c = 5431.4$, $A = 15°\ 23'\ 20''$.
14. $a = 0.87642$, $b = 0.91145$, $c = 0.33217$.

53. The area

The area S of a triangle is equal to half the product of its base and its altitude. This is a formula given in plane geometry. With the aid of trigonometry we are able to derive certain formulas which enable us to express S directly in terms of (1) *two sides and the included angle*, (2) *the three sides*, and (3) *one side and the adjacent angles.*

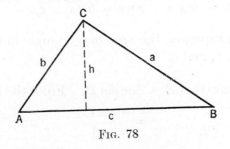

FIG. 78

Calling h the altitude from C, we have
$$S = \tfrac{1}{2} \text{ base} \times \text{altitude} = \tfrac{1}{2}\ hc.$$

Since $\dfrac{h}{b} = \sin A$, and $\dfrac{h}{a} = \sin B$, it follows that $h = b \sin A = a \sin B$. Therefore $S = \tfrac{1}{2}bc \sin A = \tfrac{1}{2}ac \sin B$. If an altitude is dropped from either A or B, it is readily seen that $S = \tfrac{1}{2}ab \sin C$. Thus, given any two sides and the included angle, the area is given by any of the formulas.

(1) $S = \tfrac{1}{2}bc \sin A = \tfrac{1}{2}ac \sin B = \tfrac{1}{2}ab \sin C.$

By identity (**17**) in Chapter VI, we can write

$$\tfrac{1}{2} \sin A = \sin \frac{A}{2} \cos \frac{A}{2}.$$

From § 51 we have $\sin \dfrac{A}{2} = \sqrt{\dfrac{(s-b)(s-c)}{bc}}$,

and

$$\cos \frac{A}{2} = \sqrt{\frac{s(s-a)}{bc}}.$$

Hence

$$\tfrac{1}{2} \sin A = \frac{\sqrt{s(s-a)\,(s-b)\,(s-c)}}{bc}.$$

Therefore $S = \tfrac{1}{2}bc \sin A$

becomes $S = bc\dfrac{\sqrt{s(s-a)(s-b)(s-c)}}{bc}$, or

(2) $$S = \sqrt{s(s-a)(s-b)(s-c)}.$$

This formula expresses the area of a triangle in terms of the three sides a, b, and c.

In (**1**) we saw that $S = \tfrac{1}{2}ac \sin B$.   From the law of sines,

$$c = \frac{a \sin C}{\sin A}.$$

Eliminating c between these two equations, we have

$$S = \frac{a^2 \sin B \sin C}{2 \sin A}.$$

Since $A = 180° - (B + C)$, and $\sin A = \sin [180° - (B + C)] = \sin (B + C)$, it follows that, given one side a and the two adjacent angles B and C, the area is expressed by

(3) $$S = \frac{a^2 \sin B \sin C}{2 \sin (B + C)}.$$

54. Radius of the inscribed circle*

Let AO, BO, and CO be the bisectors of the angles A, B, and C, respectively. The point O is the center of the inscribed circle, r is the radius, and D, E, and F are the feet of

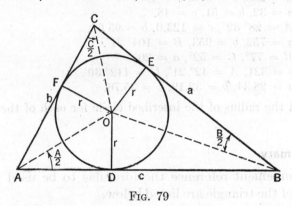

FIG. 79

the perpendiculars dropped from O upon the three sides, respectively. The area of the triangle is equal to the sum of the areas of the triangles AOB, BOC, and COA. The area of $\triangle AOB = \frac{1}{2}rc$, the area of $\triangle BOC = \frac{1}{2}ra$, and the area of $\triangle COA = \frac{1}{2}rb$. So the area S of the triangle ABC is

$$S = \frac{r(a + b + c)}{2} = rs.$$

Since it was determined in the preceding section that

$$S = \sqrt{s(s - a)(s - b)(s - c)},$$

it follows that

$$rs = \sqrt{s(s - a)(s - b)(s - c)},$$

and

$$r = \sqrt{\frac{(s - a)(s - b)(s - c)}{s}}.$$

* May be omitted for a brief course.

170   *THE GENERAL TRIANGLE*

EXERCISES

1. Find the area of each of the triangles which have the given parts:

(a) $a = 17$, $b = 25$, $C = 30°$.
(b) $a = 253$, $b = 316$, $c = 198$.
(c) $a = 32$, $b = 51$, $c = 48$.
(d) $A = 28° 32''$, $c = 123.0$, $b = 95.66$.
(e) $a = 752$, $b = 953$, $B = 104° 21'$.
(f) $B = 77°$, $C = 52°$, $a = 205$.
(g) $b = 321$, $A = 42° 21'$, $C = 112° 30'$.
(h) $a = 28.34$, $b = 32.19$, $c = 35.76$.

2. Find the radius of the inscribed circle for each of the above triangles.

55. Summary

For convenient reference the formulas to be used in the solution of the triangle are listed below.

Law of sines: $\dfrac{\sin A}{a} = \dfrac{\sin B}{b} = \dfrac{\sin C}{c}.$

This law is used in solving the triangle when two angles and a side or two sides and an opposite angle are known, and it is adapted to the use of logarithms and the slide rule.

Law of cosines: $a^2 = b^2 + c^2 - 2bc \cos A.$

$$\cos A = \frac{b^2 + c^2 - a^2}{2bc}.$$

This law is used in solving the triangle when two sides and the included angle or three sides are known, but it is not adapted to the direct use of logarithms.

Law of tangents: $\dfrac{\tan\left(\dfrac{A - B}{2}\right)}{\tan\left(\dfrac{A + B}{2}\right)} = \dfrac{a - b}{a + b}, \ a > b.$

This law is used in solving the triangle when two sides and

the included angle are known, and it is adapted to the use of logarithms.

Law of the half-angle: $\tan \dfrac{A}{2} = \sqrt{\dfrac{(s - b)(s - c)}{s(s - a)}}$,

where $s = \dfrac{a + b + c}{2}$.

This law is used in solving the triangle when three sides are known, and it is adapted to the use of logarithms.

Law of cotangents: $h = \dfrac{c}{\cot A + \cot B}$,

where h is the altitude on side c and A and B are the angles adjacent to c.

Area:

(1) $S = \frac{1}{2}ab \sin C$, where a, b are any two sides and C is the angle between them.

(2) $S = \sqrt{s(s - a)(s - b)(s - c)}$.

(3) $S = \dfrac{a^2 \sin B \sin C}{2 \sin (B + C)}$, where a is any side and B and C are the angles adjacent to that side.

EXERCISES: CHAPTER VII

1. Solve the following triangles:
   (a) $a = 2.1460$, $b = 3.9470$, $A = 27° 31' 25''$.
   (b) $a = 32.165$, $b = 24.776$, $C = 122° 41' 10''$.
   (c) $A = 31° 17' 36''$, $B = 25° 29' 15''$, $c = 756.20$.
   (d) $a = 10.165$, $b = 15.932$, $c = 20.247$.
   (e) $B = 96° 30' 36''$, $C = 18° 20' 40''$, $b = 8.1480$.
   (f) $b = 0.19348$, $c = 0.31662$, $B = 93° 25' 52''$.
   (g) $a = 1325.0$, $b = 2064.0$, $c = 1871.0$.
   (h) $C = 44° 44' 44''$, $a = 1.9936$, $b = 2.4775$.
   (i) $a = 86.432$, $b = 91.217$, $c = 63.594$.
   (j) $a = 938$, $c = 837$, $B = 59° 30' 15''$.
   (k) $A = 100° 15' 21''$, $B = 45° 33' 6''$, $c = 5.3716$.
   (l) $C = 37° 14' 20''$, $c = 75.293$, $a = 100.27$.
   (m) $A = 100° 31' 40''$, $B = 25° 6' 17''$, $a = 31.706$.
   (n) $A = 112° 6' 7''$, $b = 26.421$, $c = 34.115$.
   (o) $B = 38° 35'$, $C = 54° 40'$, $a = 4.1670$.

2. Find the area and the radius of the inscribed circle for each of the above triangles.

3. Prove that the radius of the circumscribed circle is equal to any side divided by twice the sine of the opposite angle, *i.e.*,

$$R = \frac{a}{2 \sin A} = \frac{b}{2 \sin B} = \frac{c}{2 \sin C}.$$

(See the figure which follows.)

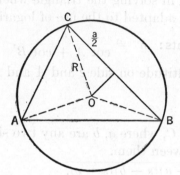

4. Show that, for any triangle, the following relation exists,

$$S = \frac{abc}{4R} = rs,$$

where S is the area, R is the radius of the circumscribed circle, r is the radius of the inscribed circle, and $s = \dfrac{a + b + c}{2}$.

5. If a, b, c and A, B, C are parts of a triangle, prove that

$$\frac{a + b}{c} = \frac{\cos \dfrac{A - B}{2}}{\sin \dfrac{C}{2}}.$$

6. The angle of depression of an object viewed from the top of a tower is 48° 12′ 53″. The angle of depression of a second object 200 feet farther away, and in a straight line with the first object and the foot of the tower, is 31° 19′ 30″. What is the height of the tower?

7. A flagpole 35 feet tall stands on a building 153 feet tall. Find to the closest minute the angle subtended by the pole from a point 376 feet from the corner of the building in a horizontal line through its base.

8. A naval officer observes the angle of elevation of an airplane to be 57° 43'; its horizontal distance from the point of observation is 863 yards. How high is the airplane, and what is its distance from the officer?

9. The sides of a triangle are in the ratio 3:5:7. Find the angles. Can you find the lengths of the sides?

10. The horizontal distance from a point on the top of a hill to a distant tower is 263.84 feet. The angle of elevation of the top of the tower is 10° 28' 23", and the angle of depression of the foot of the tower is 14° 43' 27". Find the height of the tower.

11. A parachute jumper is sighted at the same instant by two observers who are 1500 feet apart. If the jumper is between the two observers and if the angles of elevation are 74° 19' and 62° 38', respectively, what was the height of the jumper when the observations were made?

12. Find the radius of the circumscribed circle and the radius of the inscribed circle for the triangle whose sides are 139.46 inches, 215.34 inches, and 182.61 inches.

13. Two points, B and C, on opposite sides of a lake, are sighted by a surveyor from a point A at one end of the lake. The angle BAC is found to be 83° 42', AB = 138 yards, and AC = 123 yards. Find BC.

14. Find the area of a triangular field whose sides are 231.75 feet, 341.63 feet, and 419.23 feet. What are the angles of the field?

15. To find the height of a tree, a man observed from a certain point that the angle of elevation of the top of the tree was 72° 23'. He retired 50 feet from the tree in a line with the base and observed that the angle of elevation was 55° 47'. What is the height of the tree?

16. A triangle ABC on a horizontal plane has A = 50° 34', B = 65° 15', and c = 300 feet. Find the height of a flagpole standing at C if the angle of elevation of its top from A is 12° 32'.

17. A tree is growing on the side of a hill. The inclination of the hill is 24° 25'. From a point A on the hill the angle of elevation of the top of the tree is 43° 21'; from a point B, 100 feet farther up the hill, the angle of elevation of the top of the tree is 50° 40'. Find the height of the tree if it is growing vertically.

18. Two automobiles leave the same place at the same time and travel along straight roads at right angles to each other. If one car travels at the rate of 35 miles per hour and the other car travels at the rate of 40 miles per hour, how far apart are the automobiles at the end of 6 hours and 20 minutes?

19. Two trains leave the same station at the same time and travel along straight tracks making an angle of 65° with each other. If one train travels at the rate of 55 miles per hour and the other travels at the rate of 60 miles per hour, how far apart are the trains at the end of 4 hours?

20. From the top of a lighthouse 45 feet high, standing on a cliff, the angle of depression of a ship was 8° 27′; from the bottom of the lighthouse the angle of depression was 5° 20′. Find the height of the cliff and the horizontal distance of the ship from the cliff.

21. From the top of a cliff the angles of depression to two objects in the plane of the base of the cliff are observed to be 20° 31′ 53″ and 37° 22′ 48″. If the two objects are 243.75 feet apart and in the same vertical line from the foot of the cliff, find the height of the cliff.

22. From the ends of a wall 93.7 feet in length the lines of sight to a point C in front of the wall make angles of 37° 21′ 52″ and 48° 32′ 29″, respectively, with the wall. What are the distances from the ends of the wall to C? What is the perpendicular distance from the wall to C?

23. The base of a tower is at C. From two other positions, A and B, in a plane with the base of the tower, the angle CAB is found to be 72° 25′ and the angle CBA is 64° 35′. The distance $AB = 375$ feet. If the angle of elevation of the top of the tower from A is 12° 40′, how high is the tower?

24. A tree has its base at a point C. Two observers at A and B, in a plane with C, note that $\angle CAB = 59° 30′ 20″$, $\angle CBA = 40° 29′ 52″$, and the length of $AB = 2106$ feet. From D, the midpoint of AB, the angle of elevation of the top of the tree is found to be 16° 15′ 42″. Find the height of the tree.

25. A ship sails due north at a speed of 20 knots. Another ship leaves the same place an hour later and sails directly northeast at a speed of 23 knots. After the second vessel has been sailing for six hours, how far apart are the ships?

26. Two angles of a triangle are 25° 16′ and 32° 40′. If the radius of the inscribed circle is 8.19 inches, find the lengths of the sides, and the area of the triangle.

27. At one of its ends a diagonal of a parallelogram makes angles of 32° 28′ and 54° 43′ with the sides. If the diagonal is 13.5 feet in length, find the lengths of the sides.

28. A side AB of a triangle ABC is 10.93 inches in length, the radius of the circumscribed circle is 4.235 inches in length, and the angle CAB is 42° 25′. Find the remaining parts of the triangle.

29. The diagonals of a parallelogram intersect at an angle of 42° 25′ 30″. If the lengths of the diagonals are 24.360 feet and 32.480 feet, respectively, find the lengths of the sides of the parallelogram.

30. It is desired to find the distance between two points A and B situated on opposite sides of a deep ravine. The distance between two other points C and D, also on opposite sides of the ravine, is known to be 100 feet. The points A and C are on the same side of the ravine, and $AC = 54$ feet. If $BD = 73$ feet, angle $DCB = 42° 25′$, and angle $ADC = 33° 44′$, find the distance from A to B.

31. A tree, growing on the side of a hill, makes an angle of 10° with the vertical. The hill is inclined at 25° to the horizontal. At A, a point 203 feet down the hill from the base of the tree, the angle of elevation of the top of the tree is found to be 44° 28′. Find the height of the tree.

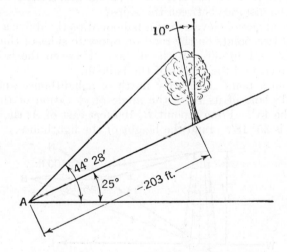

32. Two forces, F_1 and F_2, acting on a particle make angles of 102° 38′ with each other. If $|F_1| = 13.98$ pounds and $|F_2| = 16.34$ pounds, what is the magnitude of the resultant force F?

33. Two towns, L and M, are located on opposite sides of a lake. In order to go from L to M, one follows a straight road from L to P, another from P to Q, and then a third road from Q to M. If $LP = 535$ feet, $PQ = 400$ feet, $QM = 626$ feet, $\angle PLQ = 20° 19′$, and $\angle PMQ = 36° 20′$, find LM.

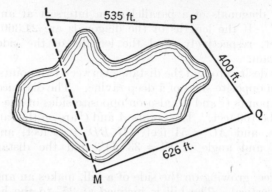

34. Two ships, *A* and *B*, are anchored offshore. In order to find the distance *AB*, two points of observation, *C* and *D*, are taken on shore. *C* and *D* are 500 feet apart, ∠*ACB* is found to be 68° 25′, ∠*ACD* = 29° 26′, ∠*ADB* = 72° 35′ and ∠*BDC* = 40° 34′. What is the distance between the ships?

35. The angles of elevation of a balloon directly above a straight road from two points on the road on opposite sides of the balloon are 54° 28′ and 46° 30′. If the distance between the two points is 2000.0 feet, find the height of the balloon.

36. From a point *A* directly north of a lighthouse and in the horizontal plane of its base, the angle of elevation of the top is noted to be 45°. From a point *B*, 100 feet east of *A*, the angle of elevation is 35° 18′. Find the height of the lighthouse.

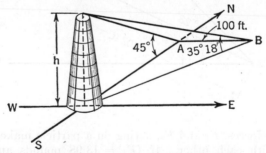

37. Three forces in the same plane act on a body and produce a condition of equilibrium. The magnitudes of two of the forces are 61.86 pounds and 73.94 pounds, respectively, the first force making an angle of 48° 20′ with the second force. Find the magnitude of the third force. *Hint*: The directed line segments representing the forces must form a triangle.

38. Find the altitudes of a triangle whose sides are 139.56, 202.37, and 186.45.

39. From the top of a hill the angles of depression of the top and bottom of a tower 30 feet high at the foot of the hill are observed to be 45° 20′ and 50° 30′, respectively. Find the elevation of the hill.

40. The area of a triangle is 52.34. If two of the angles are 45° 20′ and 64° 15′, find the length of each of the sides.

41. Two points, L and M, are on opposite sides of a river. A straight line, PQ, is run through L and the following measurements are taken: $PL = 500$ feet, $LQ = 300$ feet, $\angle MPL = 32° 24′$, $\angle MQL = 40° 35′$. Find the distance LM.

42. Two towns, P and Q, are separated by a swamp. A third town, T, is located at the intersection of two straight roads leading to P and Q, respectively. The town T is 1854 yards from P and 2063 yards from Q. A point L is taken on the road PT, 935 yards from T, and M is chosen on QT, 725 yards from T. The distance LM is found to be 640 yards. Find PQ.

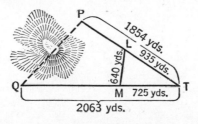

43. The corner post (vertical) of a fence is braced by two inclined members which are in vertical planes at right angles to each other, each vertical plane containing the corner post. The braces, which are 5.0 feet and 6.0 feet long, respectively, are fastened to the post at a height of 3.0 feet.

(a) How far from the foot of the post are the lower ends of the braces?

(b) What is the distance between the ends of the braces?

(c) What is the angle between the braces?

44. On the edge of a lake, there is erected a tower 100 feet high supporting a 22-foot flagpole. An observer on the opposite shore, in the same vertical plane with the tower, notes that the flagpole subtends the same angle at the point of observation as a man 6 feet tall standing at the foot of the tower. How far is the observer from the foot of the tower?

45. If the wind gives a sailboat a speed of 5 knots due east and the current gives it a speed of 3 knots N 70° 0′ E, what is the speed of the sailboat?

46. An airplane pilot wishes to follow the course N 30° W. If the velocity of the wind is 30 miles per hour N 42° W and the speed of the plane relative to the air is 150 miles per hour, on what compass bearing should he set his course?

Chapter VIII

TRIGONOMETRIC EQUATIONS AND THE INVERSE TRIGONOMETERIC FUNCTIONS*

56. Trigonometric equations

The relations between the trigonometric functions of an angle which were studied in Chapter VI were identities, since they were satisfied by every value of the angle for which the functions were defined. We shall now consider relations between the trigonometric functions which are satisfied by only certain values of the angle. We shall call these *trigonometric equations.*

Each value of the angle that satisfies an equation is called a solution of the equation. If a trigonometric equation has one solution, it has infinitely many solutions. It is usually possible to write down formulas which represent all the values of the angle that satisfy a given trigonometric equation, and this will be discussed in detail in § 58. We shall call such a formula the *general solution* of a trigonometric equation. In this section we shall be interested in finding all the *positive angles less than 360°* which satisfy the equation. Several of the various types of equations that occur and the methods used in solving them are illustrated in the following examples. After a problem has been solved, all results

---

* May be omitted for a brief course. Before the student takes up this chapter, it is essential that he make a brief but thorough review of the values of the trigonometric functions of 0°, 30°, 45°, 60°, 90°, and the angles obtained by adding $k90°$, for k a positive or negative integer, to these angles. The student should be able to evaluate these without the use of the tables.

should be checked, since some of the methods used in solving an equation may introduce extraneous solutions.

Example 1:

Solve the following equation for all positive values of $\theta < 360°$.

$$\sin \theta = \cos \theta.$$

Whenever possible it is best to put the equation in such a form that only one trigonometric function appears. Dividing both sides of the equation by $\cos \theta$,* we obtain

$$\frac{\sin \theta}{\cos \theta} = 1, \text{ or } \tan \theta = 1.$$

Hence

$$\theta = 45° \text{ or } 225°.$$

Check: Since $\sin 45° = \cos 45°$ and $\sin 225° = \cos 225°$, both of these values of θ are solutions of the equation. If it had not been possible to obtain the solutions by inspection, we should have had to use tables.

Example 2:

Solve the following equation for all positive values of $\theta < 360°$.

$$\sin \theta + 1 = 2 \cos^2 \theta.$$

Replacing $\cos^2 \theta$ by $1 - \sin^2 \theta$, we have

$$\sin \theta + 1 = 2 - 2 \sin^2 \theta.$$

This is a quadratic equation in $\sin \theta$ which may be written in the form

$$2 \sin^2 \theta + \sin \theta - 1 = 0.$$

Factoring, we have

$$(2 \sin \theta - 1)(\sin \theta + 1) = 0.$$

Equating each factor to zero and solving for $\sin \theta$, we obtain

$$\sin \theta = \tfrac{1}{2} \text{ and } \sin \theta = -1.$$

If $\sin \theta = \tfrac{1}{2}$, we have

$$\theta = 30° \text{ or } 150°;$$

* This is permissible, since the values of θ for which $\cos \theta = 0$ are not solutions of the equation.

if $\sin \theta = -1$, we have

$$\theta = 270°.$$

Check:

(1) $\sin 30° + 1 = 2 \cos^2 30°, \;$ since $\dfrac{1}{2} + 1 = 2\left(\dfrac{\sqrt{3}}{2}\right)^2.$

(2) $\sin 150° + 1 = 2 \cos^2 150°,$ since $\dfrac{1}{2} + 1 = 2\left(-\dfrac{\sqrt{3}}{2}\right)^2.$

(3) $\sin 270° + 1 = 2 \cos^2 270°,$ since $-1 + 1 = 2(0)^2.$

Therefore $\theta = 30°$, $150°$, and $270°$ are solutions.

Example 3:

Solve the following equation for all positive values of $x < 360°$.

$$\sin x - \cos x = 1.$$

In order to arrange this equation so as to involve only one trigonometric function, and also so as to avoid radicals, we write it in the form

$$\sin x = 1 + \cos x.$$

After squaring, we have

$$\sin^2 x = 1 + 2 \cos x + \cos^2 x,$$

whence $1 - \cos^2 x = 1 + 2 \cos x + \cos^2 x,$

or $2 \cos^2 x + 2 \cos x = 0.$

Factoring, we have

$$\cos x \, (\cos x + 1) = 0,$$

therefore

$$\cos x = 0 \text{ and } \cos x = -1.$$

If $\cos x = 0$,

$$x = 90° \text{ or } 270°;$$

if $\cos x = -1$,

$$x = 180°.$$

Check:

(1) $\sin 90° - \cos 90° = 1,$ since $1 - 0 = 1.$
(2) $\sin 270° - \cos 270° \neq 1,$ since $-1 - 0 \neq 1.$
(3) $\sin 180° - \cos 180° = 1,$ since $0 - (-1) = 1.$

Therefore $x = 90°$ and $180°$ are solutions. The extraneous solution $270°$ was introduced when the original equation was squared.

Example 4:

Solve the following equation for all positive values of $\theta < 360°$.

$$2 \sin 2\theta = 1.$$

Dividing both sides of the equation by 2, we have

$$\sin 2\theta = \frac{1}{2}.$$

Since we are interested in all the values of θ less than $360°$ which satisfy the equation, we have

$$2\theta = 30°, 150°, 390°, 510°,$$

and

$$\theta = 15°, 75°, 195°, 255°.$$

The student should check these results.

Example 5:

Solve the following equation for all positive values of $\theta < 360°$.
$$\sin 4x = 3 \cos 2x.$$

From the identity $\sin 2\theta = 2 \sin \theta \cos \theta$, it follows that

$$\sin 4x = \sin 2(2x) = 2 \sin 2x \cos 2x.$$

Substituting this in the original equation, we have

$$2 \sin 2x \cos 2x = 3 \cos 2x,$$
$$\cos 2x \ (2 \sin 2x - 3) = 0.$$

Therefore $\cos 2x = 0$ and $\sin 2x = \dfrac{3}{2}.$

If $\cos 2x = 0$, we have

$$2x = 90°, 270°, 450°, 630°,$$
and $$x = 45°, 135°, 225°, 315°.$$

From $\sin 2x = \dfrac{3}{2}$, we obtain no solutions.   **Why?**

The student should check the results.

Example 6:

Solve the following equation for all positive values of $\theta < 360°$.
$$2 \cos 2\theta - \cos 3\theta - \cos \theta = 0.$$

Since $\cos A + \cos B = 2 \cos\left(\dfrac{A+B}{2}\right) \cos\left(\dfrac{A-B}{2}\right)$, it follows

that $\cos 3\theta + \cos \theta = 2 \cos \dfrac{4\theta}{2} \cos \dfrac{2\theta}{2}$; so our equation becomes

$$2 \cos 2\theta - 2 \cos 2\theta \cos \theta = 0,$$

or $\qquad\qquad 2 \cos 2\theta (1 - \cos \theta) = 0.$

Therefore $\qquad\qquad \cos 2\theta = 0$ and $\cos \theta = 1.$

If $\cos 2\theta = 0$, we have

$$2\theta = 90°, 270°, 450°, 630°,$$

and $\qquad\qquad \theta = 45°, 135°, 225°, 315°.$

If $\cos \theta = 1$, we have

$$\theta = 0°.$$

Check the results.

EXERCISES

1. Solve the following equations for all of the positive angles less than 360°:

(a) $2 \sin^2 x - 1 = 0.$

(b) $\cos x + 3 \sin x = 0.$

(c) $\cos^2 x - 2 \sin x - 1 = 0.$

(d) $\cos x - 2 \sin x = 2.$

(e) $2 \cos 2\theta - 1 = 0.$

(f) $2 \sin^2 2\theta - 3 \sin 2\theta - 2 = 0.$

(g) $2 \sin x + \sin 2x = 0.$

(h) $\cos 2x - \sin x = 0.$

(i) $\sin x - 3 \cos x = 1.$

(j) $2 \sin x + \cos 3x - \cos x = 0.$

(k) $\sin 2x - \sin 4x = 0.$

(l) $\sec^2 \theta - 4 = 0.$

(m) $\sin 3x = \cos 3x.$

(n) $\cos x + \sin x - 1 = 0.$

(o) $\tan x - \sin x = 0.$

(p) $2 \cos^2 \theta + 1 = -4 \sin \theta \cos \theta.$

(q) $2 \sec x - \tan x = 2.$

(r) $1 + 2 \sin x \cos x = \sin x + \cos x.$

(s) $\tan 2\theta = 2 \sin \theta.$

(t) $1 + \csc x = \cot x.$

2. In the following equations, find the values of x which make y equal to zero:

(a) $y = \sin 2x - 2 \sin x.$

(b) $y = \sin x + \tan x.$

(c) $y = \cos 2x - 1.$

(d) $y = \sin 2x + \cos 2x.$

57. The inverse trigonometric functions

From the definitions of the trigonometric functions of an angle it follows that for any given angle there exists one, and only one, value of each trigonometric function. For example,

$$\sin 90° = 1, \cos 30° = \frac{\sqrt{3}}{2}, \sin 45° = \frac{\sqrt{2}}{2}, \tan 120° = -\sqrt{3},$$

and so on. On the other hand, there are infinitely many angles for which a particular trigonometric function has a given value. This follows immediately, since by § 10 we know that each trigonometric function generally determines two positive angles less than 360°. Furthermore, by § 12, if θ is an angle whose function is known, then *this* function of $\theta + 2k\pi$, for k any positive or negative integer, has the same value.

Thus if $\sin \alpha = \frac{1}{2}$,

$$\alpha = 30°, 150°, 390°, 510°, -330°, -210°, \cdots;$$

if $\cos \theta = \frac{\sqrt{2}}{2}$,

$$\theta = 45°, 315°, 405°, 675°, -315°, -45°, \cdots;$$

or if $\tan \phi = -\sqrt{3}$,

$$\phi = 120°, 300°, 480°, 660°, -240°, -60°, \cdots.$$

The equation $\sin y = x$ can be read, "y is the angle whose sine is x," and may be written

$$y = \text{arc} \sin x, \text{ or } y = \sin^{-1} x.$$

The index -1 must not be confused with an exponent. It is necessary to become familiar with both notations, since both are commonly used. It is most important to understand that $y = \sin^{-1} x$, $y = \text{arc} \sin x$, and $x = \sin y$ are equivalent equations. It is important to understand clearly that arc sin x is an angle or arc as its name implies. The relation $y = \sin^{-1} x$ or $y = \text{arc} \sin x$ is also read, "y is the inverse sine of x." Similarly $y = \cos^{-1} x$ or $y = \text{arc} \cos x$ is read, "y is the angle whose cosine is x," or "y is the inverse cosine of x," and $y = \tan^{-1} x$ or $y = \text{arc} \tan x$ is read, "y is the angle whose tangent is x," or "y is the inverse tangent of x," and so on for the other functions.

EXERCISES

1. In words, we read $y = \sin^{-1} x$ or $y = \text{arc sin } x$ as "y is the angle whose sine is x." Using this same language, read the following:

(a) $y = \text{arc cot } x$.   (b) $y = \text{arc sec } x$.   (c) $y = \csc^{-1} x$.

2. Rewrite each of the following so that x is a function of y:

(a) $y = \cot^{-1} x$.   (b) $y = \sec^{-1} x$.   (c) $y = \text{arc csc } x$.

3. In each of the following write the statement in the inverse form:

(a) $y = \cos x$.   (c) $y = \csc x$.   (e) $y = \cot x$.

(b) $y = \tan x$.   (d) $y = \sin x$.   (f) $y = \sec x$.

4. Prove: $a \sin x + b \cos x \equiv \sqrt{a^2 + b^2} \sin (x + \alpha)$, where a and b are constants, and $\alpha = \tan^{-1} \dfrac{b}{a}$.

5. Prove: $a \cos x + b \sin x \equiv \sqrt{a^2 + b^2} \cos (x - \alpha)$, where a and b are constants and $\alpha = \tan^{-1} \dfrac{b}{a}$.

58. The general solution of a trigonometric equation

As has already been mentioned, there are an indefinite number of solutions for $\alpha = \sin^{-1} k$. Because of this property, the inverse trigonometric functions are said to be many-valued. It is usually possible to write down a single expression which represents the general value of a given inverse trigonometric function. The following examples will illustrate the method.

Example 1:

Given $\alpha = \sin^{-1} \dfrac{\sqrt{3}}{2}$; find all the values of α.

Rewrite the equation as $\sin \alpha = \dfrac{\sqrt{3}}{2}$. Then

$\alpha = 60°, 120°, 420°, 480°, 780°, 840°, \cdots, -300°, -240°, \cdots$;
or we could have written
$\alpha = 60°, 180° - 60°, 360° + 60°, 540° - 60°, \cdots, -360° + 60°,$
$\cdots$.

This latter way of writing the values of α suggests the following method of writing the general solution in a single expression:

$$\alpha = (-1)^n \, 60° + n \, 180°,$$

for n any positive or negative integer or zero.

Theorem 1: *If α is an angle whose sine is k (i.e., $\alpha = \sin^{-1} k$), where $-1 \le k \le 1$, and if α_1 is one solution, then the general solution is*

(1) $\alpha = (-1)^n \, \alpha_1 + n \, 180°,$

for n any positive or negative integer or zero.

Proof: Since $\sin \alpha = k$, there exist, in general, two angles, α_1 and $180° - \alpha_1$, both less than $360°$,* such that $\sin \alpha_1 = k$ and $\sin (180° - \alpha_1) = k$ (see chapter II). By adding positive and negative integral multiples of $360°$ to α_1 and to $180° - \alpha_1$, we obtain infinitely many angles each having the same terminal side as either α_1 or $180° - \alpha_1$. Hence the sine of all the angles thus obtained is k. Any one of the angles may be represented either by

$$\alpha_1 + m \, 360° \text{ or } 180° - \alpha_1 + m \, 360°$$

where m is any positive or negative integer or zero. We can write

$$\alpha_1 + m \, 360° = (-1)^{2m}\alpha_1 + (2m) \, 180°,$$

and

$$180° - \alpha_1 + m \, 360° = (-1)^{2m+1}\alpha_1 + (2m + 1) \, 180°.$$

But both of these formulas can be expressed in the one formula

$$\alpha = (-1)^n\alpha_1 + n \, 180°,$$

since if n is even (*i.e.*, $n = 2m$), we have $\alpha = (-1)^{2m}\alpha_1 + (2m)180°$, and if n is odd (*i.e.*, $n = 2m + 1$), we have

$$\alpha = (-1)^{2m+1}\alpha_1 + (2m + 1)180°.$$

---

* If k is negative, $180° - \alpha_1$ will be a negative angle but we can replace it by $180° - \alpha_1 + 360°$ and so have two positive angles, both less than $360°$, such that $\sin \alpha_1 = k$ and $\sin (180° - \alpha_1 + 360°) = k$.

Example 2:

Given $\alpha = \cos^{-1} \frac{1}{2}$; find all the values of α.

Rewrite the equation as $\cos \alpha = \dfrac{1}{2}$. Then

$$\alpha = \pm 60°, \pm 300°, \pm 420°, \pm 660°, \pm 780°, \pm 1020°, \cdots$$

Or we could have written

$$\alpha = \pm 60°, \pm 360° - 60°, \pm 360° + 60°, \pm 720° - 60°,$$
$$\pm 720° + 60°, \cdots.$$

These results can be written in one formula as

$$\alpha = \pm(60° + n\,360°),$$

where n is any positive or negative integer or zero.   This is the desired formula for the general solution of

$$\alpha = \cos^{-1} \tfrac{1}{2}.$$

Theorem 2: *If α is an angle whose cosine is k* (i.e., $\alpha = \cos^{-1} k$), $-1 \leqq k \leqq 1$, *and if α_1 is one solution, then the general solution is*

(2) $\alpha = \pm(\alpha_1 + n\,360°),$

where n is any positive or negative integer or zero.

Prove Theorem 2.

Example 3:

Given $\alpha = \tan^{-1}(-1)$; find all the values of α.

Rewrite the equation as $\tan \alpha = -1$.   Then

$$\alpha = 135°, 315°, 495°, 675°, 855°, 1035°, \cdots, -45°, -225°, \cdots,$$

or we could have written

$$\alpha = 135°, 135° + 180°, 135° - 180°, 135° + 360°,$$
$$135° - 360°, \cdots.$$

Hence, all the values of α are given by

$$\alpha = 135° + n\,180°,$$

where n is any positive or negative integer or zero.

Theorem 3: *If α is an angle whose tangent is k* (i.e., $\alpha = \tan^{-1} k$), *and if α_1 is one solution, then the general solution is*

(3) $\alpha = \alpha_1 + n\,180°,$

where n is any positive or negative integer or zero.
Prove Theorem 3.

The following examples illustrate various methods of finding the general solution of a trigonometric equation.

Example 4:

Find the general solution of

$$\cos \theta = -\sin \theta$$

(a) Dividing each member by $-\cos \theta$, we obtain

$$\tan \theta = -1, \text{ or } \theta = \text{arc tan } (-1).$$

Since $\theta = 135°$ is one solution, the general solution is

$$\theta = 135° + n\,180°. \quad \text{(See Theorem 3)}.$$

Check:

$$\cos (135° + n\,180°) = -\sin (135° + n\,180°).$$

When n is even, this becomes: $\cos 135° = -\sin 135°$;
When n is odd, this becomes: $-\sin 135° = \cos 135°$.

(b) Another method of solving the above equation is as follows:
By § 14, we have $\cos \theta = \sin (90° \pm \theta + m\,360°)$, for m any positive or negative integer.
Hence, since $\cos \theta = -\sin \theta$, we have

$$\sin (90° \pm \theta + m\,360°) = -\sin \theta = \sin (-\theta).$$

Therefore

$$90° \pm \theta + m\,360° = -\theta,$$

or

$$180° - (90° \pm \theta) + m\,360° = -\theta.^*$$

When either the plus or minus sign within the parentheses is employed, the solution of the equation is

$$\theta = -45° - m\,180°.$$

Since m may be any positive or negative integer or zero, this general solution is the same as the one previously obtained.

---

* If $\sin \alpha = \sin \beta$, it follows that $\alpha = \beta + n\,360°$ or $\alpha = 180° - \beta + n\,360°$, for n any positive or negative integer or zero.

Example 5:

Find the general solution of

$$\cos 2\theta = \sin 4\theta.$$

Writing $\sin 4\theta \equiv 2 \sin 2\theta \cos 2\theta$, we have

$$\cos 2\theta = 2 \sin 2\theta \cos 2\theta.$$

After factoring, we obtain

$$\cos 2\theta \, (1 - 2 \sin 2\theta) = 0.$$

Therefore

$$\cos 2\theta = 0 \text{ and } \sin 2\theta = \frac{1}{2}.$$

If $\cos 2\theta = 0$, we have

$$2\theta = \text{arc} \cos 0 = \pm(90° + n\,360°). \quad \text{(See Theorem 2.)}$$

So

$$\theta = \pm(45° + n\,180°).$$

If $\sin 2\theta = \frac{1}{2}$, we have

$$2\theta = \text{arc} \sin \frac{1}{2} = (-1)^n\,30° + n\,180°. \quad \text{(See Theorem 1.)}$$

Consequently

$$\theta = (-1)^n\,15° + n\,90°.$$

The student should check these results.

Example 6:

Find the general solution of

$$\cos x - \sin x = \sqrt{2}.$$

After adding $\sin x$ to each member of the equation and squaring, we have

$$\cos^2 x = 2 + 2\sqrt{2} \sin x + \sin^2 x.$$

After replacing $\cos^2 x$ by $1 - \sin^2 x$, we have

$$1 - \sin^2 x = 2 + 2\sqrt{2} \sin x + \sin^2 x$$

or

$$2 \sin^2 x + 2\sqrt{2} \sin x + 1 = 0,$$

which may be written

$$(\sqrt{2} \sin x + 1)^2 = 0.$$

Hence

$$\sin x = -\frac{1}{\sqrt{2}}, \text{ or } x = \sin^{-1}\left(-\frac{1}{\sqrt{2}}\right).$$

Therefore
$$x = (-1)^n 225° + n 180°.$$

Check: Write the general solution in two parts, namely,
$$x = 225° + n 360° \text{ and } x = 315° + n 360°.$$

For $x = 225° + n 360°$, we have
$$\cos (225° + n 360°) - \sin (225° + n 360°) = -\frac{1}{2}\sqrt{2} + \frac{1}{2}\sqrt{2} = 0.$$

Therefore $x = 225° + n 360°$ is not a solution.
For $x = 315° + n 360°$, we have
$$\cos (315° + n 360°) - \sin (315° + n 360°) = \frac{1}{2}\sqrt{2} + \frac{1}{2}\sqrt{2} = \sqrt{2}.$$

Thus, $x = 315° + n 360°$ is the general solution.

Example 7:

Find the general solution of
$$\cos 4\theta = \sin 3\theta.$$

Writing $\cos 4\theta = \sin (90° \pm 4\theta + n 360°)$, we have
$$\sin (90° \pm 4\theta + n 360°) = \sin 3\theta.$$

Therefore
$$90° \pm 4\theta + n 360° = 3\theta,$$
or
$$180° - (90° \pm 4\theta) + n 360° = 3\theta.$$

Using the equation $90° + 4\theta + n 360° = 3\theta$ in our solution for θ, we obtain
$$\theta = -90° - n 360°.$$

Using the equation $90° - 4\theta + n 360° = 3\theta$ to solve for θ, we obtain
$$\theta = (90°/7) + (n 360°/7).$$

The student should check these results.

Example 8:

Given $y = \text{arc cos } 3x$, find x as a function of y.

By definition $3x = \cos^{-1}y$ and hence,

$$x = \frac{1}{3}\cos^{-1}y.$$

EXERCISES

1. Explain what is meant by the notation: $\sin^{-1}\theta$, arc cos θ, arc tan θ, $\sec^{-1}\theta$.

2. Write the formulas for the general solution of $\alpha = \cos^{-1}k$, $\alpha = \sec^{-1}k$, and $\alpha = \text{arc cot } k$.

3. Find two positive angles less than $360°$ satisfying the following:

(a) $\theta = \cos^{-1}\dfrac{\sqrt{3}}{2}$.

(g) $\alpha = \text{arc cot }(-\sqrt{3})$.

(b) $\alpha = \text{arc tan } 1$.

(h) $\beta = \sec^{-1}\sqrt{2}$.

(c) $\beta = \sin^{-1}0.33333$.

(i) $\theta = \csc^{-1}\left(-\dfrac{2}{\sqrt{3}}\right)$.

(d) $\theta = \text{arc cos }(-0.21794)$.

(j) $\alpha = \tan^{-1}1.9863$.

(e) $\beta = \text{arc tan }\sqrt{3}$.

(k) $\theta = \text{arc sin }(-\tfrac{1}{2})$.

(f) $\theta = \cot^{-1}(-1)$.

(l) $\beta = \cos^{-1}\dfrac{1}{2}$.

4. Write the general solutions for each of the equations in the above exercises.

5. Construct two angles θ if $\theta = \sin^{-1}(\sqrt{2}/3)$, and find the other five inverse trigonometric functions in each case.

6. Construct two angles θ if $\theta = \tan^{-1}(-2)$, and find the other five inverse trigonometric functions in each case.

7. If $\theta = \text{arc cos } k$, find the other five inverse trigonometric functions.

8. Prove:

(a) $\sin^{-1}k \equiv \csc^{-1}\dfrac{1}{k}$.

(b) $\cos^{-1}l \equiv \sec^{-1}\dfrac{1}{l}$.

(c) $\text{arc tan } m \equiv \text{arc cot }\dfrac{1}{m}$.

9. Rewrite each of the following so that x is a function of y:

(a) $y = \text{arc sin } 2x$.   (e) $y = \dfrac{1}{2} \cos^{-1} x$.

(b) $y = 2 \text{ arc cos } 3x$.   (f) $y = \cot^{-1} \pi x$.

(c) $y = \text{arc tan } \dfrac{x}{2}$.   (g) $y = \dfrac{\sec^{-1} 2x}{2}$.

(d) $y = 3 \sin^{-1} \dfrac{x}{2}$.   (h) $y = 3 \text{ arc sin } 2x$.

10. Rewrite each of the following so that y is a function of x:

(a) $x = \sin 3y$.   (e) $x = 2 \sin \dfrac{y}{2}$.

(b) $x = 3 \cos \dfrac{y}{2}$.   (f) $x = \dfrac{\cos y}{2}$.

(c) $x = 2 \tan y$.   (g) $x = \dfrac{\sec 3y}{3}$.

(d) $x = \cot \pi y$.   (h) $x = \dfrac{3}{2} \tan 5y$.

11. Find the general solution of $\cos x - \sin x = \sqrt{2}$ by using the result of problem 14, § 57.

12. Find the general solutions of the following:

(a) $\cos 2\theta + 2 \cos^2 \theta = 0$.   (i) $\sin 5\theta - \sin 3\theta - \sin \theta$
(b) $\sin 9\theta = \sin 3\theta$. $= 0$.
(c) $\tan 2\theta = \tan 5\theta$.   (j) $\cos k\theta - \cos l\theta = 0$.
(d) $\cos 4\theta = \sin 2\theta$.   (k) $\sin 4\theta = \cos 3\theta$.
(e) $\tan \theta \tan 3\theta = 1$.   (l) $4 \sin^2 \theta - \sin 3\theta = 0$.
(f) $\sin 5\theta = \sin 3\theta + \sqrt{3} \cos 4\theta$.   (m) $\sin \theta \cot \dfrac{\theta}{2} = 1$.
(g) $2 \cos^2 \theta - \sin 2\theta = 0$.
(h) $\sin k\theta + \sin l\theta = 0$.   (n) $\cos 3\theta + 8 \cos^3 \theta = 0$.

59. Applications of the inverse trigonometric functions

Example 1:

Show that there exist angles such that

$$\tan^{-1} 1 = \sin^{-1} \dfrac{1}{\sqrt{2}}.$$

Let $\theta = \tan^{-1} 1$, then $\tan \theta = 1$, and
                 $\theta = 45°, 225°, 405°, 585°, \ldots.$

Let $$\phi = \sin^{-1}\frac{1}{\sqrt{2}}, \text{ then } \sin \phi = \frac{1}{\sqrt{2}},$$

and $$\phi = 45°, 135°, 405°, 495°, \ldots$$

Hence there are angles for which $\tan^{-1} 1 = \sin^{-1}\frac{1}{\sqrt{2}}$. But the equation is not an identity, and because of the many-valued property of the inverse functions great care must be taken in the choice of the angles.

Example 2:

Show that a positive acute angle exists such that

$$\text{arc sin } \frac{3}{5} = \text{arc cos } \frac{4}{5}.$$

Let $$\theta = \text{arc sin } \frac{3}{5}; \text{ then } \sin \theta = \frac{3}{5}.$$

Let $$\phi = \text{arc cos } \frac{4}{5}; \text{ then } \cos \phi = \frac{4}{5}.$$

We must prove that $\theta = \phi$, where θ and ϕ are positive acute angles. Since $\sin \theta = \frac{3}{5}$, it follows that $\cos \theta = \frac{4}{5}$. But by hypothesis $\cos \phi = \frac{4}{5}$. Therefore

$$\cos \theta = \cos \phi$$
and $$\theta = \phi,$$

with the provision that they are positive acute angles.

Example 3:

Find the value of $\sin\left(\sin^{-1}\frac{\sqrt{3}}{2}\right)$.

Let $$\theta = \sin^{-1}\frac{\sqrt{3}}{2}; \text{ then } \sin \theta = \frac{\sqrt{3}}{2}.$$

Therefore $$\sin\left(\sin^{-1}\frac{\sqrt{3}}{2}\right) = \frac{\sqrt{3}}{2}.$$

Example 4:

Find the value of $\cos (\tan^{-1} \sqrt{3})$.

Let $$\theta = \tan^{-1} \sqrt{3}; \text{ then } \tan \theta = \sqrt{3}.$$

But if $\qquad$ $\tan \theta = \sqrt{3}, \cos \theta = \pm\dfrac{1}{2}.$

Therefore

$$\cos(\tan^{-1}\sqrt{3}) = \pm\frac{1}{2}. \quad \text{(See the figure below.)}$$

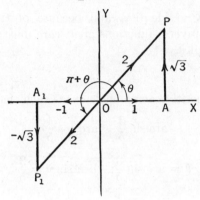

Example 5:

Prove that for all positive acute angles

$$\cos^{-1}\sqrt{1-x^2} \equiv \sin^{-1} x.$$

Proof:

Let $\qquad \theta = \cos^{-1}\sqrt{1-x^2}$; then $\cos\theta = \sqrt{1-x^2}.$

Let $\quad \phi = \sin^{-1}x$; then $\sin\phi = x$, and $\cos\phi = \sqrt{1-x^2}.$

Therefore $\qquad \cos\theta = \cos\phi$, or $\theta = \phi.$

Hence $\cos^{-1}\sqrt{1-x^2} = \sin^{-1}x$ for all positive acute angles.

Example 6:

Show that there exists a *positive angle* θ such that, if

$$\theta = 2 \text{ arc tan } \tfrac{1}{2} + \text{arc cos } \tfrac{4}{5}, \text{ then } \cos\theta = 0.$$

Proof:

Let $\qquad \alpha = \text{arc tan } \dfrac{1}{2}$; then $\tan\alpha = \dfrac{1}{2}.$

Let $\qquad \beta = \text{arc cos } \dfrac{4}{5}$; then $\cos\beta = \dfrac{4}{5}.$

We shall regard α and β as positive acute angles. By hypothesis, we have

$$\theta = 2\alpha + \beta,$$

so

$$\cos \theta = \cos (2\alpha + \beta) = \cos 2\alpha \cos \beta - \sin 2\alpha \sin \beta.$$

Since $\cos 2\alpha \equiv \cos^2 \alpha - \sin^2 \alpha$, and $\sin 2\alpha \equiv 2 \sin \alpha \cos \alpha$, we have

(1) $\cos \theta = (\cos^2 \alpha - \sin^2 \alpha) \cos \beta - 2 \sin \alpha \cos \alpha \sin \beta.$

Since $\tan \alpha = \dfrac{1}{2}$, we have $\sin \alpha = \dfrac{1}{\sqrt{5}}$ and $\cos \alpha = \dfrac{2}{\sqrt{5}}.$ Since $\cos \beta = \dfrac{4}{5}$, we have $\sin \beta = \dfrac{3}{5}.$ Substituting these values in (1), we have

$$\cos \theta = \left(\frac{4}{5} - \frac{1}{5}\right)\frac{4}{5} - 2\left(\frac{1}{\sqrt{5}}\right)\left(\frac{2}{\sqrt{5}}\right)\frac{3}{5} = 0,$$

which was to be proved.

Example 7:

Considering x to be less than $90°$, solve for x if it is given that

$$\text{arc sin } x + \text{arc cos } 2x = \frac{\pi}{2}.$$

Let $\theta = \text{arc sin } x$; then $\sin \theta = x$ and $\cos \theta = \sqrt{1 - x^2}.$

Let $\phi = \text{arc cos } 2x$; then $\cos \phi = 2x$ and $\sin \phi = \sqrt{1 - 4x^2}.$

By hypothesis,

$$\theta + \phi = \frac{\pi}{2}.$$

Hence

$$\sin (\theta + \phi) = \sin \theta \cos \phi + \cos \theta \sin \phi = \sin \frac{\pi}{2}.$$

Therefore

$$x(2x) + \sqrt{1 - x^2}\sqrt{1 - 4x^2} = 1,$$

or

$$\sqrt{1 - x^2}\sqrt{1 - 4x^2} = 1 - 2x^2.$$

After squaring both sides, we have

$$(1 - x^2)(1 - 4x^2) = (1 - 2x^2)^2,$$
$$1 - 5x^2 + 4x^4 = 1 - 4x^2 + 4x^4,$$

or

$$x = 0.$$

Therefore $x = 0$ is the desired solution to the problem, for it checks in the given relationship.

60. Principal values of the inverse functions*

It is desirable in certain investigations to make the inverse functions single-valued. The one value assigned to an inverse function is known as the *principal value* and is defined as follows:

Principal values of $y = \sin^{-1} x$ lie in the
    interval $-\pi/2 \leqq y \leqq \pi/2$.
Principal values of $y = \cos^{-1} x$ lie in the
    interval $0 \leqq y \leqq \pi$.
Principal values of $y = \tan^{-1} x$ lie in the
    interval $-\pi/2 < y < \pi/2$.

Note that arc tan x does not take on the values $-\pi/2$ and $\pi/2$. This is indicated in the interval symbol by the omission of the equality signs before and after the y.

Principal values of $y = \cot^{-1} x$ lie in the
    interval $0 < y < \pi$.
Principal values of $y = \sec^{-1} x$ lie in the
    intervals $0 \leqq y < \pi/2$ and $\pi/2 < y \leqq \pi$.
Principal values of $y = \csc^{-1} x$ lie in the
    intervals $-\pi/2 \leqq y < 0$ and $0 < y \leqq \pi/2$.

In order to distinguish the principal values, we shall write the symbol for the inverse function with a capital letter. So $\text{Sin}^{-1} (-1) = -\pi/2$, $\text{Tan}^{-1} (-1) = -\pi/4$, $\text{Cos}^{-1} 0 = \pi/2$, Arc sec $(-2/\sqrt{3}) = 5\pi/6$, Arc cot $(1/\sqrt{3}) = \pi/3$, and Arc csc $1 = \pi/2$.

EXERCISES

Find the value of each of the following:

1. Arc cos $1/2$.   **2.** $\text{Sin}^{-1} \dfrac{\sqrt{3}}{2}$

---

* See Chapter IX for graphs of the principal values of the inverse functions.

3. $\text{Tan}^{-1}(-1)$.

4. Arc sec 1.

5. Arc cot $\sqrt{3}$.

6. $\text{Cos}^{-1}(-1/2)$.

7. Arc sin $\left(-\dfrac{1}{\sqrt{2}}\right)$.

8. Arc tan 0.1834.

9. Arc sin 0.58463.

10. Arc cos (-0.61774).

11. $\text{Sin}^{-1}(-0.89662)$.

12. Tan^{-1} 2.4635.

13. Cot^{-1} 1.1483.

14. $\text{Cos}^{-1}(-0.52146)$.

EXERCISES: CHAPTER VIII

1. Solve for all positive angles less than 360° and check each result:

(a) $2\cos^2 x - \sin^2 x + \dfrac{1}{4} = 0$.

(b) $3\sec^2 \theta = 4$.

(c) $\sin 7y = \sin 3y$.

(d) $\cos 3y + \cos 2y + \cos y = 0$.

(e) $\tan 2x + \cot 2x = 2$.

(f) $2\csc x - 3\sin x = -1$.

(g) $2\sin x = 3\cos x$.

(h) $6\sin^2 x + \cos x - 5 = 0$.

(i) $\sqrt{3}\sin\theta - \cos\theta = 1$.

(j) $\cos 2x = \cos x - \sin x$.

(k) $\csc y - \cot y = -\sqrt{3}$.

(l) $3\sin x + \cos x = 1$.

(m) $\sin 3\theta \cos\theta - \cos 3\theta \sin\theta = 1$.

(n) $\sin 2\phi = 2\cos\phi$.

(o) $\sin\theta \cos\theta = \dfrac{-1}{2}$.

(p) $\sec A + \tan A = 2$.

(q) $\tan 2x = \cot x$.

(r) $\sin x + 2\cos x = 2$.

(s) $\sin 3\theta = \dfrac{1}{2}$.

(t) $\tan x = 2\cos x$.

(u) $3\cos x - 4\sin x = 3$.

(v) $2\sin 2\theta = 3\cos\theta$.

(w) $\sin 3x + \sin 2x + \sin x = 0$.

(x) $\sin 3y - \sin y = 0$.

(y) $2\cos^2\theta - 1 = 2\sqrt{3}\sin\theta \cos\theta$.

(z) $\sin 2x + 2 \sin x = 2 \cos x + 2.$

(aa) $\sin 3\theta + \sin 5\theta = 0.$

(ab) $\cos \theta + \cos 5\theta + \cos 3\theta = 0.$

(ac) $\cos \theta + \sin^2 \dfrac{\theta}{2} + \cos^2 \dfrac{\theta}{2} = 2.$

(ad) $\cos 5\theta - \cos 3\theta = 0.$

(ae) $\sin^4 x - 2 \sin^2 x = -1.$

(af) $\sin 2\theta \cos \theta + \cos 2\theta \sin \theta = \dfrac{1}{\sqrt{2}}.$

(ag) $\cos 5x = \sin 9x - \sin x.$

(ah) $3 \cos^4 \theta + \sin^2 \theta - 3 = 0.$

(ai) $\tan^4 \theta - 1 = 0.$

(aj) $\sin^4 \theta - \cos^4 \theta = 0.$

(ak) $\sin x - \cos x + 1 = 0.$

(al) $3 \tan x - 2 - \cot x = 0.$

(am) $\sin^2 4\theta + \sin 2\theta + \cos^2 4\theta = 2.$

(an) $3 \sin \theta + 4 \cos \theta = 3.$

(ao) $\cos 3\theta \cos \theta + \sin 3\theta \sin \theta = \dfrac{1}{\sqrt{2}}.$

2. Find the general solution of each of the above equations.

3. Prove that:

(a) $\tan^{-1} \dfrac{x}{\sqrt{1 - x^2}} \equiv \sin^{-1} x.$

(b) $\cos^{-1} x \equiv \sin^{-1} \sqrt{1 - x^2}.$

(c) $\sec^{-1} \dfrac{1}{\sqrt{1 - x^2}} \equiv \sin^{-1} x.$

(d) $\csc^{-1} \dfrac{1}{x} \equiv \cos^{-1} \sqrt{1 - x^2}.$

4. Find all the positive angles less than 360° satisfying each of the following inverse functions:

(a) $\sin^{-1} \dfrac{1}{2}.$

(b) $\cos^{-1} 1.$

(c) $\tan^{-1} \left(\dfrac{-1}{\sqrt{3}} \right).$

(d) $\sin^{-1} (-1).$

(e) $\operatorname{arc} \cot \dfrac{1}{\sqrt{3}}.$

(f) $\operatorname{arc} \cos 0.$

(g) $\operatorname{arc} \csc (-1).$

(h) $\operatorname{arc} \sec 2.$

5. What are the principal values of the inverse functions of exercise 4?

6. Evaluate the following:

(a) $\cos\left(\text{Arc cos }\dfrac{1}{2}\right)$.

(i) $\sin\left(\text{Sec}^{-1}\dfrac{5}{2}\right)$.

(b) $\sin\left(\text{Sin}^{-1}\dfrac{1}{\sqrt{2}}\right)$.

(j) $\cos\left(\text{Tan}^{-1} 2\right)$.

(c) $\tan\left(\text{Tan}^{-1}(-1)\right)$.

(k) $\cot\left(\text{Arc sin }\dfrac{2}{3}\right)$.

(d) $\sin\left(\text{Cos}^{-1}\dfrac{\sqrt{3}}{2}\right)$.

(l) $\sin\left(\text{Arc cot }\dfrac{3}{4}\right)$.

(e) $\cos\left[\text{Arc sin}\left(-\dfrac{1}{2}\right)\right]$.

(m) $\tan\left(\text{Cos}^{-1}\dfrac{5}{6}\right)$.

(f) $\tan\left[\text{Sin}^{-1}\left(-\dfrac{1}{\sqrt{2}}\right)\right]$.

(n) $\sin\left[\text{Cos}^{-1}(-0.49344)\right]$.

(g) $\tan\left[\text{Arc sin}\left(-\dfrac{1}{2}\sqrt{3}\right)\right]$.

(o) $\cos\left[\text{Sin}^{-1}(-0.1365)\right]$.

(h) $\sec\left[\text{Sin}^{-1}\left(-\dfrac{1}{2}\sqrt{2}\right)\right]$.

(p) $\tan\left[\text{Cot}^{-1}(-1.1234)\right]$.

7. Find values for each of the following expressions:

(a) $\sin\left(\sin^{-1} x\right)$.

(f) $\sin\left(3 \text{ arc sin } x\right)$.

(b) $\sin\left(2 \text{ arc sin } x\right)$.

(g) $\tan\left(\sin^{-1} x\right)$.

(c) $\cos\left(2 \text{ arc sin } x\right)$.

(h) $\sin\left(\text{arc sin } x + \text{arc cos } x\right)$.

(d) $\tan\left(2 \tan^{-1} 2\right)$.

(i) $\cos\left(\sin^{-1}\dfrac{1}{2} + \sin^{-1}\dfrac{\sqrt{3}}{2}\right)$.

(e) $\sin\left(\sin^{-1} x + \sin^{-1} 2x\right)$.

(j) $\tan\left(\text{arc sin }\dfrac{s}{\sqrt{1+s^2}}\right)$.

8. Considering the angles to be positive acute angles, solve for x and check:

(a) $\sin^{-1} x = \cos^{-1}(1-x)$.

(b) $\text{arc cos } x + \text{arc cos } 2x = \dfrac{\pi}{2}$.

(c) $\text{arc tan } x + \text{arc tan }(x-1) = \dfrac{\pi}{4}$.

(d) $\cos^{-1}\dfrac{\sqrt{3}}{2} + \sin^{-1} 3x = \dfrac{\pi}{2}$.

(e) $\sin^{-1} x + \text{arc sin } 2x = 60°$.

(f) arc sin $(2x^2 - 1) = 2$ arc sin $\dfrac{\sqrt{2}}{2}$.

(g) arc tan $x = \dfrac{\pi}{2} - \sin^{-1} x$.

9. Rewrite each of the following such that x is a function of y:

(a) $y = 2 \sin 3x$.

(b) $y = \pi \cos 2x$.

(c) $y = \frac{1}{3} \tan \dfrac{x}{2}$.

(d) $y = 2 \cot \pi x$.

(e) $y = \frac{1}{3} \sec \pi x$.

(f) $y = 5 \csc \dfrac{x}{3}$.

(g) $y = \dfrac{\sin 2x}{3}$.

(h) $y = \dfrac{1}{\pi} \cos \dfrac{2}{3} x$.

10. Rewrite each of the following such that y is a function of x:

(a) $x = 3 \sin^{-1} y$.

(b) $x = \frac{1}{2}$ arc cos $\dfrac{y}{2}$.

(c) $x = 2$ arc tan $3y$.

(d) $x = \pi \cot^{-1} y$.

(e) $x = \frac{1}{3}$ arc cos πy.

(f) $x = \dfrac{\sec^{-1} y}{4}$.

(g) $x = \frac{1}{2}$ arc sin $\dfrac{y}{3}$.

(h) $x = \frac{2}{3} \tan^{-1} \dfrac{y}{\pi}$.

11. Prove that

(a) $\tan^{-1} x + \tan^{-1} y \equiv \tan^{-1} \dfrac{x + y}{1 - xy}$.

(b) $\sin (2 \text{ arc sin } x) \equiv 2x \sqrt{1 - x^2}$.

(c) $2 \text{ arc tan } \sqrt{\dfrac{x}{a}} \equiv \cos^{-1} \dfrac{a - x}{a + x}$.

(d) $\cos^{-1} x \equiv 2 \sin^{-1} \sqrt{\dfrac{1 - x}{2}}$.

(e) $\tan (2 \tan^{-1} x) \equiv 2 \tan (\tan^{-1} x + \tan^{-1} x^3)$.

Chapter IX

GRAPHS[*]

61. The graph of $y = \sin x$

In § 4 we divided the plane into four parts by means of two mutually perpendicular lines and we determined a point in the plane by means of its distances from the two fixed lines. The fixed lines were called the x-axis and the y-axis, and the point was designated $P(x,y)$. If, in the equation $y = \sin x$, arbitrary values are assigned to x, values of y are determined. Geometrically we may consider these related values of x and y as representing the co-ordinates of points in the plane. If we join the points thus obtained by a smooth curve, we obtain a graph of $y = \sin x$.

To draw the graph of $y = \sin x$:

(1) Construct a table of values of x and y. Take the unit of measure along the x-axis to be one radian.

TABLE I

x	0	$\dfrac{\pi}{6}$	$\dfrac{2\pi}{6}$	$\dfrac{3\pi}{6}$	$\dfrac{4\pi}{6}$	$\dfrac{5\pi}{6}$	$\dfrac{6\pi}{6}$
$y = \sin x$	0	$\dfrac{1}{2}$	$\dfrac{\sqrt{3}}{2}$	1	$\dfrac{\sqrt{3}}{2}$	$\dfrac{1}{2}$	0
x		$\dfrac{7\pi}{6}$	$\dfrac{8\pi}{6}$	$\dfrac{9\pi}{6}$	$\dfrac{10\pi}{6}$	$\dfrac{11\pi}{6}$	$\dfrac{12\pi}{6}$
$y = \sin x$		$-\dfrac{1}{2}$	$-\dfrac{\sqrt{3}}{2}$	-1	$-\dfrac{\sqrt{3}}{2}$	$-\dfrac{1}{2}$	0

[*] May be omitted for a brief course.

(2) Draw the x-axis and the y-axis and plot the points given in Table I. If more points are required between the ones selected, choose x-values between those appearing in Table I and find the corresponding y-values from a table of the natural functions.

(3) Join the points by a smooth curve and so obtain a graph of a section of the curve which has the equation $y = \sin x$.

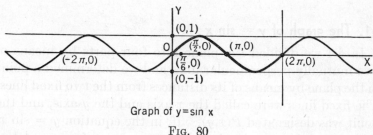

Graph of y = sin x

Fig. 80

By extending Table I to include negative values of x and values of x greater than 2π, we are able to extend the curve indefinitely to the right and to the left. In § 12 we saw that $\sin (2k\pi + x) \equiv \sin x$, if k is any positive or negative integer; hence, in Table I, if we replace each value of x by $x \pm 2\pi$, the corresponding value of $y = \sin (x \pm 2\pi) = \sin x$ is unchanged. Consequently, the graph of the curve repeats itself in intervals of 2π. (See Fig. 80.) Because of this property the function is said to be periodic with the period 2π, where the period is the length of the smallest interval of repetition.* The maximum value of the function is called the amplitude, so the amplitude of $y = \sin x$ is 1.

The heavy section of the curve as drawn in Figure 80 represents a portion of the curve included within an interval of one period. This portion of the curve is sometimes called a *cycle* of the curve.

In § 9 we discussed the variation of the sine of an angle

---

* This is sometimes referred to as the *primitive period* to distinguish it from 4π, 6π, etc., which are also intervals of repetition.

by means of a unit circle. The graph of $y = \sin x$ gives us another method of determining the change in $\sin x$ as x varies from 0 to 2π. Since the ordinate of each point on the curve represents a value of $\sin x$, it is seen that as the angle x increases from 0 to $\pi/2$, $\sin x$ increases from 0 to 1; as x increases from $\pi/2$ to $3\pi/2$, $\sin x$ decreases from 1 to -1; as x increases from $3\pi/2$ to 2π, $\sin x$ increases from -1 to 0. The figure illustrates clearly that $\sin x$ is never greater than 1 or less than -1.

NOTE: Another method of sketching this curve is given in problem 7 at the end of § 64.

62. The graph of y = cos x

Again we construct a table of values of x and y.

TABLE II

x	0	$\dfrac{\pi}{6}$	$\dfrac{2\pi}{6}$	$\dfrac{3\pi}{6}$	$\dfrac{4\pi}{6}$	$\dfrac{5\pi}{6}$	$\dfrac{6\pi}{6}$
$y = \cos x$	1	$\dfrac{\sqrt{3}}{2}$	$\dfrac{1}{2}$	0	$-\dfrac{1}{2}$	$-\dfrac{\sqrt{3}}{2}$	-1

x	$\dfrac{7\pi}{6}$	$\dfrac{8\pi}{6}$	$\dfrac{9\pi}{6}$	$\dfrac{10\pi}{6}$	$\dfrac{11\pi}{6}$	$\dfrac{12\pi}{6}$
$y = \cos x$	$-\dfrac{\sqrt{3}}{2}$	$-\dfrac{1}{2}$	0	$\dfrac{1}{2}$	$\dfrac{\sqrt{3}}{2}$	1

Again taking each related pair of values of x and y to represent a point $P(x,y)$ in the plane, and joining the points by a *smooth* curve, we obtain the graph of a section of the curve $y = \cos x$.   (See Fig. 81.)

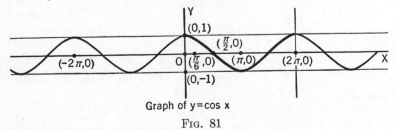

Graph of y=cos x

FIG. 81

By extending our table, we can extend the curve indefinitely to the right and to the left. Since cos $(2k\pi + x)$ $\equiv \cos x$, when k is any positive or negative integer, the graph of the curve repeats itself in intervals of length 2π. Hence the function is periodic with the period 2π. The amplitude of $y = \cos x$ is also 1. Why?

A cycle of the curve, *i.e.*, the portion of the curve included within an interval of length equal to the period, has been indicated in heavy type in Figure 81.

From the graph we are able to trace clearly the change of cos x as x varies from 0 to 2π. As x increases from 0 to π, cos x decreases from 1 to -1. As x increases from π to 2π, cos x increases from -1 to 1. From the figure it is clear that cos x is never greater than 1 nor less than -1.

NOTE: See problem 8 at the end of § 64 for a different method of sketching $y = \cos x$.

63. The graph of $y = \tan x$

Letting x assume the values 0, $\pi/6$, $\pi/3$, $\pi/2$, and multiples of these, we construct Table III. Plotting these points and joining them by a *smooth* curve, we obtain the graph of a section of $y = \tan x$. (See Fig. 82.)

TABLE III

x	0	$\dfrac{\pi}{6}$	$\dfrac{2\pi}{6}$	$\dfrac{3\pi}{6}$	$\dfrac{4\pi}{6}$	$\dfrac{5\pi}{6}$	$\dfrac{6\pi}{6}$
$y = \tan x$	0	$\dfrac{\sqrt{3}}{3}$	$\sqrt{3}$	Does not exist	$-\sqrt{3}$	$-\dfrac{\sqrt{3}}{3}$	0
x	$\dfrac{7\pi}{6}$	$\dfrac{8\pi}{6}$	$\dfrac{9\pi}{6}$	$\dfrac{10\pi}{6}$	$\dfrac{11\pi}{6}$	$\dfrac{12\pi}{6}$	
$y = \tan x$	$\dfrac{\sqrt{3}}{3}$	$\sqrt{3}$	Does not exist	$-\sqrt{3}$	$-\dfrac{\sqrt{3}}{3}$	0	

Since tan $(x + k\pi) \equiv \tan x$ when k is any positive or negative integer, the graph of $y = \tan x$ repeats itself in intervals of length π. Thus the function is periodic with the period π. A cycle of the curve is drawn in heavy type in Figure 82.

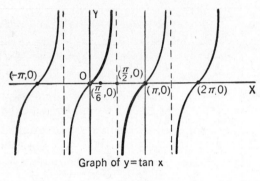

Graph of y = tan x

Fɪɢ. 82

The graph is especially helpful in illustrating that tan 90° does not exist and that, as x varies from 0 to $\pi/2$, tan x increases indefinitely.

If we draw the vertical line through the point $\left(\dfrac{\pi}{2}, 0\right)$, we find that as we plot the curve $y = \tan x$ in the interval from $x = 0$ to $x = \dfrac{\pi}{2}$ the distance from the line to the curve approaches zero as the function increases indefinitely. When a line and a curve are related to each other in this way, the line is called an *asymptote* to the curve. Since tan x is periodic with period π, all the vertical lines through the points $\left(\dfrac{\pi}{2} + k\pi, 0\right)$, where k is any positive or negative integer, are asymptotes. As x varies from $\pi/2$ to π, tan x continues to *increase* from negative values back to zero. (See Fig. 82.) The graph also illustrates clearly how the curve behaves on either side of $x = \pi/2$.

64. The graph of $y = \sec x$

We construct Table IV. Plotting these points and joining them by a *smooth* curve we obtain a section of the graph of $y = \sec x$. (See Fig. 83.)

TABLE IV

x	0	$\dfrac{\pi}{6}$	$\dfrac{2\pi}{6}$	$\dfrac{3\pi}{6}$	$\dfrac{4\pi}{6}$	$\dfrac{5\pi}{6}$	$\dfrac{6\pi}{6}$
$y = \sec x$	1	$\dfrac{2\sqrt{3}}{3}$	2	Does not exist	-2	$-\dfrac{2\sqrt{3}}{3}$	-1

x	$\dfrac{7\pi}{6}$	$\dfrac{8\pi}{6}$	$\dfrac{9\pi}{6}$	$\dfrac{10\pi}{6}$	$\dfrac{11\pi}{6}$	$\dfrac{12\pi}{6}$
$y = \sec x$	$-\dfrac{2\sqrt{3}}{3}$	-2	Does not exist	2	$\dfrac{2\sqrt{3}}{3}$	1

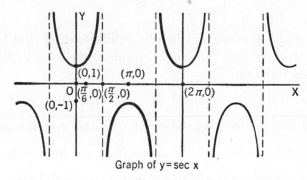

Graph of $y = \sec x$

FIG. 83

Since $\sec (2k\pi + x) \equiv \sec x$ when k is any positive or negative integer, the graph of $y = \sec x$ repeats itself in intervals of length 2π, and therefore the function is periodic with the period 2π. A cycle of the curve is indicated in heavy type in Figure 83.

Here again the graph is extremely useful in illustrating where the function does not exist. At $x = 0$ we find that $\sec 0 = 1$, and as x increases toward $\pi/2$, $\sec x$ increases indefinitely. At $x = \pi/2$, sec x does not exist. The vertical line through the point $(\pi/2, 0)$ is an asymptote of the curve, as are all the vertical lines through the points $\left(\dfrac{\pi}{2} + k\pi, 0\right)$, when k is a positive or negative integer. The graph illustrates clearly how the function behaves on either side of its asymptotes and also shows us that sec x never takes on values between 1 and -1.

EXERCISES

1. Draw the graphs of the following in the interval -2π to 0:
(a) $y = \sin x$.   (b) $y = \cos x$.   (c) $y = \tan x$.
Hint: Make a table of values for x and y in this interval.

2. Draw the graphs of the following in the interval 2π to 4π:
(a) $y = \tan x$.   (b) $y = \cos x$.   (c) $y = \sin x$.

3. Draw the graph of $y = \cot x$ in the interval 0 to 2π.

4. Draw the graph of $y = \csc x$ in the interval 0 to 2π.

5. What are the periods of $y = \cot x$ and $y = \csc x$? Give reasons.

6. Discuss the changes in cot x and csc x from their graphs as x varies from 0 to 2π.

7. Draw the unit circle with center at $(-1, 0)$. With this point as the vertex and the x-axis as the initial side, construct the angles $\theta = 0$, $\pi/6$, $2\pi/6$, $3\pi/6$, $\cdots$, $12\pi/6$. Locate the points where the terminal sides of these angles intersect the circumference of the circle. From each of these points draw a horizontal segment to the y-axis and *extend* it to the right of the y-axis a distance equal in length to the arc at that point. Join the ends of these segments by a smooth curve. This is the graph of a section of $y = \sin x$. Why? *Hint:* The formula for length of arc is $s = r\theta$, where r is the radius of the circle and θ is the angle in radians (see § 3). In this exercise $r = 1$, hence $s = \theta$.

8. Make a graph of $y = \cos x$ by a similar method.

65. The graph of $y = a \sin bx$

Since the sine of an angle is never greater than 1, the greatest value that $a \sin bx$ can have is $|a|$. Since the period of $\sin \theta$ is 2π, we know that $\sin (bx + 2\pi) = \sin bx$.

If x is replaced by $x + \dfrac{2\pi}{b}$, sin bx becomes $\sin b\left(x + \dfrac{2\pi}{b}\right)$
$= \sin (bx + 2\pi) = \sin bx$. Hence sin bx is periodic with
period $\dfrac{2\pi}{|b|}$. So $y = a$ sin bx has the period $\dfrac{2\pi}{|b|}$ and the
amplitude $|a|$. One method of graphing this function is by
plotting-points. A simpler way is to start at the origin and
mark off on the x-axis intervals equal to $\dfrac{2\pi}{|b|}$ in length. Then
measure the amplitude $|a|$ upon the y-axis, and draw the
lines $y = |a|$ and $y = -|a|$. As a convenience, divide
each interval into four equal parts; then in each interval
draw a cycle of a curve similar in shape to the sine curve. A
curve that is drawn in this way, without plotting a lot of
points, will be said to have been *sketched*.

Example 1:

Sketch $y = 3$ sin $2x$. The amplitude is 3, and the period is
$\dfrac{2\pi}{2} = \pi$. Draw the lines $y = +3$, $y = -3$. Starting from the
origin, mark off intervals equal in length to π. Divide each
interval into four parts, and draw the curve as shown in Figure 84.

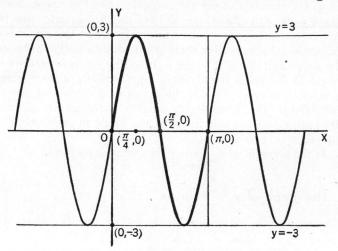

FIG. 84

Example 2:

Sketch $y = 2 \sin \dfrac{2x}{3}$. The amplitude is 2, and the period is

$\dfrac{2\pi}{(2/3)} = 3\pi$. Proceeding as in the previous example, draw the

curve. (See Fig. 85.)

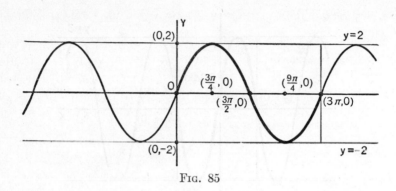

Fɪɢ. 85

66. The graph of y = a sin (bx + θ)

Here a, b, and θ are constants. The amplitude is $|a|$ and

the period is $\dfrac{2\pi}{|b|}$. The angle θ is known as the *phase angle*.

When θ is positive it is called a lead angle and when it is

negative it is called a lag angle. When $bx + \theta = 0$,

$x = -\dfrac{\theta}{b}$ and $y = 0$. To draw this curve, plot the point

$\left(-\dfrac{\theta}{b},0\right)$. Then, *starting at this point*, mark off on the x-axis

intervals equal in length to $\dfrac{2\pi}{|b|}$. Mark off on the y-axis the

amplitude $|a|$ and draw the lines $y = |a|$ and $y = -|a|$.

Divide each *interval* into four equal parts and in each interval

draw a cycle of a curve similar in shape to the sine curve.

Example:

Sketch $y = 3 \sin (2x + 3)$. The amplitude is 3, the period is π, and the lead angle is 3 radians.

When $x = -\frac{3}{2}$, $y = 0$. Locate this point and from it mark off on the x-axis intervals equal in length to the period π. Draw the lines $y = 3$ and $y = -3$. Divide each interval of length π into four equal parts and draw the curve. (See Fig. 86.)

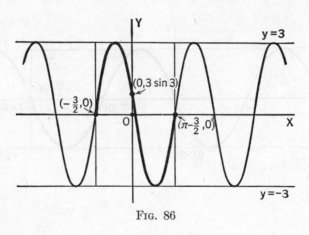

FIG. 86

67. The graph of $y = a \cos (bx + \theta)$

Again a, b, and θ are constants. The amplitude is $|a|$, the period is $\dfrac{2\pi}{|b|}$, and the phase angle is θ. To sketch the curve we proceed as follows: Starting from the point $\left(-\dfrac{\theta}{b}, 0\right)$, mark off on the x-axis intervals equal in length to $\dfrac{2\pi}{|b|}$. Draw the lines $y = |a|$ and $y = -|a|$ and in the intervals draw cycles of a curve similar in shape to the cosine curve. The following examples illustrate the process.

Example 1:

Sketch $y = 2 \cos 3x$. The period is $2\pi/3$, and the amplitude is 2. Draw the lines $y = 2$ and $y = -2$. Starting from $(0,0)$ mark off on the x-axis intervals $2\pi/3$ in length, divide each interval into four equal parts, and draw the curve. (See Fig. 87.)

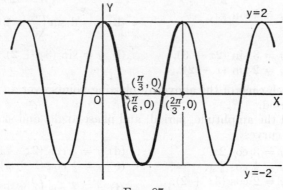

FIG. 87

Example 2:

Sketch $y = 3 \cos (2x - 3)$. The amplitude is 3, the period π, and the phase angle -3. Locate the point $(\frac{3}{2},0)$. From this point mark off on the x-axis intervals of length π. Draw the lines $y = 3$ and $y = -3$ and, after dividing each interval into four equal parts, draw the curve. (See Fig. 88.)

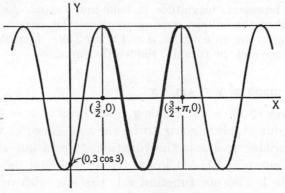

FIG. 88

EXERCISES

1. Find the amplitude, period, and phase angle, and sketch the following:

(a) $y = 2 \sin 3x$.

(f) $y = \frac{1}{2} \sin x$.

(b) $y = 3 \sin \frac{x}{2}$.

(g) $y = \sin \left(\frac{2x}{3} - \frac{1}{2} \right)$.

(c) $y = \frac{1}{2} \sin \pi x$.

(h) $y = 3 \sin \left(\frac{x}{3} - 2 \right)$.

(d) $y = 3 \sin (2x + 3)$.

(i) $y = \sin (3x + 2)$.

(e) $y = 2 \sin (x - 2)$.

2. Sketch each of the above by plotting points over an interval of one period.

3. Find the amplitude, period, and phase angle, and sketch the following curves:

(a) $y = 3 \cos 2x$.

(d) $y = 3 \cos (2x - 1)$.

(b) $y = \frac{1}{2} \cos \frac{2}{3} x$.

(e) $y = \frac{1}{2} \cos (x + \pi)$.

(c) $y = 2 \cos (3x + 2)$.

(f) $y = \frac{2}{3} \cos \left(\frac{1}{2} x + \frac{\pi}{2} \right)$.

4. Find the period of $y = \tan 2x$, and sketch the curve. *Hint*: The period of $\tan \theta$ is π. Show that the period of $\tan kx$ is π/k. Then draw the tangent curve in the interval from 0 to π/k. Plot some points.

5. Sketch the following curves and give the period of each:

(a) $y = 2 \tan \frac{x}{2}$.   (b) $y = \frac{1}{3} \tan 3x$ (c) $y = 4 \tan \pi x$.

6. If y represents magnitude in volts and t stands for time in seconds, then the voltage causing an alternating current of electricity is given by an equation $y = 120 \sin 250t$. Find the maximum voltage and the period. Sketch the curve.

68. The graph of $y = \sin^{-1} x$

If we rewrite $y = \sin^{-1} x$ or $y = \text{arc} \sin x$ as $x = \sin y$ we see that our graph is going to be the sine curve in which y is the variable and x is the function. From our study of the sine curve (§ 61) we know it has a period 2π and an amplitude 1. So our function x is periodic with period 2π and has an amplitude 1. To sketch $y = \sin^{-1} x$ we draw the lines $x = -1$ and $x = 1$. We know the curve lies entirely within these lines. Why? Then, starting from the origin, mark off intervals of 2π along the y-axis and in each interval draw a cycle of the sine curve. (See Fig. 89.)

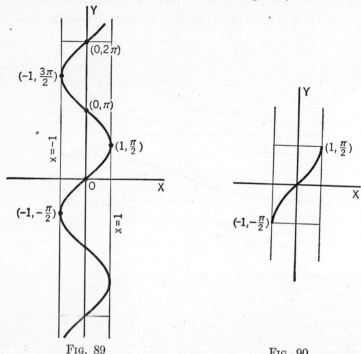

Fig. 89   Fig. 90

The principal values of the function lie in the interval from $y = -\dfrac{\pi}{2}$ to $y = \dfrac{\pi}{2}$. It should be noted that in this interval to each value of x there corresponds *one* and *only one* value of y. (See Figure 90.) This is the graph of $y = \operatorname{Sin}^{-1} x$.

Another method of sketching this curve is to notice that $x = \sin y$ is obtained from $y = \sin x$ by interchanging x and y. But a point $P_1(y,x)$ is a reflection, or image, of a point $P(x,y)$ with respect to the line $y = x$. Hence if the curve $y = \sin x$ is reflected about the line $y = x$, we obtain the curve $x = \sin y$ or $y = \sin^{-1} x$.

69. The graph of $y = \tan^{-1} x$

Rewriting $y = \tan^{-1} x$ as $x = \tan y$, we see that the function x has a period of π and no amplitude. So, starting from the origin, we mark off intervals π units in length along the y-axis and in each interval put cycles of the tangent curve.

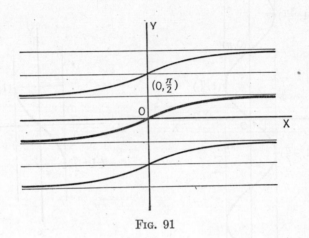

FIG. 91

The graph of the principal part of the curve, *i.e.*, the graph of $y = $ Arc tan x, is heavily marked in the interval $-\dfrac{\pi}{2} < y < \dfrac{\pi}{2}$. (See Fig. 91.)

The curve $y = \tan^{-1} x$ is also a reflection of $y = \tan x$ about the line $y = x$.

70. The graph of $y = \sec^{-1} x$

Rewriting the equation as $x = \sec y$, we draw the secant curve about the y-axis. The period of the function x is 2π. The curve does not exist within the interval $-1 < x < 1$. Why?

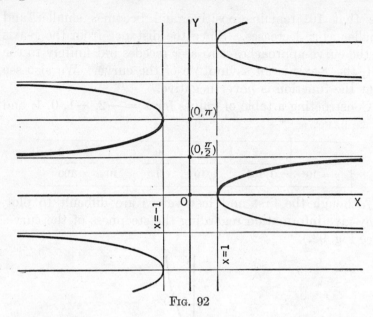

FIG. 92

Again the principal part of the curve, or the graph of $y = \text{Sec}^{-1} x$, has been heavily marked. (See Fig. 92.)

This graph, too, can be obtained by a reflection of $y = \sec x$ about the line $y = x$.

EXERCISES

1. Sketch the graphs of the following:

(a) $y = \arccos x$.   (b) $y = \tan^{-1} x$.   (c) $y = \cot^{-1} x$.
(d) $y = \text{arc sec } x$.   (e) $y = \csc^{-1} x$.

2. In the graphs of the above problem trace with colored pencil the interval of the principal values.

71. The graph of $y = 10^x$

By determining the outstanding characteristics of the curve and then plotting a few points we are able to make a good sketch of the function $y = 10^x$. When x increases through positive values, 10^x is positive and increases much more rapidly than x. As x is assigned negative values we see that 10^x remains positive and becomes smaller and smaller as x decreases. Since the distance from the x-axis to the curve approaches zero as x recedes indefinitely to the left, the x-axis is an asymptote of the curve. We also see that the function is never negative.

Constructing a table of values for $x = -2, -1, 0, 1$, and 2, we have:

x	-2	-1	0	1	2
$y = 10^x$	1/100	1/10	1	10	100

Although the first and last values are difficult to plot, they give information regarding the steepness of the curve. (See Fig. 93.)

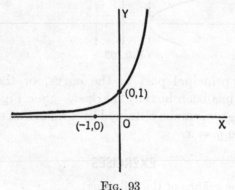

Fɪɢ. 93

EXERCISES

Sketch the following:

1. $y = 2^x$.   **2.** $y = -3^x$.   **3.** $y = \frac{1}{2}x$.   **4.** $y = 2(3^x)$.

5. $y = 2^{-x}$.   **6.** $y = \dfrac{1}{3^x}$.   **7.** $y = 10^{-x}$.

72. The graph of $y = \log_{10} x$

In order to sketch this function we first write it so that x is a function of y. So we have

$$x = 10^y.$$

Proceeding as before, we find that as y increases, x is positive and increases much more rapidly than y. As y takes on negative values, $x = 10^y$ remains positive and becomes smaller and smaller as y decreases. Since the distance from the y-axis to the curve approaches zero as y decreases indefinitely, it follows that the y-axis is an asymptote. A table of values showing the relation between x and y and a sketch of the curve are shown below.

y	-2	-1	0	1	2
$x = 10^y$	$\frac{1}{100}$	$\frac{1}{10}$	1	10	100

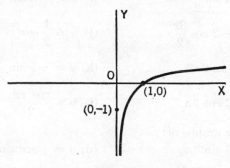

Fig. 94

.Turning back to the chapter on logarithms, we see that the above graph illustrates clearly the following facts:

(1) $\log_{10} 1 = 0$.

(2) As the number increases, the logarithm of the number increases but not as rapidly as the number.

(3) A real logarithm of a negative number does not exist.*

(4) The logarithm of a positive number less than 1 is negative.

EXERCISES: CHAPTER IX

1. Prove that the graph of $y = \log_{10} x$ is a reflection of $y = 10^x$ about the line $y = x$.

* See note at the bottom of page 65.

2. Sketch the following curves:

(a) $y = \log_3 x$.

(b) $y = \log_5 x$.

(c) $y = \log_{10} (x + 2)$.

(d) $y = \log_{10} (x - 2)$.

(e) $y = \log_{10} x^2$.

(f) $y = \log_{10} (x^2 - 4)$.

(g) $y = \log_2 x$.

(h) $y = \log_3 (x - 2)$.

(i) $y = \log_{10} \left(\dfrac{x}{2} \right)$.

3. Find the period and amplitude and sketch each of the following curves:

(a) $y = \sin 2x$.

(b) $y = 2 \cos 3x$.

(c) $y = 3 \sin \dfrac{x}{2}$.

(d) $y = -2 \cos \dfrac{3x}{2}$.

(e) $y = \tan 2x$.

(f) $y = 2 \cot 3x$.

(g) $y = \sec \dfrac{x}{2}$.

(h) $y = \csc 3x$.

(i) $y = -3 \sin \dfrac{2x}{3}$.

(j) $y = \dfrac{1}{2} \cos \dfrac{x}{3}$.

(k) $y = -\pi \sin \dfrac{x}{3}$.

(l) $y = \dfrac{\cos \pi x}{2}$.

4. Draw the graphs of:

(a) $y = 3 \sin^{-1} x$.

(b) $y = 2 \cos^{-1} \dfrac{x}{2}$.

(c) $y = 3 \tan^{-1} 2x$.

(d) $y = \frac{1}{3}$ arc sin $2x$.

(e) $y = \frac{1}{2}$ arc cos $3x$.

(f) $y = 2 \sec^{-1} 3x$.

5. Write each part of problems 3 and 4 so that x is a function of y.

6. Sketch the following:

(a) $y = $ Arc sin x.

(b) $y = $ Arc tan x.

(c) $y = \text{Cos}^{-1} x$.

(d) $y = \text{Sec}^{-1} x$.

(e) $y = \text{Cot}^{-1} x$.

(f) $y = $ Arc csc x.

(g) $y = \log_3 \dfrac{x}{2}$.

(h) $y = 2^x$.

(i) $y = \left(\frac{1}{3} \right) x$.

(j) $y = 4^{-x}$.

(k) $y = \log_{10} (x^2 - 1)$.

(l) $y = \log_{10} x^3$.

(m) $y = 2(3^x)$.

(n) $y = \log_{10} (1 + x^2)$.

(o) $y = -2^x$.

APPENDIX

APPENDIX

IMPORTANT FORMULAS

1. π radians = 180 degrees = 3200 mils.

2. $s = r\theta$.

3. $\csc \theta \equiv \dfrac{1}{\sin \theta}$, $\sec \theta \equiv \dfrac{1}{\cos \theta}$, $\cot \theta \equiv \dfrac{1}{\tan \theta}$.

4. $\sin^2 \theta + \cos^2 \theta \equiv 1$, $1 + \tan^2 \theta \equiv \sec^2 \theta$, $1 + \cot^2 \theta \equiv \csc^2 \theta$.

5. $\tan \theta \equiv \dfrac{\sin \theta}{\cos \theta}$, $\cot \theta \equiv \dfrac{\cos \theta}{\sin \theta}$.

6. $\sin (\alpha + \beta) \equiv \sin \alpha \cos \beta + \cos \alpha \sin \beta$.

7. $\sin (\alpha - \beta) \equiv \sin \alpha \cos \beta - \cos \alpha \sin \beta$.

8. $\cos (\alpha + \beta) \equiv \cos \alpha \cos \beta - \sin \alpha \sin \beta$.

9. $\cos (\alpha - \beta) \equiv \cos \alpha \cos \beta + \sin \alpha \sin \beta$.

10. $\tan (\alpha + \beta) \equiv \dfrac{\tan \alpha + \tan \beta}{1 - \tan \alpha \tan \beta}$.

11. $\tan (\alpha - \beta) \equiv \dfrac{\tan \alpha - \tan \beta}{1 + \tan \alpha \tan \beta}$.

12. $\sin \left(\dfrac{\pi}{2} - \theta\right) \equiv \cos \theta$, $\sin \left(\dfrac{\pi}{2} + \theta\right) \equiv \cos \theta$.

13. $\cos \left(\dfrac{\pi}{2} - \theta\right) \equiv \sin \theta$, $\cos \left(\dfrac{\pi}{2} + \theta\right) \equiv -\sin \theta$.

14. $\tan \left(\dfrac{\pi}{2} - \theta\right) \equiv \cot \theta$, $\tan \left(\dfrac{\pi}{2} + \theta\right) \equiv -\cot \theta$.

15. $\sin (\pi - \theta) \equiv \sin \theta$, $\sin (\pi + \theta) \equiv -\sin \theta$.

16. $\cos (\pi - \theta) \equiv -\cos \theta$, $\cos (\pi + \theta) \equiv -\cos \theta$.

17. $\tan (\pi - \theta) \equiv -\tan \theta$, $\tan (\pi + \theta) \equiv \tan \theta$.

18. $\sin (2\pi - \theta) \equiv -\sin \theta$, $\sin (-\theta) \equiv -\sin \theta$.

19. $\cos (2\pi - \theta) \equiv \cos \theta$, $\cos (-\theta) \equiv \cos \theta$.

20. $\tan (2\pi - \theta) \equiv -\tan \theta$, $\tan (-\theta) \equiv -\tan \theta$.

21. $\sin 2\theta \equiv 2 \sin \theta \cos \theta$, $\cos 2\theta \equiv \cos^2 \theta - \sin^2 \theta$.

22. $2 \sin^2 \dfrac{\theta}{2} \equiv 1 - \cos \theta, \ 2 \cos^2 \dfrac{\theta}{2} \equiv 1 + \cos \theta.$

23. $2 \sin \alpha \cos \beta \equiv \sin (\alpha + \beta) + \sin (\alpha - \beta).$

24. $2 \cos \alpha \sin \beta \equiv \sin (\alpha + \beta) - \sin (\alpha - \beta).$

25. $2 \cos \alpha \cos \beta \equiv \cos (\alpha + \beta) + \cos (\alpha - \beta).$

26. $-2 \sin \alpha \sin \beta \equiv \cos (\alpha + \beta) - \cos (\alpha - \beta).$

27. $\sin x + \sin y \equiv 2 \sin \dfrac{x + y}{2} \cos \dfrac{x - y}{2}.$

28. $\sin x - \sin y \equiv 2 \cos \dfrac{x + y}{2} \sin \dfrac{x - y}{2}.$

29. $\cos x + \cos y \equiv 2 \cos \dfrac{x + y}{2} \cos \dfrac{x - y}{2}.$

30. $\cos x - \cos y \equiv -2 \sin \dfrac{x + y}{2} \sin \dfrac{x - y}{2}.$

31. $\log_a (MN) = \log_a M + \log_a N.$

32. $\log_a \dfrac{M}{N} = \log_a M - \log_a N.$

33. $\log_a M^k = k \log_a M.$

34. $\log_b M = \dfrac{\log_a M}{\log_a b}.$

35. $\dfrac{\sin A}{a} = \dfrac{\sin B}{b} = \dfrac{\sin C}{c}$, law of sines.

36. $a^2 = b^2 + c^2 - 2bc \cos A$, law of cosines.

37. $\tan \left(\dfrac{A - B}{2} \right) = \dfrac{a - b}{a + b} \tan \left(\dfrac{A + B}{2} \right)$, law of tangents.

38. $r = \sqrt{\dfrac{(s - a)(s - b)(s - c)}{s}}$, r is the radius of the inscribed circle and

$s = \dfrac{a + b + c}{2}.$

39. $\tan \dfrac{A}{2} = \dfrac{r}{s - a}$, law of the half-angle.

40. Area of a triangle:

$S = \dfrac{1}{2} bc \sin A; \ S = \sqrt{s(s - a)(s - b)(s - c)};$

$S = \dfrac{a^2 \sin B \sin C}{2 \sin (B + C)}.$

41. $y = \operatorname{arc sin} x$ or $y = \sin^{-1} x$ is the same as $x = \sin y.$

THE MIL

The mil is a unit of measure for the angle which is used extensively by the United States Army. If the circumference of a circle is divided into 6400 equal parts, the central angle which is subtended by one of these parts is called an angle of 1 mil. It is approximately the angle subtended by an arc of 1 yard at a distance of 1000 yards and, for this reason, is found very convenient for rapid calculations. In the aiming of all types of artillery the mil is used almost exclusively.

In many applications it will be necessary to know the relation that exists between degrees, radians, and mils. The student should verify the following results.

$$360° \quad = 2\pi \text{ radians} \quad = 6400 \text{ mils.}$$
$$90° \quad = \frac{\pi}{2} \text{ radians} \quad = 1600 \text{ mils.}$$
$$1° \quad = 0.0175 \text{ radians} = 17.778 \text{ mils.}$$
$$1 \text{ radian} = 57° \, 17' \, 45'' \quad = 1018.6 \text{ mils.}$$
$$1 \text{ mil} \quad = 0.0563° \quad = 0.000982 \text{ radians.}$$
$$1 \text{ mil} \quad = 3.375'.$$

An approximation formula for length of arc is given by

$$S = \frac{r\theta}{1000} \text{ where } \theta \text{ is in mils.}$$

EXERCISES

1. Change the following angles into mils: 30°, 24°, 100°, 30° 10′ 20″, 26° 15′ 30″, 2 radians, 0.1 radians, 0.4 radians, and 0.001 radians.

2. Change the following angles into degrees, minutes, and seconds: 100 mils, 35.3 mils, 4 radians, 23 radians, 325 mils, and 0.5 radians.

3. Change the following angles into radians: 20 mils, 1015 mils, 36°, 3524 mils, and 25°.

4. An angle of 5 mils is subtended by what arc, if the radius is 3000 yards?

5. How many mils are there in the central angle that is subtended by an arc of 30 feet if the radius of the circle is 40 feet?

6. What length of arc at 1000 yards will 1 mil intercept; 2.4 mils; 6 mils?

7. Solve the following triangles.

(a) $A = 534$ mils, $C = 1600$ mils, $b = 10$ yds.
(b) $a = 20$ ft., $b = 10$ ft., $C = 1600$ mils.
(c) $a = 100$ ft., $A = 243$ mils, $B = 450$ mils.
(d) $B = 628$ mils, $C = 1600$ mils, $c = 100$ ft.

8. An observer notes that a wall 6 feet high subtends an angle of 100 mils. How far is the observer from the base of the wall?

9. A gun is so built that it can be traversed through an angle of 2300 mils. If the range of the gun is 18,000 yards, what length of arc can the gun keep under fire?

ANSWERS

§ 3; page 8

1. $\pi/6, 3\pi/4, -\pi/12, -5\pi/6$.
3. $720°/\pi, 41.40°/\pi, 90°/\pi, -30°$.
5. $960°/\pi$.

7. 40π ft.
9. 7.85 ft./sec.

§ 5; page 13

3. No. No.
5. (a) $\sqrt{61}$.
5. (c) $\sqrt{89}$.
5. (e) 6.
7. (7, 0).

12. A straight line parallel to the x-axis and three units below it.
14. A circle of radius 5 with center at the origin.

EXERCISES: CHAPTER I; PAGE 14

1. $7\pi/36, 53\pi/36, 2\pi/3, -7\pi/4, 5\pi/4, 17\pi/4, 7\pi/72, -29\pi/12$.
3. $60°, -120°, -270°/\pi, 360°/\pi, 180°, -720°/\pi, 90°/\pi, 135°$.
5. $16° \ 11' \ 15''$.
7. $14° \ 50' \ 10''$.
13. $6\frac{2}{3}$ ft.
15. 5 ft.
17. 8π ft.
19. 12.35 P.M.
21. 829.16 mi.
23. 2072.93 mi.
25. 120 radians, $60/\pi$ revolutions.

27. 1145.9° in 1 sec.; 11,459° in 10 sec.
29. $\theta = \frac{1}{8}$ radian.
31. $44\pi/3$ in., $104\pi/3$ in.
33. $-90°, -1080°, -64800°$.
35. $5'$.
37. 1800° per sec.
39. $40\pi/3$ in.; $-20°$.
41. $(x, -y); (-x, y); (-x, -y)$.
43. 10.

45. (6, 3) and (6, −1); or (−2, 3) and (−2, −1).
47. A straight line parallel to the y-axis and three units to the left of it.
49. A straight line through the origin and making an angle of 45° with the positive x-axis.

§ 7; page 19

1. $A = l^2$, where A is the area and l is the length of a side.

3. $A = \frac{1}{2}bh$, where b is the base and h is the altitude.

5. $d = \sqrt{2}\,s$.   **7.** $p = \dfrac{k}{v}$; $v = \dfrac{k}{p}$.   **9.** $r = \sqrt{A/\pi}$.

§ 8; page 23

3. (a) $\dfrac{4}{5}, \dfrac{3}{5}, \dfrac{4}{3}$.

(c) $\dfrac{3}{5}, -\dfrac{4}{5}, -\dfrac{3}{4}$.

(e) $\dfrac{-12}{13}, \dfrac{5}{13}, \dfrac{-12}{5}$.

3. (g) $\dfrac{5}{\sqrt{41}}, \dfrac{-4}{\sqrt{41}}, -\dfrac{5}{4}$.

5. $\dfrac{1}{\sqrt{2}}, \dfrac{-1}{\sqrt{2}}, -1$.

7. $\dfrac{-1}{\sqrt{2}}, \dfrac{1}{\sqrt{2}}, -1$.

§ 9; page 27

5. sine, cosine, secant, cosecant are restricted.

$-1 \leqq \sin \theta \leqq 1$; $-1 \leqq \cos \theta \leqq 1$; $\left.\begin{array}{c}\sec \theta \\ \csc \theta\end{array}\right\}$ never take values between -1 and 1.

7. $0, 0, 0, -1, 1, 1, 0, 0, 0$.

§ 10; page 30

3. $\sin \theta = -\dfrac{\sqrt{5}}{3}$, $\tan \theta = -\dfrac{\sqrt{5}}{2}$, $\cot \theta = -\dfrac{2}{\sqrt{5}}$, $\sec \theta = \dfrac{3}{2}$,

$\csc \theta = -\dfrac{3}{\sqrt{5}}$.

5. $\sin \theta = \dfrac{\sqrt{3}}{2}$, $\cos \theta = \dfrac{1}{2}$, $\tan \theta = \sqrt{3}$, $\cot \theta = \dfrac{1}{\sqrt{3}}$, $\csc \theta = \dfrac{2}{\sqrt{3}}$.

7. $\sin \theta = -\dfrac{7}{\sqrt{58}}$, $\cos \theta = -\dfrac{3}{\sqrt{58}}$, $\tan \theta = \dfrac{7}{3}$, $\sec \theta = -\dfrac{\sqrt{58}}{3}$,

$\csc \theta = -\dfrac{\sqrt{58}}{7}$.

9. $\sin \theta = -\dfrac{5}{13}$, $\tan \theta = \dfrac{5}{12}$, $\cot \theta = \dfrac{12}{5}$, $\sec \theta = -\dfrac{13}{12}$,

$\csc \theta = -\dfrac{13}{5}$.

11. $\sin \theta = \dfrac{3}{5}$, $\cos \theta = -\dfrac{4}{5}$, $\tan \theta = -\dfrac{3}{4}$, $\cot \theta = -\dfrac{4}{3}$, $\sec \theta = -\dfrac{5}{4}$.

13. $\sin \theta = \dfrac{12}{13}$, $\cos \theta = -\dfrac{5}{13}$, $\tan \theta = -\dfrac{12}{5}$, $\cot \theta = -\dfrac{5}{12}$,

$\csc \theta = \dfrac{13}{12}$.

15. $\sin \theta = \dfrac{\sqrt{24}}{5}$, $\tan \theta = \sqrt{24}$, $\cot \theta = \dfrac{1}{\sqrt{24}}$, $\sec \theta = 5$,

$\csc \theta = \dfrac{5}{\sqrt{24}}$.

§ 11; page 33

1. $\sin \theta = \frac{3}{5}$, $\cos \theta = \frac{4}{5}$, $\tan \theta = \frac{3}{4}$, $\cot \theta = \frac{4}{3}$, $\sec \theta = \frac{5}{4}$, $\csc \theta = \frac{5}{3}$.

3. $\sin \theta = \sqrt{2/7}$, $\cos \theta = \sqrt{5/7}$, $\tan \theta = \sqrt{2/5}$, $\cot \theta = \sqrt{5/2}$,

$\sec \theta = \sqrt{7/5}$, $\csc \theta = \sqrt{7/2}$.

5. $\sin \theta = \dfrac{3}{7}$, $\cos \theta = \dfrac{\sqrt{40}}{7}$, $\tan \theta = \dfrac{3}{\sqrt{40}}$, $\cot \theta = \dfrac{\sqrt{40}}{3}$,

$\sec \theta = \dfrac{7}{\sqrt{40}}$, $\csc \theta = \dfrac{7}{3}$.

§ 12; page 41

1. (a) $\sin 40°$.   (i) $-\tan 42° 34' 20''$.

    (c) $-\tan 50°$.   (k) $\cos 60° 20'$.

    (e) $\sin 15°$.   (m) $-\tan 34° 29' 30''$.

    (g) $-\sec 57° 44'$.   (o) $-\csc 20° 10' 30''$.

§ 14; page 44

1. $\theta = 30°$.   **5.** $28\frac{1}{3}°$.

3. $\theta = 33\frac{1}{3}°$.   **7.** $\theta = 46°$.

EXERCISES: CHAPTER II; PAGE 44

3. In general, two positive angles less than 360° may be constructed for any given trigonometric function.

5. $\sin \theta = -\dfrac{1}{\sqrt{10}}$, $\cos \theta = \dfrac{3}{\sqrt{10}}$, $\tan \theta = -\dfrac{1}{3}$, $\sec \theta = \dfrac{\sqrt{10}}{3}$,

$\csc \theta = -\sqrt{10}$.

7. $\sin \theta = \dfrac{1}{7}$, $\cos \theta = -\dfrac{\sqrt{48}}{7}$, $\tan \theta = \dfrac{-1}{\sqrt{48}}$, $\cot \theta = -\sqrt{48}$,

$\sec \theta = -\dfrac{7}{\sqrt{48}}$.

11. No. $\sin \theta \not> 1$. $\sin \theta$, $\cos \theta$, $\sec \theta$, $\csc \theta$ are restricted in value. $\tan \theta$ and $\cot \theta$ are not restricted in value.

14. (b) $\sin (90° - \theta) = \cos \theta$, $\cot (90° - \theta) = \tan \theta$,
    $\cos (90° - \theta) = \sin \theta$, $\sec (90° - \theta) = \csc \theta$,
    $\tan (90° - \theta) = \cot \theta$, $\csc (90° - \theta) = \sec \theta$.

14. (d) $\sin (270° - \theta) = -\cos \theta$, $\cot (270° - \theta) = \tan \theta$,
    $\cos (270° - \theta) = -\sin \theta$, $\sec (270° - \theta) = -\csc \theta$,
    $\tan (270° - \theta) = \cot \theta$, $\csc (270° - \theta) = -\sec \theta$.

16. (a) $\sin 60°$,   (f) $\sin 60°$,   (k) $\sin 0°$,
        $-\cos 60°$, $-\cos 60°$, $\cos 0°$,
        $-\tan 60°$. $-\tan 60°$. $\tan 0°$.

    (b) $-\sin 45°$, (g) $\sin 60°$,   (l) $\sin 0°$,
        $\cos 45°$, $-\cos 60°$, $-\cos 0°$,
        $-\tan 45°$. $-\tan 60°$. $-\tan 0°$.

    (c) $-\sin 60°$, (h) $-\sin 45°$, (m) $\sin 84°$,
        $\cos 60°$, $\cos 45°$, $\cos 84°$,
        $-\tan 60°$. $-\tan 45°$. $\tan 84°$.

    (d) $\sin 30°$, (i) $-\sin 45°$, (n) $\sin 15°$,
        $-\cos 30°$, $\cos 45°$, $\cos 15°$,
        $-\tan 30°$. $-\tan 45°$. $\tan 15°$.

    (e) $\sin 30°$, (j) $-\sin 45°$, (o) $\sin 56° 41' 31''$,
        $-\cos 30°$, $\cos 45°$, $-\cos 56° 41' 31''$,
        $-\tan 30°$. $-\tan 45°$. $-\tan 56° 41' 31''$.

18. (a) $\cos 30°$, (d) $\cos 60°$, (g) $-\cos 45°$,
        $\sin 30°$, $-\sin 60°$, $\sin 45°$,
        $\cot 30°$. $-\cot 60°$. $-\cot 45°$.

    (b) $\cos 62°$, (e) $-\cos 60°$, (h) $-\cos 5°$,
        $\sin 62°$, $-\sin 60°$, $-\sin 5°$,
        $\cot 62°$. $\cot 60°$. $\cot 5°$.

    (c) $\cos 22°$, (f) $-\cos 40°$, (i) $-\cos 70°$,
        $-\sin 22°$, $-\sin 40°$, $\sin 70°$,
        $-\cot 22°$. $\cot 40°$. $-\cot 70°$.

(j) —cos 40°,   (m)   cos 30°,   (p)   cos 75°,
    —sin 40°,   sin 30°,   sin 75°,
    cot 40°.   cot 30°.   cot 75°.

(k) —cos 60°,   (n)   cos 50°,   (q)   cos 45°,
    sin 60°,   —sin 50°,   —sin 45°,
    —cot 60°.   —cot 50°.   —cot 45°.

(l)   cos 45°,   (o) —cos 30°,   (r) —cos 60°,
    —sin 45°,   —sin 30°,   —sin 60°,
    —cot 45°.   cot 30°.   cot 60°.

20. (a) 32°.   (g) 65°.   (k) 45°.
    (c) 19°.   (i) 25°.   (m) 5°.
    (e) 22 ° 30′.

§ 16; page 52

1. 5.13×10^3; 3.13×10^{-2}; 1.31×10^4; 6.05×10^{-1}.
2. (b) 9.01.   (d) 1.19.   (f) 1.0×10^3.

§ 17; page 54

In each of the following the answers are given for the sine, cosine, and tangent in that order.

1. (a) 0, −1, 0.
   (c) 0, 1, 0.

2. (a) $\dfrac{\sqrt{3}}{2}, -\dfrac{1}{2}, -\sqrt{3}$.   (q) $\dfrac{1}{2}, \dfrac{\sqrt{3}}{2}, \dfrac{1}{\sqrt{3}}$.

   (c) $-\dfrac{1}{\sqrt{2}}, -\dfrac{1}{\sqrt{2}}, 1$.   (s) $\dfrac{\sqrt{3}}{2}, -\dfrac{1}{2}, -\sqrt{3}$.

   (e) $-\dfrac{1}{\sqrt{2}}, \dfrac{1}{\sqrt{2}}, -1$.   (u) $\dfrac{1}{\sqrt{2}}, \dfrac{1}{\sqrt{2}}, 1$.

   (g) $-\dfrac{\sqrt{3}}{2}, -\dfrac{1}{2}, \sqrt{3}$.   (w) $\dfrac{1}{2}, \dfrac{\sqrt{3}}{2}, \dfrac{1}{\sqrt{3}}$.

   (i) $\dfrac{1}{2}, -\dfrac{\sqrt{3}}{2}, -\dfrac{1}{\sqrt{3}}$.   (y) 1, 0, *Doesn't exist.*

                                 (aa) −1, 0, *Doesn't exist.*

   (k) $-\dfrac{1}{\sqrt{2}}, \dfrac{1}{\sqrt{2}}, -1$.   (ac) $-\dfrac{1}{2}, -\dfrac{\sqrt{3}}{2}, \dfrac{1}{\sqrt{3}}$.

   (m) $-\dfrac{1}{\sqrt{2}}, \dfrac{1}{\sqrt{2}}, -1$.

   (o) 0, −1, 0.

6. Perimeter: $(\sqrt{2} + 1)37$ ft.; Area: $(1369/4)$ sq. ft.

8. $361\sqrt{3}$ sq. in.

10. (a) $AC = CB = 5\sqrt{2}, \angle B = 45°.$
   (c) $CB = 194, AB = 224, \angle B = 30°.$
   (e) $AC = 23, CB = 40, \angle A = 60°.$
   (g) $AC = \sqrt{3}, \angle A = 30°, \angle B = 60°.$
   (i) $AB = 2, \angle A = 60°, \angle B = 30°.$

§ 18; page 58

1. 0.38349.
3. 0.93633.
5. 0.47614.
7. 0.21529.
9. 0.28234.

11. 0.89623.
13. 1.6909.
15. 0.92499.
17. −0.98270.
19. −0.25924.

21. −0.36108.
23. −0.37388.
25. −3.4124.
27. 0.71813.
29. −0.91449.

§ 19; page 62

1. (a) 0.52051.
   (c) 0.18684.
   (e) 1.1287.

   (g) 5.3553.
   (i) −0.63904.
   (k) −0.52505.

   (m) −0.99179.
   (o) 2.4885.
   (q) −0.79483.

2. (a) $42° 9' 44''.$
      $137° 50' 16''.$
   (c) $17° 44' 11'',$
      $197° 44' 11''.$
   (e) $73° 39' 39'',$
      $253° 39' 39''.$

   (g) $17° 44' 48'',$
      $197° 44' 48''.$
   (i) $112° 56' 57''.$
      $292° 56' 57''.$
   (k) $102° 8' 36'',$
      $257° 51' 24''.$

   (n) $72° 28' 23'',$
      $252° 28' 23''.$
   (o) $110° 0' 31'',$
      $249° 59' 29''.$
   (q) $207° 32' 28'',$
      $332° 27' 32''.$

EXERCISES: CHAPTER III; PAGE 63

1. In each of the following the answers are given for the sine, cosine, and tangent in that order.

(a) $\dfrac{\sqrt{3}}{2}, -\dfrac{1}{2}, -\sqrt{3}.$ (d) $\dfrac{1}{2}, -\dfrac{\sqrt{3}}{2}, -\dfrac{1}{\sqrt{3}}.$ (g) $\dfrac{\sqrt{3}}{2}, -\dfrac{1}{2}, -\sqrt{3}.$

(b) $-\dfrac{1}{\sqrt{2}}, \dfrac{1}{\sqrt{2}}, -1.$ (e) $\dfrac{1}{2}, -\dfrac{\sqrt{3}}{2}, -\dfrac{1}{\sqrt{3}}.$ (h) $-\dfrac{1}{\sqrt{2}}, \dfrac{1}{\sqrt{2}}, -1.$

(c) $-\dfrac{\sqrt{3}}{2}, \dfrac{1}{2}, -\sqrt{3}.$ (f) $-\dfrac{\sqrt{3}}{2}, -\dfrac{1}{2}, \sqrt{3}.$ (i) $-\dfrac{1}{\sqrt{2}}, \dfrac{1}{\sqrt{2}}, -1.$

(j) $-\dfrac{1}{\sqrt{2}}, \dfrac{1}{\sqrt{2}}, -1.$ (n) $\dfrac{1}{2}, \dfrac{\sqrt{3}}{2}, \dfrac{1}{\sqrt{3}}.$ (r) $-\dfrac{1}{\sqrt{2}}, -\dfrac{1}{\sqrt{2}}, 1.$

(k) $\dfrac{1}{2}, \dfrac{\sqrt{3}}{2}, \dfrac{1}{\sqrt{3}}.$ (o) $0, 1, 0.$ (s) $-\dfrac{1}{2}, -\dfrac{\sqrt{3}}{2}, \dfrac{1}{\sqrt{3}}.$

(l) $-\dfrac{\sqrt{3}}{2}, -\dfrac{1}{2}, \sqrt{3}.$ (p) $\dfrac{1}{2}, -\dfrac{\sqrt{3}}{2}, -\dfrac{1}{\sqrt{3}}.$ (t) $-1, 0,$ *Doesn't exist.*

(m) $1, 0,$ *Doesn't exist.* (q) $-\dfrac{\sqrt{3}}{2}, -\dfrac{1}{2}, \sqrt{3}.$ (u) $-\dfrac{1}{\sqrt{2}}, -\dfrac{1}{\sqrt{2}}, 1.$

2. (b) $-0.93784.$ (h) $1.6916.$ (n) $0.64622.$
    (d) $1.9909.$ (j) $-0.43322.$ (p) $-0.57032.$
    (f) $-0.71031.$ (l) $0.59198.$

3. (b) $43° 49' 51''.$ (h) $227° 19' 12''.$ (l) $127° 7'.$
    (d) $13° 52' 17''.$ (j) $69° 45'.$ (n) $159° 5' 30''.$
    (f) $66° 49' 57''.$

4. (a) $41° 48' 38'',$ (g) $75° 31' 21'',$ (m) $158° 11' 55'',$
       $138° 11' 22''.$ $284° 28' 39''.$ $338° 11' 55''.$
    (c) $30° 57' 50'',$ (i) $53° 7' 45'',$ (o) $221° 48' 38'',$
       $210° 57' 50''.$ $233° 7' 45''.$ $318° 11' 22''.$
    (e) $70° 31' 44'',$ (k) $53° 7' 48'',$ (q) $238° 59' 48'',$
       $289° 28' 16''.$ $306° 52' 12''.$ $301° 0' 12''.$

5. 290.9 rods.

§ 20; page 65

1. (a) $81;$ $64;$ $729;$ $\tfrac{8}{27};$ $27;$ $1;$ $3.$
    (c) $4;$ $2;$ $\tfrac{1}{8};$ $4;$ $\tfrac{3}{16};$ $\tfrac{8}{3}.$

§21; page 66

1. (a) $\log_3 9 = 2.$ (g) $\log_{10} .001 = -3.$ (m) $\log_5 \tfrac{1}{5} = -1.$
    (c) $\log_5 125 = 3.$ (i) $\log_8 1 = 0.$ (o) $\log_{10} .1 = -1.$
    (e) $\log_2 \tfrac{1}{8} = -3.$ (k) $\log_8 4 = \tfrac{2}{3}.$ (q) $\log_{10} 1 = 0.$

2. (a) $3^2 = 9.$ (i) $2^{-3} = \tfrac{1}{8}.$ (o) $2^5 = 32.$
    (c) $2^0 = 1.$ (k) $6^2 = 36.$ (q) $25^{-\frac{3}{2}} = \tfrac{1}{125}.$
    (e) $\sqrt{9} = 3.$ (m) $3^3 = 27.$ (s) $27^{\frac{1}{3}} = 3.$
    (g) $5^1 = 5.$

3. (b) $3.$ (h) $16.$ (n) $4.$
    (d) $2.$ (j) $8.$ (p) $\tfrac{1}{8}.$
    (f) $\tfrac{2}{3}.$ (l) $10.$ (r) $b^a.$

§ 22; page 68

2. (b) 1.17609.
(d) 0.17609.
(f) 2.
(h) 0.23299.
(j) 1.69897.

(l) −3.
(n) 0.38908.
(p) 1.50515.
(r) −0.22185.

(t) 4.70436.
(v) 1.47712.
(x) 0.87506.
(z) 3.16992.

§ 24; page 72

1. 0.
3. −2.
5. −5.

7. −3.
9. −2.
11. 0.

13. 0.
15. −1.
17. 4.

§ 27; page 78

1. (a) 2.45325.
2. (a) 2898.5.
3. (a) 0.0141.
(c) 1.43.
(e) 0.1123.

(c) 9.80711 − 10.
(c) 5.2928.
(g) 3.2984.
(i) 0.0000087454.

(e) 7.72768 − 10.
(e) 0.0048466.
(k) −0.7184.
(m) 0.29445.

§ 28; page 80

1. (a) 6.80535 − 10.
(c) 9.01884 − 10.
(e) 8.40572 − 10.
(g) 1.98767.

(i) 9.03483 − 10.
(k) 3.89575.
(m) 6.59435 − 10.

(o) 1.83246.
(q) 0.53880.
(s) 1.56785.
(t) 90.717.

§ 29; page 82

1. (a) 9.72797 − 10.

(c) 9.80121 − 10.

(e) 9.89904 − 10.

(g) 0.22572.

2. (a) $\begin{cases} 40°\,28'\,36''. \\ 139°\,31'\,24''. \end{cases}$

(c) $\begin{cases} 54°\,29'\,7''. \\ 234°\,29'\,7''. \end{cases}$

(e) $\begin{cases} 33°\,36'\,29''. \\ 146°\,23'\,31''. \end{cases}$

(g) $\begin{cases} 39°\,36'\,53''. \\ 219°\,36'\,53''. \end{cases}$

§ 30; page 83

1. 0.0172.
3. 201.
5. 5.17.

7. 0.303.
9. 1870.

11. 48.3.
13. 0.539.

EXERCISES: CHAPTER IV; PAGE 83

1. (a) $9.68950 - 10$.   (k) $11,122,000,000$.   (u) $21,764,000$.
   (c) $9.98134 - 10$.   (m) 7.19342.   (w) -1713.
   (e) $9.55575 - 10$.   (o) 0.02475.   (y) 28.375.
   (g) $9.84079 - 10$.   (q) 1.8258.   (aa) -1.0345.
   (i) $9.81259 - 10$.   (s) 0.0077873.

2. (b) $-\frac{3}{10}$.   (j) $3° 5', 183° 5'$.
   (d) -2.   (l) $54° 0' 27'', 125° 59' 33''$.
   (f) 0.024983.   (n) $64° 27', 295° 33'$.
   (h) 0.00092358.

3. (b) 206.41.   (d) 5.3931.   (f) 0.0043774.
4. (b) -0.95.   (d) -1.2.
6. $130,430$ cu. in.   8. 96.81 cu. ft.

§ 32; page 89

1. $A = 64° 45', c = 165.8, b = 70.74$.
3. $B = 6° 14' 42'', a = 140.01, c = 140.85$.
5. $A = 43° 32', a = 11.838, c = 17.187$.
7. $A = 46° 44', a = 6.6598, b = 6.2686$.
9. $A = 33° 46' 51'', B = 56° 13' 10'', b = 519$.
11. $A = 29° 58', B = 60° 2', b = 8.03$.
13. $A = 22° 39' 40'', B = 67° 20' 20'', b = 5.904$.
15. $B = 57° 44', b = 149.94, c = 177.33$.
17. $A = 27° 44' 24'', a = 1547.0, c = 3323.7$.
19. $A = 64° 51' 51'', B = 25° 8' 9'', a = 5.607$.
21. $B = 61° 15', a = 4.983, b = 9.0828$.

§ 33; page 93

1. $a = 26.1, b = 38.7, B = 56°$.
3. $b = 43.2, A = 32° 45', B = 57° 15'$.
5. $c = 59.2, A = 59° 12', B = 30° 48'$.
7. $c = 38.6, A = 35° 24', B = 54° 36'$.

§ 34; page 100

1. 22.1.
3. $AD = 7.8, DC = 8.7$.
4. (b) $b = c = 129$ ft., $A = 110° 28'$.
   (d) $a = 328$ ft., $c = 248$ ft., $A = 82° 48', B = C = 48° 36'$.
   (f) $A = 2\pi/3$ radians, $C = \pi/6$ radians, $a = 79.7$ yd.,
       $b = 46.0$ yd.

5. (a) $c = 225$ ft., $a = 171$ ft., $C = 99°\ 23'$.
   (c) $c = 54.6$ in., $A = 38°\ 39'$, $B = 96°\ 21'$.
   (e) $a = 0.251$ mi., $c = 0.205$ mi., $B = 69°\ 54'$.
6. $r = 15.6$ in., $R = 18$ in.
8. 2.3 in.
10. $x = 3.16$ in., $y = 4.73$ in.

§ 35; page 106

1. 296 ft.
3. 90.5 mi. S, 90.5 mi. E.
5. 136 mi. W., 44.2 mi. N.
7. 32 ft., 45°.

9. 398 yd.
11. 257 ft.
13. 219. ft.
15. 24.1 ft., 17.9 ft.

§ 36; page 112

1. $|F| = 365$ lb., $\alpha = 26°\ 30'$.
3. $|F_t| = 175$ lb., $\alpha = 39°\ 15'$.
5. Upstream 48° 11' with the horizontal; 8 min.
7. 139.1 mi.
9. Vertical speed 1400 ft. per sec.   Muzzle speed 1980 ft.

EXERCISES: CHAPTER V; PAGE 113

1. (a) $B = 44°\ 40'$, $a = 96.013$, $b = 94.90$.
   (c) $A = 69°\ 16'\ 37''$, $B = 20°\ 43'\ 23''$, $a = 3.0397$.
   (e) $A = 24°\ 8'\ 52''$, $B = 65°\ 51'\ 8''$, $b = 100.37$.
   (g) $A = 30°$, $c = 2.0784$, $a = 1.0392$.
   (i) $A = 60°$, $b = 152$, $a = 263.27$.

2. (b) Side 11.607, base angle 57° 46'.
   (d) Base angle 79° 52' 6'', vertex angle 20° 15' 48''.
   (f) Vertex angle 91° 39' 28'', base 34.830.
   (h) Base angle 57° 47' 40'', vertex angle 64° 24' 40'', side 5.8654.

3. 36° 7' 47''.
5. 65.449 ft.
7. 136.10 yd.
9. $|F_h| = 70.823$ lb.
   $|F_v| = 44.773$ lb.
11. 911.48 lb.
13. Has driven 204 miles.   27.553 miles from first road.
15. 14.3 ft., $\theta = 40°\ 56'$.
17. 9.33 in., $\theta = 40°\ 36'$.

§ 37; page 119

1. $\sin \theta, \quad \pm\sqrt{1 - \sin^2 \theta}, \quad \dfrac{\sin \theta}{\pm\sqrt{1 - \sin^2 \theta}}, \quad \dfrac{\pm\sqrt{1 - \sin^2 \theta}}{\sin \theta},$

$\dfrac{1}{\pm\sqrt{1 - \sin^2 \theta}}, \quad \dfrac{1}{\sin \theta}.$

§ 40; page 126

1. $\dfrac{\sqrt{2}(1 + \sqrt{3})}{4}.$

3. $\sin (\alpha + \beta) = 0, \cos (\alpha + \beta) = 1; \; \sin (\alpha + \beta) = 0,$

$\cos (\alpha + \beta) = -1; \; \sin (\alpha + \beta) = \dfrac{\sqrt{3}}{2}, \cos (\alpha + \beta) = -\dfrac{1}{2};$

yes.

5. $\cos \alpha, \; -\sin \alpha.$

7. $\sin (\alpha + \beta) = -\dfrac{3\sqrt{3} + 4}{10}, \cos (\alpha + \beta) = \dfrac{-\sqrt{3}(4 - \sqrt{3})}{10}.$

9. $\sin (\alpha - \beta) = -\sqrt{3}/2, \cos (\alpha - \beta) = -1/2;$
$\sin (\alpha - \beta) = 0, \cos (\alpha - \beta) = -1;$
$\sin (\alpha - \beta) = -\sqrt{3}/2, \cos (\alpha - \beta) = 1/2.$

12. (b) $-\cos \alpha, \; -\sin \alpha.$
   (d) $-\sin \alpha, \cos \alpha.$

§ 41; page 128

2. $\tan 75° = 2 + \sqrt{3}, \tan 105° = -2 - \sqrt{3}, \tan 255° = 2 + \sqrt{3}.$

4. (a) $\tan (\alpha + \beta) = -2 + \sqrt{3},$ or $2 - \sqrt{3},$ or $-2 - \sqrt{3}.$

$\cot (\alpha + \beta) = \dfrac{1}{-2 + \sqrt{3}},$ or $\dfrac{1}{2 - \sqrt{3}},$ or $\dfrac{-1}{2 + \sqrt{3}}.$

(c) $\tan (\alpha + \beta) = -\dfrac{3\sqrt{3} + 4}{3 - 4\sqrt{3}}, \quad \cot (\alpha + \beta) = -\dfrac{3 - 4\sqrt{3}}{3\sqrt{3} + 4}.$

5. $2 - \sqrt{3}; \; -(2 - \sqrt{3}); \; -(2 + \sqrt{3}).$

7. $8 - 5\sqrt{3}, \; -(8 + 5\sqrt{3})/11.$

§ 42; page 129

1. $1; \; 0; \;$ doesn't exist.

3. $\sin \theta \equiv 2 \sin \dfrac{\theta}{2} \cos \dfrac{\theta}{2}, \cos \theta \equiv \cos^2 \dfrac{\theta}{2} - \sin^2 \dfrac{\theta}{2},$

$\tan \theta \equiv \dfrac{2 \tan \dfrac{\theta}{2}}{1 - \tan^2 \dfrac{\theta}{2}}.$

5. $\sin 2\theta = \dfrac{3\sqrt{7}}{8}$, $\sin 2\theta = \dfrac{-3\sqrt{7}}{8}$.

7. $\sin 4\theta \equiv 2 \sin 2\theta \cos 2\theta$, $\cos 4\theta \equiv \cos^2 2\theta - \sin^2 2\theta$,

$\tan 4\theta \equiv \dfrac{2 \tan 2\theta}{1 - \tan^2 2\theta}$.

9. $\sin 2\theta = \dfrac{-24}{25}$, $\cos 2\theta = \dfrac{7}{-25}$, $\tan 2\theta = \dfrac{24}{7}$.

§ 43; page 131

1. (a) $\sin 15° = \dfrac{\sqrt{2 - \sqrt{3}}}{2}$. 　　**(i)** $\sin 67\frac{1}{2}° = \dfrac{\sqrt{2 + \sqrt{2}}}{2}$.

(c) $\tan 15° = 2 - \sqrt{3}$. 　　**(k)** $\tan 67\frac{1}{2}° = \sqrt{\dfrac{\sqrt{2} + 1}{\sqrt{2} - 1}}$.

(e) $\sin 22\frac{1}{2}° = \dfrac{\sqrt{2 - \sqrt{2}}}{2}$. 　**(m)** $\cos (-22\frac{1}{2}°) = \dfrac{\sqrt{2 + \sqrt{2}}}{2}$.

(g) $\tan 22\frac{1}{2}° = \sqrt{\dfrac{\sqrt{2} - 1}{\sqrt{2} + 1}}$. 　**(o)** $\sin (-15°) = -\dfrac{\sqrt{2 - \sqrt{3}}}{2}$.

5. $\sin \dfrac{\theta}{2} = \pm\dfrac{1}{\sqrt{10}}$; 　$\cos \dfrac{\theta}{2} = \pm\dfrac{3}{\sqrt{10}}$; 　$\tan \dfrac{\theta}{2} = \dfrac{1}{3}$; 　$\cot \dfrac{\theta}{2} = 3$.

$\sin \dfrac{\theta}{2} = \pm\dfrac{3}{\sqrt{10}}$; 　$\cos \dfrac{\theta}{2} = \pm\dfrac{1}{\sqrt{10}}$; 　$\tan \dfrac{\theta}{2} = 3$; 　$\cot \dfrac{\theta}{2} = \dfrac{1}{3}$.

7. $\sin \dfrac{\theta}{2} = \pm\dfrac{3}{5}$; 　$\cos \dfrac{\theta}{2} = \pm\dfrac{4}{5}$; 　$\tan \dfrac{\theta}{2} = \dfrac{3}{4}$; 　$\cot \dfrac{\theta}{2} = \dfrac{4}{3}$.

$\sin \dfrac{\theta}{2} = \pm\dfrac{4}{5}$; 　$\cos \dfrac{\theta}{2} = \pm\dfrac{3}{5}$; 　$\tan \dfrac{\theta}{2} = \dfrac{4}{3}$; 　$\cot \dfrac{\theta}{2} = \dfrac{3}{4}$.

§ 44; page 133

6. (b) $\sqrt{3} \sin 10°$. 　　　　　**(j)** $2 \sin \dfrac{3x}{2} \cos \dfrac{x}{2}$.

(d) $-\sin 10°$. 　　　　　　**(l)** $\sqrt{3} \sin 50°$.

(f) $-\dfrac{1}{\sqrt{2}}$. 　　　　　　**(n)** $2 \cos 6x \cos 4x$.

(h) $\sqrt{3} \sin 15°$. 　　　　　**(p)** $-\sqrt{2} \sin 9°$.

7. (b) $\dfrac{\cos 10° - \cos 70°}{2}$.   (h) $\dfrac{\cos 90° + \cos 10°}{2}$.

     (d) $\dfrac{\sin 34° - \sin 14°}{2}$.   (j) $\dfrac{\sin 6x - \sin 2x}{2}$.

     (f) $\dfrac{\cos 3x + \cos 2x}{2}$.

9. (a) $\tan 35°$.   (c) $\cot 15°$.

11. $\tan\left(\dfrac{\alpha + \beta}{2}\right) \cot\left(\dfrac{\alpha - \beta}{2}\right)$.

EXERCISES: CHAPTER VI; PAGE 136

1. $\dfrac{\tan\theta}{\sqrt{1 + \tan^2\theta}}$, $\dfrac{1}{\sqrt{1 + \tan^2\theta}}$ $\tan\theta$, $\dfrac{1}{\tan\theta}$, $\sqrt{1 + \tan^2\theta}$,

$\dfrac{\sqrt{1 + \tan^2\theta}}{\tan\theta}$.

3. $\dfrac{\sqrt{\sec^2\theta - 1}}{\sec\theta}$, $\dfrac{1}{\sec\theta}$, $\sqrt{\sec^2\theta - 1}$, $\dfrac{1}{\sqrt{\sec^2\theta - 1}}$, $\sec\theta$,

$\dfrac{\sec\theta}{\sqrt{\sec^2\theta - 1}}$.

5. (a) $\dfrac{\cos\theta + \sin\theta}{\sqrt{2}}$.   **5.** (e) $\dfrac{1 - \sqrt{3}\tan\theta}{\sqrt{3} + \tan\theta}$.

     (c) $\dfrac{\cos\theta - \sqrt{3}\sin\theta}{2}$.   (g) $\dfrac{1 + \tan\theta}{1 - \tan\theta}$.

6. $\sin(\theta + \phi) = \dfrac{-(3 + \sqrt{105})}{16}$, $\cos(\theta + \phi) = \dfrac{3\sqrt{15} + \sqrt{7}}{16}$.

12. $\sin\alpha = \dfrac{1}{5\sqrt{2}}$, $\cos\alpha = \dfrac{7}{5\sqrt{2}}$.

14. $\sin 2\alpha = \dfrac{-24}{25}$, $\cos 2\alpha = \dfrac{7}{25}$, $\tan 2\alpha = -\dfrac{24}{7}$.

16. (a) $-\dfrac{7}{25}$.   (c) 1.   (e) $-\dfrac{7}{24}$.

19. $\tan 3\alpha \equiv \dfrac{3\tan\alpha - \tan^3\alpha}{1 - 3\tan^2\alpha}$.

§ 47; page 150

1. (a) $C = 119°\ 15'$, $a = 67.268$, $b = 75.228$.
   (c) $B = 28°\ 29'\ 52''$, $C = 107°\ 38'\ 8''$, $c = 12.627$.
   (e) $C = 37°\ 24'\ 30''$, $A = 12°\ 20'\ 10''$, $a = 42.337$.
   (g) $B = 75°\ 15'$, $a = 425.47$, $b = 473.13$.
   (i) No solution.
   (k) $B = 37°\ 1'\ 49''$, $a = 2.8873$, $b = 1.7676$.
   (m) $A = 18°\ 35'\ 13''$, $C = 101°\ 4'\ 17''$, $c = 4.4213$.
   (o) No solution.
   (q) No solution.
   (s) $A = 21°\ 7'\ 40''$, $C = 133°\ 21'\ 50''$, $c = 547.81$.
   (u) $B = 86°\ 19'\ 16''$, $b = 2529.1$, $c = 2246.4$.
2. 238.6 yd. from B; 200.9 yd. from A.
4. 84.3 ft.
6. 20 knots.
8. $x = \sqrt{y^2 - r^2 \sin^2 \theta} + r \cos \theta$.

§ 48; page 154

1. (a) $c = 10.29$, $B = 43°\ 59'$, $A = 72°\ 44'$.
   (c) $a = 15.2$, $C = 44°\ 4'$, $B = 23°\ 56'$.
   (e) $A = 40°\ 41'$, $B = 53°\ 39'$, $C = 85°\ 39'$.
   (g) $b = 334$, $A = 27°\ 14'$, $C = 43°\ 22'$.
2. 125.4 mi.
4. 9 ft., $B = 81°\ 52'$.
6. 1533 mi.
8. $|F| = 106$ lb.
10. $|F| = 646$ lb.

§ 49; page 158

1. (a) $h = 37.5$.   1. (c) 240.
2. 1382 ft.   4. 5.21.

§ 50; page 161

1. $A = 22°\ 14'\ 33''$, $B = 125°\ 16'\ 57''$, $c = 30.44$.
3. $A = 30°\ 5'\ 50''$, $C = 35°\ 39'\ 28''$, $b = 338.56''$.
5. $B = 32°\ 19'\ 14''$, $C = 22°\ 10'\ 16''$, $a = 9332$.
7. $C = 93°\ 41'\ 20''$, $B = 41°\ 0'\ 40''$, $a = 30.806$.
9. $B = 132°\ 20'$, $A = 17°\ 57'$, $c = 0.4571$.

§ 52; page 161

1. $B = 16° 18' 0''$, $C = 48° 26' 34''$, $a = 4.1839$.
3. $A = 37° 20' 0''$, $B = 54° 46' 8''$, $C = 87° 53' 56''$.
5. $A = 6° 7' 45''$, $C = 154° 58' 44''$, $c = 4.7307$.
7. $C = 69° 11' 46''$, $a = 232.62$, $b = 281.49$.
9. $C = 20° 53' 25''$, $B = 13° 36' 35''$, $b = 2.6521$.
11. $A = 70° 19' 48''$, $B = 9° 20' 25''$, $b = 1.0205$.
13. $C = 118° 20' 38''$, $B = 46° 16' 2''$, $a = 1637.7$.

§ 54; page 170

1. (a) 106.25.   (e) 155,900.
   (c) 746.18.   (g) 75452.

EXERCISES: CHAPTER VII; PAGE 171

1. (a) $\begin{cases} B = 121° 47' 38'', C = 30° 40' 57'', c = 2.3697. \\ B = 58° 12' 22'', C = 94° 16' 13'', c = 1.6310. \end{cases}$
   (c) $C = 123° 13' 9''$, $a = 469.51$, $b = 388.97$.
   (e) $A = 65° 8' 44''$, $a = 7.4413$, $c = 2.5811$.
   (g) $A = 38° 58'$, $B = 78° 24' 34''$, $C = 62° 37' 30''$.
   (i) $A = 65° 2' 58''$, $B = 73° 6' 32''$, $C = 41° 50' 38''$.
   (k) $C = 34° 11' 33''$, $a = 9.4058$, $b = 6.8235$.
   (m) $C = 54° 22' 3''$, $c = 26.21$, $b = 13.682$.
   (o) $A = 86° 45'$, $b = 2.6029$, $c = 3.4048$.

7. $4° 25'$.
9. $A = 21° 47' 12''$, $B = 38° 12' 48''$, $C = 120° 0' 0''$.
11. 1879 ft.
13. 174 yd.
15. 138 ft.
17. 124 ft.
19. 248 mi.
21. 179.06 ft.
23. 112 ft.
25. 106.40 mi.
27. 11.0 ft., 7.26 ft.
29. 10.958 ft., 26.535 ft.
31. 82.1 ft.
33. 638 ft.
35. 1202.5 ft.
37. 124.0 lb.
39. 181 ft.
41. 294 ft.
43. (a) 4.0 ft., 5.2 ft.
    (b) 6.6 ft.
    (c) $73° 6'$.
45. $|V| = 7.9$ k.p.h.
    $\alpha = $ N. $82° 32'$ E.

§ 56; page 183

1. (a) $45°, 135°, 225°, 315°$.
  (c) $0°, 180°$.
  (e) $30°, 150°, 210°, 330°$.
  (g) $0°, 180°$.
  (i) $90°, 233° 7' 49''$.
  (k) $0°, 90°, 180°, 270°, 30°, 150°, 210°, 330°$.

1. (m) $15°, 75°, 135°, 195°, 255°, 315°$.
  (o) $0°, 180°$.
  (q) $0°, 53° 7' 49''$.
  (s) $0°, 180°, 120°, 240°$.

2. (a) $0°, 180°$.

2. (c) $0°, 180°$.

§ 57; page 185

2. (b) $x = \sec y$.
3. (a) $x = \text{arc cos } y$.

3. (c) $x = \csc^{-1} y$.
  (e) $x = \text{arc cot } y$.

§ 58; page 191

3. (a) $30°, 330°$.
  (c) $19° 28' 16'', 160° 31' 44''$.
  (e) $60°, 240°$.

  (g) $150°, 330°$.
  (i) $240°, 300°$.
  (k) $210°, 330°$.

6. $$\theta_1 = \sin^{-1}\frac{2}{\sqrt{5}} = \cos^{-1}\left(-\frac{1}{\sqrt{5}}\right) = \cot^{-1}\left(-\frac{1}{2}\right)$$
$$= \sec^{-1}(-\sqrt{5}) = \csc^{-1}\frac{\sqrt{5}}{2}.$$
$$\theta_2 = \sin^{-1}\left(-\frac{2}{\sqrt{5}}\right) = \cos^{-1}\frac{1}{\sqrt{5}} = \cot^{-1}\left(-\frac{1}{2}\right) = \sec^{-1}\sqrt{5}$$
$$= \csc^{-1}\left(-\frac{\sqrt{5}}{2}\right).$$

9. (b) $x = \frac{1}{3}\cos\frac{y}{2}$.
  (d) $x = 2\sin\frac{y}{3}$.
  (f) $x = \frac{1}{\pi}\cot y$.

10. (a) $y = \frac{1}{3}\sin^{-1} x$.
  (c) $y = \tan^{-1}\frac{x}{2}$.
  (e) $y = 2\sin^{-1}\frac{x}{2}$.
  (g) $y = \frac{1}{3}\text{arc sec } 3x$.

12. (a) $\begin{cases}\theta = \pm 60° + n\,360°.\\ \theta = \pm 120° + n\,360°.\end{cases}$
  (c) $\theta = n\,60°$.
  (e) $\theta = \pm 22\frac{1}{2}° + n\,90°$.
  (g) $\begin{cases}\theta = \pm 90° + n\,360°.\\ \theta = 45° + n\,180°.\end{cases}$
  (i) $\begin{cases}\theta = n\,180°.\\ \theta = \pm 15° + n\,90°.\end{cases}$
  (k) $\theta = \dfrac{90° + n\,360°}{7}$.
  $\theta = 90° + n\,360°$.
  (m) $\begin{cases}\theta = n\,360°.\\ \theta = \pm 90° + n\,720°.\\ \theta = \pm 270° + n\,720°.\end{cases}$

§ 60; page 196

1. 60°.	**7.** −45°.
3. −45°.	**9.** 35° 46′ 37″.
5. 30°.	**11.** −63° 43′.
	13. 41° 3′.

EXERCISES: CHAPTER VIII; PAGE 197

1. (a) 60°, 120°, 240°, 300°.

(c) 18°, 54°, 90°, 126°, 162°, 198°, 234°, 270°, 306°, 342°, 0°, 180°.

(e) $22\frac{1}{2}°$, $112\frac{1}{2}°$, $202\frac{1}{2}°$, $292\frac{1}{2}°$.

(g) 56° 18′ 36″, 236° 18′ 36″.

(i) 60°, 180°.

(k) 240°.

(m) 45°, 225°.

(o) 135°, 315°.

(q) 30°, 150°, 210°, 330°, 90°, 270°.

(s) 10°, 50°, 130°, 170°, 250°, 290°.

(u) 0°, 253° 44′ 24″.

(w) 120°, 240°, 0°, 90°, 270°, 180°.

(y) 15°, 105°, 195°, 285°.

(aa) 0°, 45°, 90°, 135°, 180°, 225°, 270°, 315°.

(ac) 0°.

(ae) 90°, 270°.

(ag) 18°, 54°, 90°, 126°, 162°, 198°, 234°, 270°, 306°, 342°, $7\frac{1}{2}°$, $37\frac{1}{2}°$, $97\frac{1}{2}°$, $127\frac{1}{2}°$, $187\frac{1}{2}°$, $217\frac{1}{2}°$, $277\frac{1}{2}°$, $307\frac{1}{2}°$.

(ai) 45°, 135°, 225°, 315°.

(ak) 0°, 270°.

(am) 45°, 225°.

(ao) $22\frac{1}{2}°$, $157\frac{1}{2}°$, $202\frac{1}{2}$, $337\frac{1}{2}°$.

4. (a) 30°, 150°.

(c) 150°, 330°.

(e) 60°, 240°.

(g) 270°.

6. (b) $\dfrac{1}{\sqrt{2}}$.

(d) $\frac{1}{2}$.

6. (f) −1.

(h) $\sqrt{2}$.

(j) 0.44722.

(l) 0.80000.

(n) −0.86978.

(p) −0.89015.

7. (b) $2x\sqrt{1 - x^2}$.

(d) $-\frac{4}{3}$.

(f) $3x - 4x^3$.

(h) 1.

(j) s.

8. (b) $\dfrac{1}{\sqrt{5}}$.

   (d) $\dfrac{\sqrt{3}}{6}$.

   (f) $\doteq 1$.

9. (a) $x = \frac{1}{3} \sin^{-1} \dfrac{y}{2}$.

   (c) $x = 2 \text{ arc tan } 3y$.

   (e) $x = \dfrac{1}{\pi} \text{ arc sec } 3y$.

(g) $x = \frac{1}{2} \sin^{-1} 3y$.

10. (a) $y = \sin \dfrac{x}{3}$.

    (c) $y = \frac{1}{3} \tan \dfrac{x}{2}$.

    (e) $y = \dfrac{1}{\pi} \cos 3x$.

    (g) $y = 3 \sin 2x$.

§ 64; page 207

5. $y = \cot x$ has period π.

   $y = \csc x$ has period 2π.

§ 67; page 212

		Amplitude	Period	Phase Angle
1.	(a)	2	$2\pi/3$	
	(c)	$\frac{1}{2}$	2	
	(e)	2	2π	-2
	(g)	1	3π	$\frac{1}{2}$
	(i)	1	$2\pi/3$	2
3.	(a)	3	π	
	(c)	2	$2\pi/3$	2
	(e)	$\frac{1}{2}$	2π	π
4.			$\pi/2$	
5.	(b)		$\pi/3$	
6.		120	$\pi/125$	

EXERCISES: CHAPTER IX; PAGE 217

		Amplitude	Period			Amplitude	Period
3.	(a)	1	π		(g)		4π
	(c)	3	4π		(i)	3	3π
	(e)		$\pi/2$		(k)	π	6π

INDEX

243